CW00404998

Arms and Armour

review

Converted at the rate of exchange on the day of sale.

SBN 0-86248-032-9

Printed by Apollo Press, Dominion Way, Worthing, Sussex, England.
Bound by R.J. Acford, Chichester, Sussex, England.

 Published on the same day in Canada by Academic Press Canada, Limited, Toronto.

The Library of Congress Cataloged This Serial as Follows:

The Lyle official arms and armour review.
(Galashiels, Scot., Lyle Publications)

v. ill. 22 cm.

Annual.
Began with 1976 vol. Cf. New serial titles.
Other title: Arms and armour, 1980-

1. Arms and armor–Catalogs. 2. Military paraphernalia–Catalogs. 1. Title: Arms and armour.

U800.L93 739.7'029'4 80-648147
MARC-S

ISBN 0-698-11116-8

Distributed in the United States by Coward, McCann & Geoghegan, Inc.,
200 Madison Avenue, New York, N. Y. 10016

The Lyle official Arms and Armour *review* 1982

Acknowledgements

COMPILED AND EDITED BY TONY CURTIS

CHRISTINE O'BRIEN
JANICE MONCRIEFF
SHONA BROWN
NICOLA PARK
CARMEN MILIVOYEVICH
ELAINE HARLAND
KAREN KILGOUR
MAY MUTCH
MARGOT RUTHERFORD
JENNIFER KNOX
TANYA FAIRBAIRN
MARION McKILLOP
JOSEPHINE McLAREN
SUSAN LOWER

All photographs and text throughout this book relate
to recent sales at the Lewes Auction Room of
Messrs. WALLIS & WALLIS
to whom the publishers are deeply indebted.

INTRODUCTION

Compiled in close co-operation with Messrs. Wallis & Wallis, world renowned Arms, Armour and Militaria Auctioneers, the Lyle Official Arms and Armour Review is an essential work of reference for all Dealers, Collectors and Investors.

Here are 416 pages packed with thousands of photographs of all things military, each accompanied by a description and current value of the object illustrated derived from recent auctions.

For ease of reference, the contents of the book are divided under four main headings: Edged Weapons, Flintlock and Matchlock Weapons, Militaria and Percussion Weapons. These groups are then further subdivided into categories arranged alphabetically, with individual items arranged in price order.

A companion volume to the universally famed Lyle Official Antiques Review and the Lyle Official Arts Review, this volume will prove itself an invaluable work of reference, not only to arms and armour dealers, but to all antique dealers and collectors for, even more than in other fields of collecting, prices in arms and armour tend to change rapidly and it is essential to keep abreast of the field.

This, the Lyle Official Arms & Armour Review 1982, is the seventh edition of an annual review of current values in a field which is gaining a steadily widening circle of devotees.

TONY CURTIS

Contents

Arms and Armour *review*

There is rarely a cloud without a silver lining and while the Arms and Armour world has been suffering, like all other branches of collecting, from the effects of recession, eager buyers with eyes for bargains have been able to snap up some remarkable buys.

The area of the Militaria market that has shown the most marked halt in its previous steady upward progress of prices is guns. The modest buyer with limited funds has found this market closed in the past beacause of the bouyancy of the demand for guns but now, with the flattening off in prices, this could be the time to pick up buys that will certainly yield benefits in the future.

In the rest of the Arms and Armour world, the set back has not been so obvious. In particular, as far as Eastern edged weapons, swords, helmets and uniforms are concerned prices have continued to rise during the past year though these rises could be said to be slightly slower than in the past. This is certainly the time for private buyers with discrimination and money to spend to have a good chance of picking up choice items without finding themselves pushed out in the price race.

This is not to deny that when a truly rare item comes up for sale that it does not demand a prime price. Arms and Armour salerooms all over the country confirm this . . . . .
'Of one thing we are always sure,' said Mr Butler of Wallis and Wallis in Lewes, 'if we are given a truly good item to sell, we are able to get an excellent price for it. There are always buyers for quality goods, recession or no recession.'

Like other auction houses however Mr Butler confirmed that guns are static at the moment. 'Some sellers have been holding on to their best pieces,' he told us, 'this has created a sort of vicious circle because if there are not many good quality guns coming up for sale the market levels off and that makes other sellers hold their things back.'

This levelling off in guns even extends to the American Colt revolver which was in such demand eighteen months ago by collectors on the other side of the Atlantic. They too it seems, have been affected by the recession. Nevertheless, some guns have sold for good money though run of the mill items have tended to stay at the same price or at prices even marginally lower than they were last year.

Some examples of guns that have made good prices in spite of the current climate however include a Scottish all steel military pistol by McVey made between 1793 and 1799 for the 2nd Breadalbane Fencibles, certainly not the most famous of regiments. This rare gun was bought by Edinburgh Castle for £1,100 and will be displayed in the Castle's armoury museum along with other examples of fine guncraft.

Another unusual firearm that came up for sale was a cased percussion revolver that had been made for the captain of the famous tea clipper, the 'Cutty Sark.' It once sailed on the fast tea run to the east and is now laid up as a tourist attraction at Greenwich on the River Thames. The 'Cutty Sark's' captain's gun made over £100 in auction though it was a relatively ordinary weapon. What gave it a fairly high price was the fact that its past ownership and history was well proved by contemporary documentation and correspondence. Any item with a proved provenance always makes an augmented price.

Quality always fetches too in bad times and a pair of 52-bore percussion duelling pistols by Joseph Manton, signed and ornately engraved and with silver safety plugs, made £2,100. Another unusual pair of 22-bore Bohemian double shot percussion duelling pistols by M. Fiala of Bistrici, sold for £1,500.

Another prime example of a pair of pistols was a set of long 20-bore Flemish flintlock holster pistols from around 1720 – sold for £1,800.
A pair of Queen Anne double barrelled silver mounted boxlock flintlocks, made by Perry of London around 1780, sold for the very high price of £2,300.

A 24-bore Scottish all steel Military flintlock belt pistol by John McVey for The 2nd Bn. Breadalbane Fencibles (1793-1799), 11¾in., barrel 6½in. with raised breech. **$2,376 £1,100**

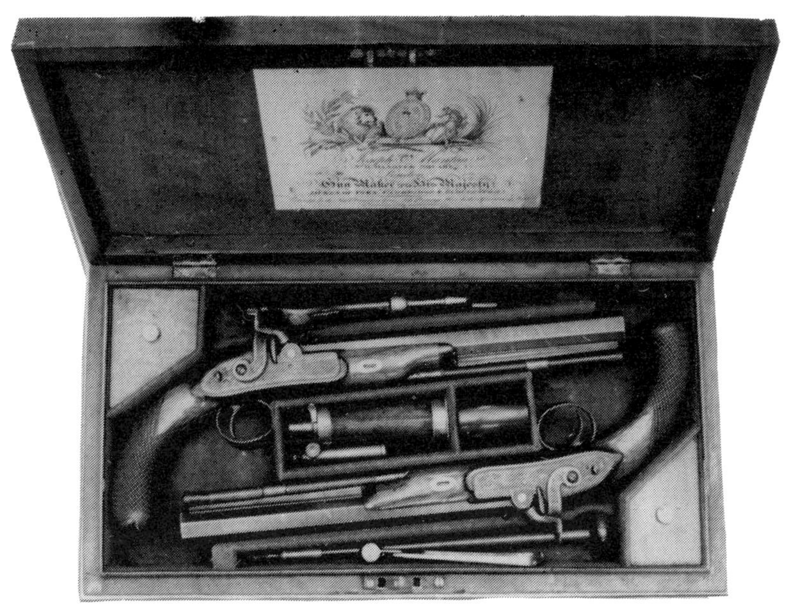

A pair of 52-bore percussion duelling pistols by Joseph Manton, No. 1978, 15in., octagonal twist browned barrels 10in. with fixed sights. Contained in their green baize lined fitted mahogany case with trade label. **$5,124 £2,100**

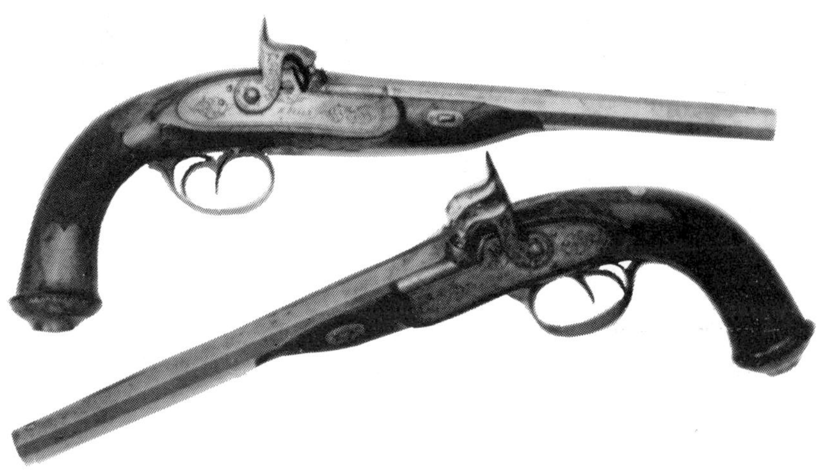

An unusual pair of 22-bore Bohemian double shot superimposed loading rifled percussion duelling pistols by M. Fiala of Bistrici, 16in. overall, octagonal barrels 10in. engraved 'M. Fiala W. Bistrici'. **$3,600 £1,500**

History again played a part in determining the price of a 10-bore Brown Bess flintlock musket which was believed to have been used during the American Revolutionary Wars. The musket was stamped '29 Regt' and it is known that the 29th Worcestershire Regiment served in Canada from 1776 to 1787. The musket sold for £1,100.

Another unusual, but much cheaper, firearm was a highly decorated 10-bore Balkan miquelet flintlock musket which fetched £400. This eye-catching gun had a barrel that was etched for its full length with silver arabesques and had also a gold damascened Kurdish lock. The stock was entirely overlaid with diamond-shaped bone and wooden sections. History does not recall who made this magnificent piece.

Also under £1,100 were two sets of cased percussion revolvers. The first set by Beaumont Adams sold for £900 and the second, a Trent Patent, for £950. However, it has to be remembered that twenty years ago neither of these sets of guns would have fetched more than £25.

To go to the other price extreme as a finishing up item in the guns section, a record price of £2,750 was recorded this year for a .451 cased Whitworth Patent Percussion target rifle made around 1860.

Gun collectors do not have to be told that their treasures represent big money either now or in the future and, of course, they should always be kept well oiled, wrapped and in a dry, safe place.

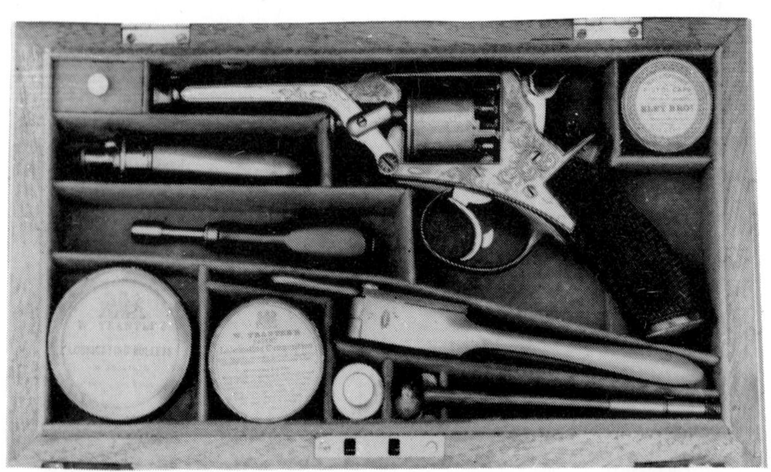

A 5-shot 80-bore Tranter's patent double action percussion revolver, No. 16820T, 9½in., octagonal barrel 4½in., Birmingham proved, engraved 'R. R. Rodda & Co Gun Makers by Appointment' on top flat. In its green baize lined fitted mahogany case with Dixon flask etc. **$2,050 £950**

If the gun market was relatively slow however, distinct growth has been seen this year in the world of military helmets. The top of the helmet pops was the Tarleton which is the sort of helmet made of metal and leather and with a crest of fur or plumes extending from the nape of the neck up over the crown of the helmet. Tarletons were worn by the British Army between 1790 till 1828, but the only regiment to go on wearing them after 1815 was the Royal Artillery. Because of the short period of their vogue, Tarletons are therefore fairly rare in the saleroom and as such examples have been known to make as much as £4,000. This year three Tarletons came up for sale – a Tarleton helmet of the Northhamptonshire Yeomanry, with a bearskin fur crest and white over red feather plume, sold for £2,700; a similar helmet of the Dorset Yeomanry made £1,400 and a helmet from an unidentified regiment did not let its anonymity stop it making a creditable £1,000.

A rare Georgian Tarleton helmet of The Northamptonshire Yeomanry, leather skull with brass peak and side binding, green linen turban and brass chains, ear to ear brass title 'Northamptonshire Yeomanry', white over red feather plume, bear skin fur crest. **\$6,480 £2,700**

A North Italian (probably Milanese) half-armour of so-called Pisan type, circa 1560-70, comprising one-piece cabaset with pear-stalk finial, itegral brim with roped border and twin peaks. Breast plate of 'peascod' form ensuite with back plate. Articulated pauldrons, elbow cops and lower arms with roped borders. **$5,075 £2,350**

Other helmets, apart from the Tarleton, are also keenly collected. Today an officer's helmet which could have been bought for £25 a couple of decades ago can fetch over £2,500. Cavalry regiments dating up to the end of the 1940's are fetching between £400 and £500. Blue cloth helmets from infantry regiments that used to change hands for as little as £5 cannot be bought now under £100 and a good example will demand as much as £300. The collectors' enthusiasm also extends to foreign helmets and this year two First World War German Garde du Corps helmets with Imperial eagles on the crowns sold for £1,200 and £1,400.

A Victorian full dress sabretache of The Royal Wiltshire (Prince of Wales's Own) Yeomanry Cavalry. **$885 £410**

All the fittings of the fighting man arouse enthusiasm in militaria collectors . . . . uniforms are perennially popular and so, of course, are suits of armour. Some high-born fighting man took the field in the 16th century in a fine suit of half armour which changed hands this summer for £2,350 – a knights ransom when the armour was first fashioned by an armourer in Pisa, north Italy.

Other glamourous accoutrements of war that are collected include sabretaches which were the pouches that hung beside a soldier's sword. A very fine collection of officer's full dress sabretaches were sold this summer and each of the 33 items made over £300. Badges are also collected and cap badges that used to fetch a modest 3/6d cannot now be bought for less than £10 and the price shows no signs of slackening. A part collection of other ranks' Glengarry badges made £1,514 this year, an average price of £30 a badge.

An officer's silvered helmet plate of The Hertfordshire Rifle Volunteers.
$144 £70

The ideal military hero was, of course, medalled and there have been medal collectors around for many years. Perhaps because, like guns, this has traditionally been a strong market it too has shown signs of slackening during the recession. In spite of that however, quality always counts and some interesting prices have been recorded for more unusual items.

Only a few years ago a Waterloo medal was undervalued at only £3.50 but today such a medal awarded to a man in a good regiment can cost over £300. Similarly another great British victory, the Battle of Trafalgar, was also commemorated by the granting of the Trafalgar Bar. A Naval General Service Medal with a Trafalgar Bar today costs over £500 – fifteen years ago the price was £5. More heroism from the past was recorded this year in the sale of an Army Gold medal (small field size) awarded for the Battle of Albufera of 1811 in the Peninsular Wars. The medal was still in its original case and inscribed with the name of the recipient, Lt Col Alexander William Campbell. It was bought by a medal collector for £2,550. Heroism from the enemy side does not go unregarded either in the saleroom and this year a German citation, for the Knight's Cross, inscribed on a sheet of vellum, dated December 1941 and signed by Adolf Hitler sold for £1,000. 'It is only a piece of paper but Hitler's signature put the price up,' said the auctioneer.

Over the past two years military swords have shown a steady rise in price that has still not slowed down and prices overall are up by more than 25% in two years. A rare patterned 1814 Household Cavalry officer's

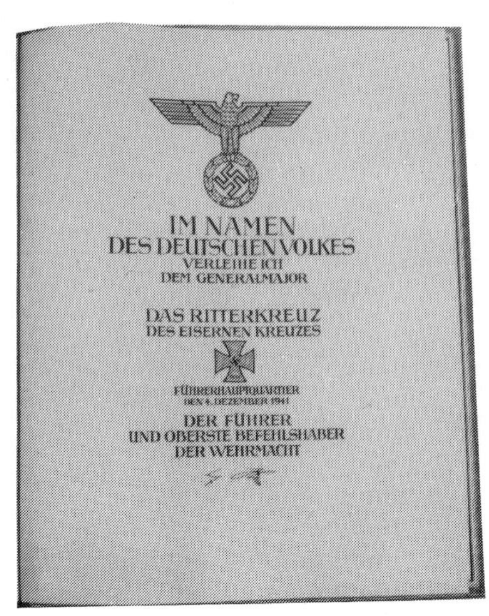

IM NAMEN
DES DEUTSCHEN VOLKES
VERLEIHE ICH
DEM GENERALMAJOR

DAS RITTERKREUZ
DES EISERNEN KREUZES

DER FÜHRER
UND OBERSTE BEFEHLSHABER
DER WEHRMACHT

A rare original Nazi Citation for the Knights Cross of The Iron Cross, on vellum, signed by Hitler, 13½ x 17½in.
$2,160 £1,000

sword sold this year for £570 and a Georgian hallmarked silver hilted 1796 Heavy Cavalry officer's dress sword for £1,550. It was inscribed from the officer's of the 2nd Battalion 44th Regiment to their Colonel, Robert Garden and dated 1809. These prices show a marked rise over last year's prices for similar weapons.

Dirks and daggers shared the popularity of swords. Four Scottish dirks, all dating from the late 19th century, three with silver and one with copper mounting, sold for prices between £290 and £440. Another fine sword was a 18th century European processional two-handed broadsword with a 50½ inch blade and a leather covered grip. It fetched £450.

In the sword world enthusiasm for European weapons was only exceeded

A late Victorian Scottish officer's dress dirk set of The Highland Light Infantry. Scallop back blade 11½in. In its latent leather sheath with four gilt mounts.

$950 £440

by the keenness of the collectors of Oriental items. The Japanese buyers continued to secure the very best of their native weaponry that appeared in British salerooms. Mr Butler of Wallis and Wallis said with conviction; 'Every good Japanese weapon that passes through our hands ends up eventually back in Japan. No. matter how keen most collectors are they cannot withstand the vast sums being offered for really good Japanese items.'

This year his Lewes saleroom has seen the sale of an interesting pair of Japanese 'daisho', signed and dated 1666 and 1681 which fetched £1,400. Another Japanese 'taichi', from the late 19th century, sold for £1,150 and a 'katana', signed and dated 1807 with a leather bound 'tsuka' and 'tsuba' damascened with Buddhist symbols, went for £3,100.

The vogue for Orientalism also applied to Arab, Indian and near Eastern weapons. A Turkish yataghan, a single edged blade with a silver gilt foliate mount and inlaid in gold foliate patterns on the leather covered scabbard, sold for the good price of £400 which shows a rising interest in this sort of weapon. The Arab blade market however is fraught with danger for the amateur collector because of the proliferation of modern weapons brought back from the Middle East by people who have been working there over the past fifteen years. The market price for a really good Arab dagger is continually rising and is now up to around £100 for a dagger that five years ago would not have fetched £50. However, the keynote word is 'good'. Really valuable daggers have to date from not later than the end of the 19th century and above all they should be of good and sophistacated workmanship. Modern examples are often too crude unless they have been made specially for a presentation or for some high dignitary. Collectors should take great care when buying Arab daggers.

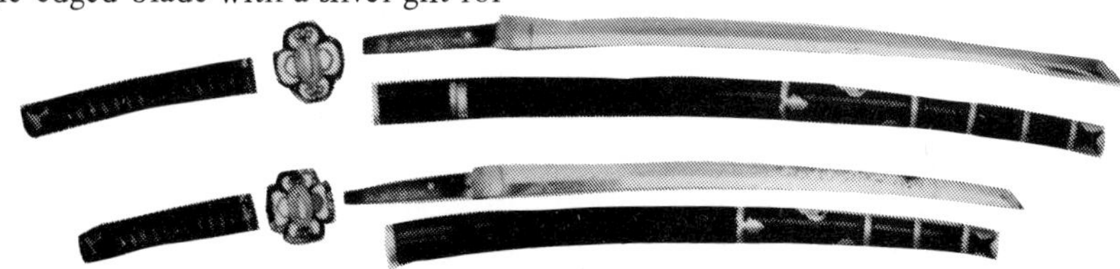

A pair of Japanese swords, daisho, katana, 57.5cm. Signed Nagasone Okisato Niudo Kotetsu, dated Kwanbun 6th year (1666 A.D.). Wakizashi 51cm, dated Genroku 3rd year (1681 A.D.). Silver mounted black lacquered sayas.

$3,024 £1,400

A Britain's Royal Engineers four-horse carriage and pontoon bridge section, two drivers in full dress, wooden pontoon and two bridge sections.

$367 £170

Caution also should be excercised in the world of Indian arms because since the mid 1970's there has been a brisk business in reproducing them. Some of the copies are very good and an example in point is the ankus or elephant goad. These are only metal hooks which mahouts used for urging on their elephants but they could also be used as fairly lethal weapons of war. Because of the simplicity of their design they are easy to copy and a specialist's advice is to hold one in the hand and 'listen to your intuition.' If in doubt it is always best to consult a specialist because pitfalls and pointers once recognised make it easier to spot the fakes.

There are several companies now in operation reproducing Eastern weapons and it is a good idea to get their catalogues in order to see the sort of thing that are being made. Serious collectors should also consider tracking down a copy of the weapon collectors' Bible – 'Stone's Glossary on Weapons'. This is still the most comprehensive study of weapons even though it was written as long ago as the 1920's. Copies can still be found, from time to time, in second-hand bookshops and they are excellent investments at the current asking price of between £10 and £20.

As always the Militaria market this year has contained one or two quirky items to spark collectors' interests. One such magnificent bronze figure of a mounted warrior made by a Japanese artist in the late 19th century. It was sold this year by the dealer who had owned it for several years and it fetched £1,700.

Another specialist field that is rapidly growing and which has the added appeal of childhood nostalgia is the world of toy soldiers. Once played with in every nursery, lead soldiers are now banned because of the toxicity of the lead. When they appear for sale however, their appeal is undiminished among the grown up 'war game' fanatics who snap them up for prices many times more than they originally cost. Some of the best prices are summoned for toys made by the famous firm, Britains and this year a four horse carriage with a pontoon bridge building unit by them sold for £170. Its original price could only have been pennies. Anyone with toy soldiers in their possession should be warned that no matter how chipped or battered they look they should be left in that state. Any attempt to repaint them or smarten them up takes pounds off the price. So leave your wounded soldiers unrepaired!

LIZ TAYLOR

EDGED WEAPONS

BAYONETS

A scarce Austrian sword-socket bayonet for the M. 1849 Augustin rifle, single edge straight fullered blade 23in. with arsenal mark, socket handle with muzzle slots, stamped with arsenal marks on elbow. $90 £36

A scarce Austrian sword-socket bayonet for the M. 1849 Augustin rifle, single edge straight fullered blade 23½in. with arsenal marks, socket handle with muzzle slots and securing ring, stamped with arsenal stamps on elbow. $105 £45

A Prussian 1871 dress bayonet, plated, slightly curved blade 19¼in., etched with military trophies, pickelhaube.crossed cannon, cuirass, and other trophies, foliage etc., plated reversed crosspiece, gilt hilt, with hatched grip and in its leather scabbard. $140 £58

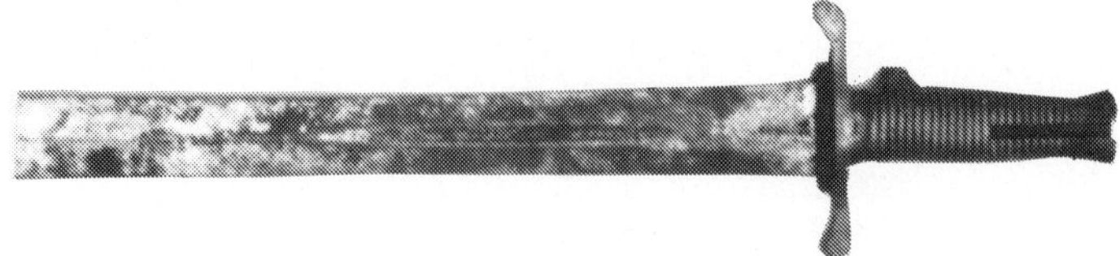

A rare British pattern 1848 brass hilted Brunswick bayonet, double edged spatulate blade 22¼in., with narrow central fuller at forte, stamped with Goverment Ordnance mark crowned E over 6, crowned 'VR' and 'Enfield', with ribbed brass grip, iron sprung latch. $130 £60

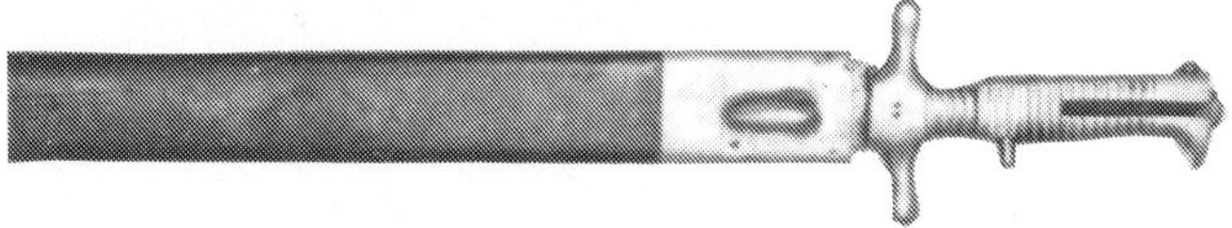

A scarce Italian brass hilted sword bayonet for the M. 1856 Bersaglieri carbine, double edged blade 17¾in., ribbed brass grip, straight crosspiece, in its brass mounted leather scabbard. $150 £70

An unusual unidentified sword bayonet for use with a double barrelled weapon, recurving blade 17¼in., steel crosspiece, horn hilt with leaf spring, in its leather scabbard with brass mounts. $165 £75

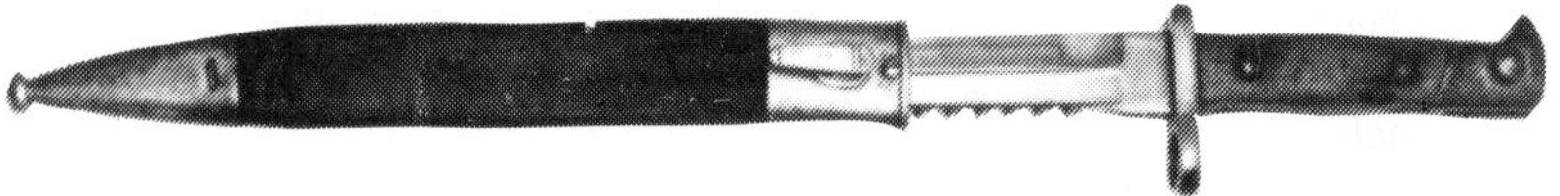

A rare German M. 1871/84 bayonet with saw-backed blade 9¾in. by 'Alex Coppel', stamped on backstrap with crown above 'W.88', steel mounts, wood grips, the crosspiece stamped with machine gunner markings '71.R.M.G., 23in. in its steel mounted leather scabbard. $225 £92

A rare Weimar Republic Police Dress bayonet, plated blade 17in. by Carl Eickhorn, plated white metal shellguard with Weimar Eagle, eagle's head pommel, stag horn grips with plated mounts, and leather frog. $540 £220

An early 18th century Scandinavian Cavalry backsword, single edged blade 34in. struck with a small mark, iron looped basket guard, thumb ring, steel wire bound grip. $135 £65

An early 18th century broadsword, double edged, slightly tapering blade 30½in., with traces of 'Running Wolf' mark, and signed in short fuller 'Inimini', also with ordnance stamp, brass hilt with double shell guard, single knucklebow with double loop at base, large rounded pommel, brass wire grip with 'Turks head' finials. $200 £96

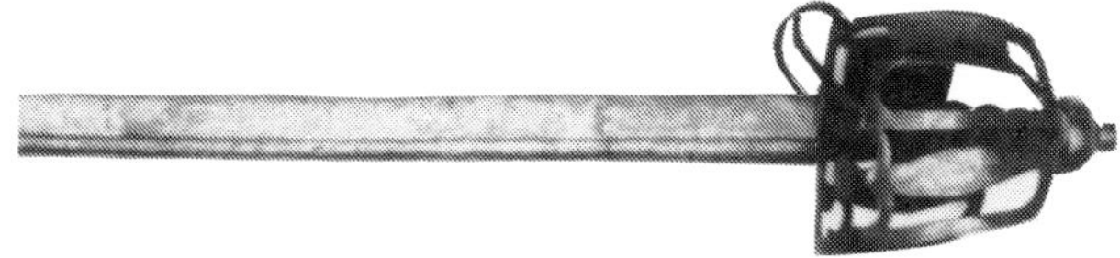

An 18th century English Horseman's broadsword straight single edged blade 34in., narrow back fuller, traces of etching, steel basket guard, with blank panels, spiral wooden grip, flattened circular pommel. $220 £100

An Austrian Heavy Cavalry Trooper's broadsword, circa 1824, straight blade 33in. stamped 'Fischer' on backstrap, steel, pierced guard, flattened knucklebow, steel mounts, leather covered ribbed grip, in its steel scabbard. $300 £145

A 17th century European broadsword, tapering double edged blade 33in., multi-fullered, iron swept hilt with loop guard around ricasso and reversed crosspiece, single knuckelbow and acorn pommel, the hilt chiselled overall with oak-leaf type patterns. $440 £200

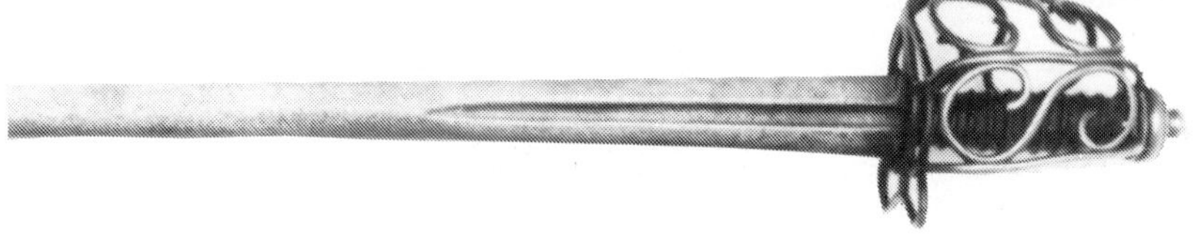

An English brass basket hilted broadsword, circa 1760, broad double edged single fullered straight blade 33in. Basket hilt composed of letter 'S' within bars, turned bun pommel. Fabric covered ribbed grip. $435 £210

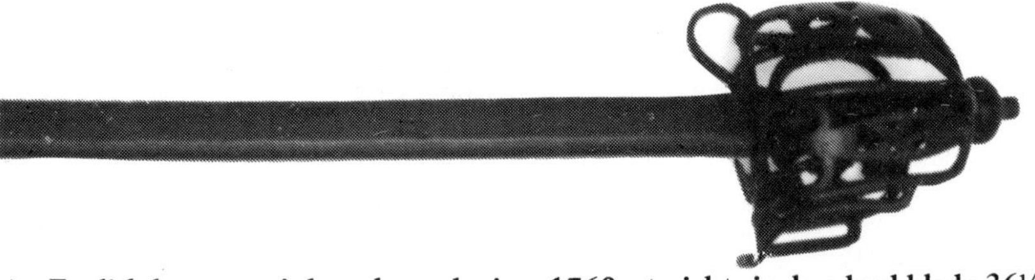

An English horseman's broadsword, circa 1760, straight single edged blade 36½in. with single back fuller, and with Shotley Bridge running fox mark and 'S.H.', iron basket guard, the bars panels pierced with heart pattern etc., wire bound fishskin covered grip. $625 £260

A Prussian 1732 Model Cuirassier broadsword, double edged, tapering blade 36½in., cast brass semi-basket guard, with pommel, wirebound, leather covered grip, thumb ring. $575 £285

A Victorian Scottish officer's broadsword, straight double fullered blade 32in., by Carter, Pall Mall, etched with crown, 'Royal Scots Fusiliers', regimental badge, crown foliage etc., fitted with undress cruciform hilt, plated crossguard and mounts, wirebound fishskin covered grip, in its leather covered Field Service scabbard with plated tip. $170 £80

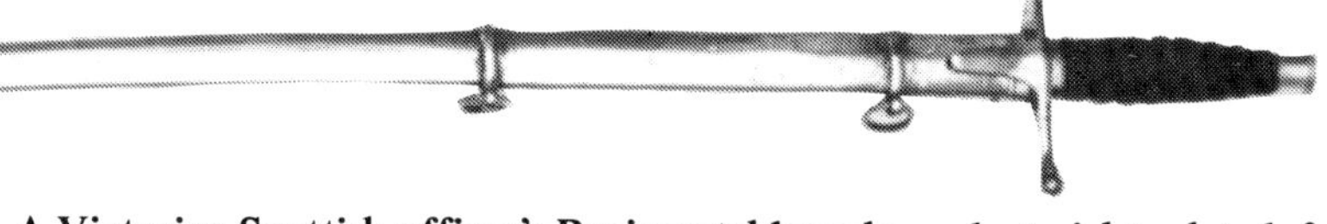

A Victorian Scottish officer's Regimental broadsword, straight, plated, fullered blade 32½in., by 'Leckie Graham, Glasgow', etched with Regimental badge of 'H.L.I.', thistles etc., fitted with undress hilt, with plated crosspiece and pommel, wirebound fishskin covered grip, in its plated scabbard. $190 £86

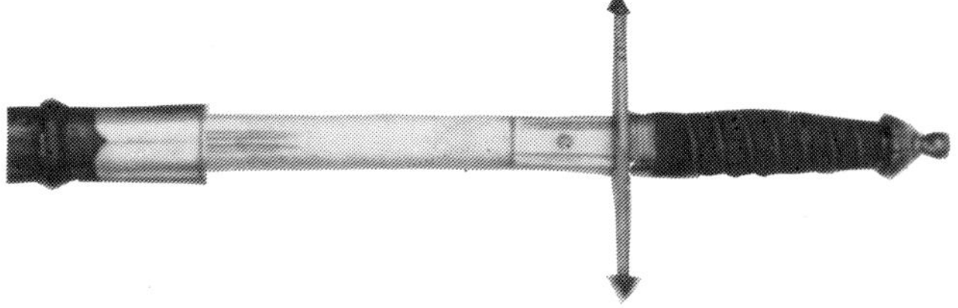

An Edward VII Scottish officer's Military broadsword, straight, double fullered blade 32in., by Hawkes, etched with 'The King's Own Scottish Borderers', Royal Cypher etc., 'Egypt' honour and sphinx, fitted with undress cruciform hilt, steel crosspiece and mounts, wirebound fishskin covered grip, in its leather covered Field Service scabbard with steel mounts. $180 £95

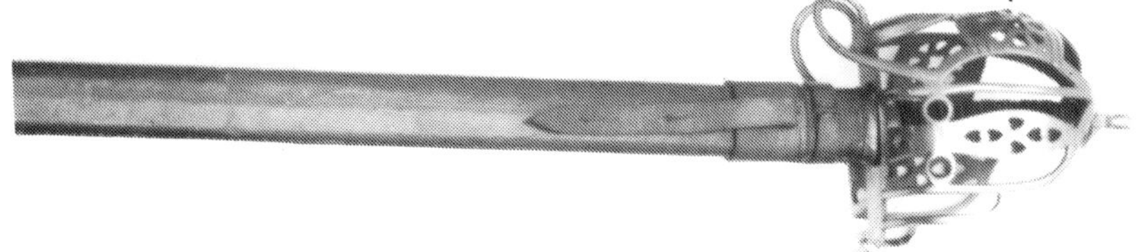

A Victorian Scottish officer's Military broadsword, straight, double edged plated blade, 32in., with double central fullers, by 'Ponder, Duke Street, St. James', etched with crown, 'V.R.', Regt. 'LXXIV Highlanders', plated basket guard of traditional pattern, fluted domed pommel, copper wirebound fishskin covered grip, in its leather covered Field Service scabbard. $205 £95

A Scottish basket hilted broadsword, circa 1900, straight double edged double fullered blade 32¼in., etched 'Brook & Son, 87 George Street, Edinburgh'. Pierced plated basket guard of traditional form with hearts in rosette form. Sharkskin covered grip, in its leather covered Field Service scabbard. $255 £105

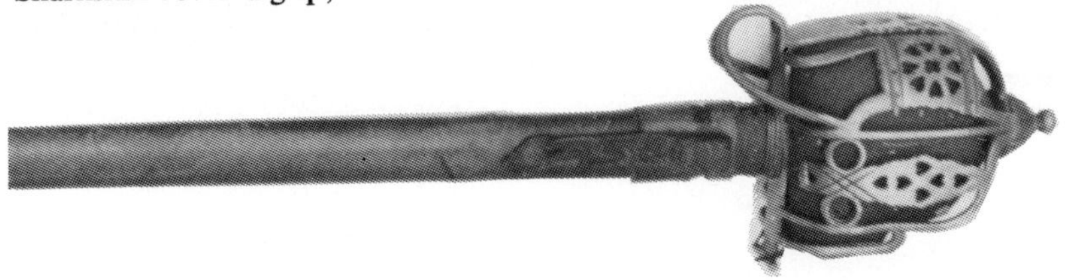

A George V Scottish officer's broadsword, straight, double fullered blade 32in., etched with foliage and thistle, and 'E. Lawson The Black Watch', white metal basket hilt pierced with traditional patterns, wirebound fishskin covered grip, in its leather covered Field Service scabbard. $260 £110

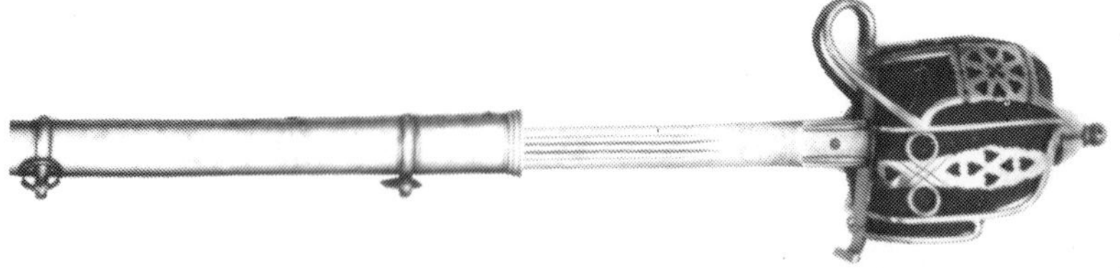

A Victorian Scottish officer's Military broadsword, straight, double edged fullered blade 32in., by 'E. Thurkle, Soho, London', etched with crown 'V.R.', Regt. 'Royal Scots Fusiliers', Regimental badges etc., steel basket guard of traditional pattern, wirebound fishskin covered grip, in its steel scabbard. $265 £120

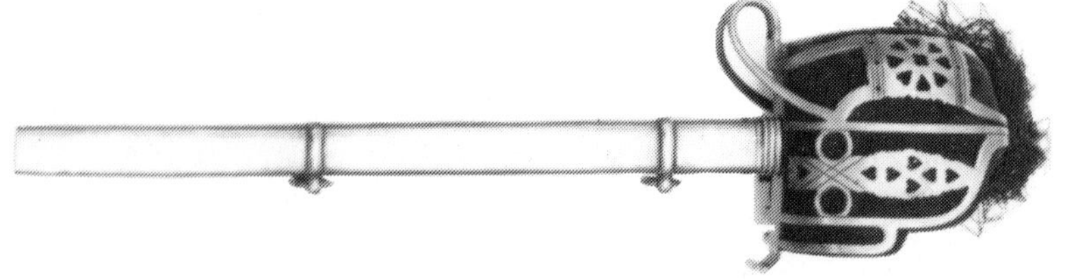

A Victorian Highland Regiment officer's broadsword, double edged, bi-fullered blade 32in., etched with 'V.R.' cypher and scrolled panels, steel basket guard, wirebound leather grip, crimson tassels, in its steel scabbard. $285 £120

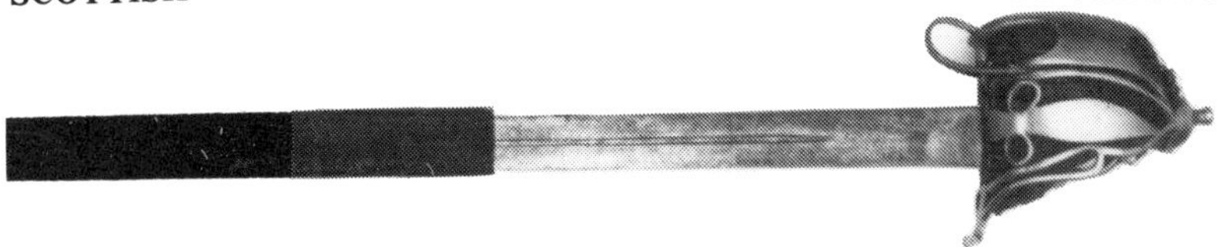

A Scottish officer's broadsword, circa 1800, plain, single edged tapering blade 32in., short narrow central fuller, copper gilt basket guard, plain panels, flattened ovoid pommel, crimson tassel, wirebound fishskin covered grip, in a leather scabbard. $275 £125

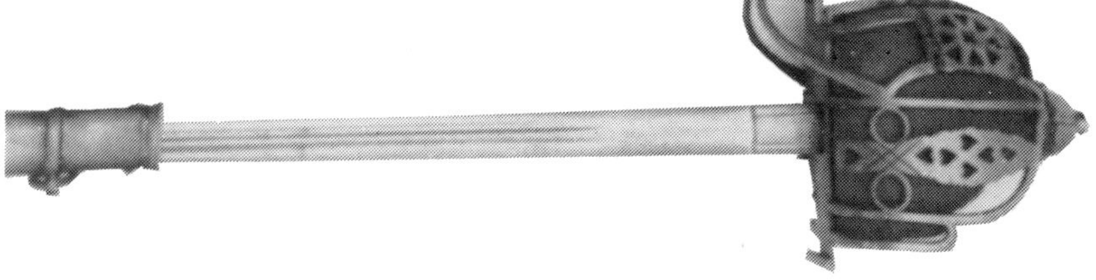

A Victorian Scottish officer's dress military broadsword, double fullered double edged blade 33in., etched with crown, 'V.R.', regiment 'H.L.I.' with regimental devices, thistles and foliage, steel basket guard, in its steel scabbard. $275 £125

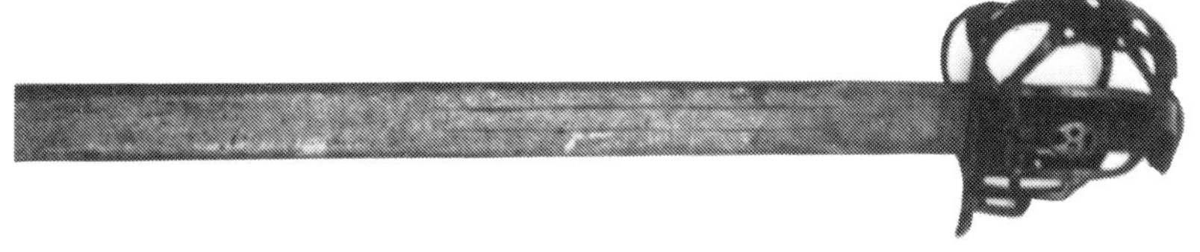

An early 18th century Scottish Military broadsword, broad, double edged blade, 33in., with short narrow fullers, iron basket hilt, with rein loop and some bars pierced in traditional style, reinforced at the back quillon and top of the guard, flattened 'Wheel' pommel, wooden grip. $280 £128

A Scottish Military broadsword, circa 1800, straight, single edged blade 30½in., broad and narrow fullers, iron basket guard of traditional pattern, flattened circular pommel, spiral fishskin covered grip. $390 £160

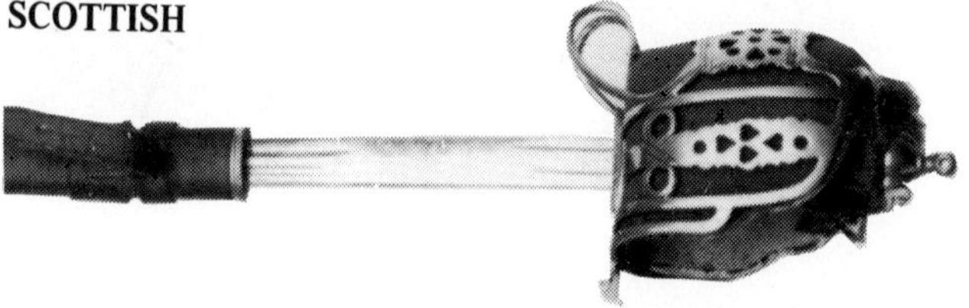

A George V Scottish officer's dress Military broadsword, straight, double fullered blade 32in., by 'Fenton Brothers, Sheffield', etched with Royal Arms and cypher and foliate sprays, German silver hilt of traditional basket form, original crimson tassel, wirebound fishskin covered grip, in its leather covered Field Service scabbard. $380 £165

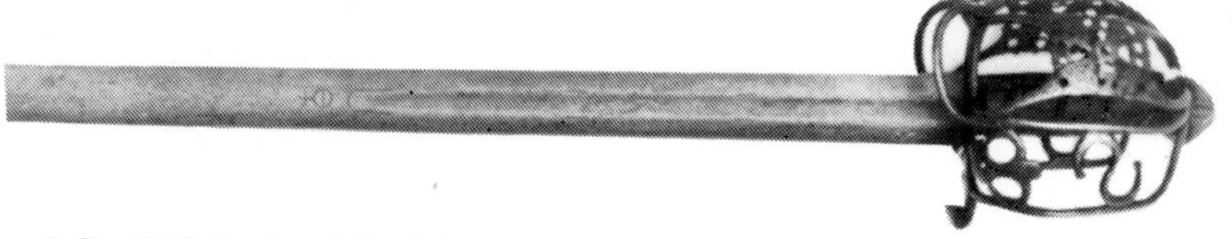

A Scottish basket hilted broadsword, circa 1720, double edged straight blade 32½in., with single fullers at forte, struck with running wolf and orb marks. Small basket guard incorporating pierced panels, stylised fleur de lys and letter 'S' within basket. Iron pommel with line decoration. $495 £240

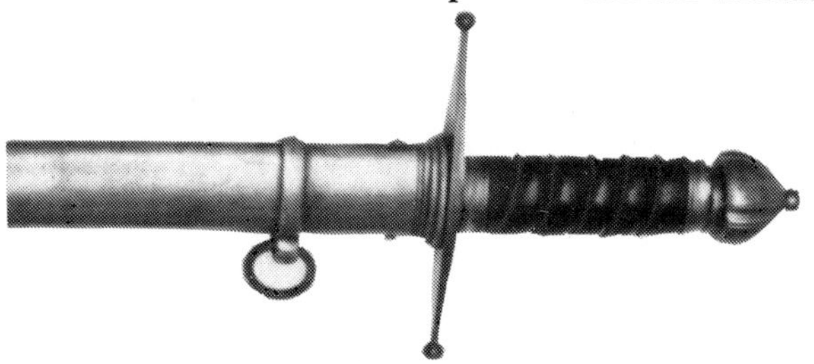

An unusual early 19th century Scottish officer's broadsword, double edged blade 34in., with long central fuller etched in large lettering 'Andrea Ferrara' cruciform hilt with plain steel crosspiece, copper wirebound, black wood ribbed grip, fluted conical steel pommel, steel mounts, in its steel scabbard.

$720 £300

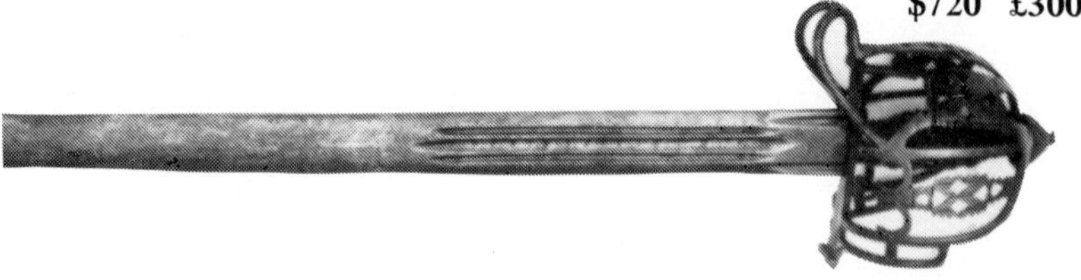

A late 18th century Scottish broadsword, broad double edged blade 31½in., multi-fullered at forte, and signed in the fuller 'Andrea Ferrara', steel basket guard pierced with traditional patterns, fluted conical pommel, wirebound fishskin covered grip. $835 £380

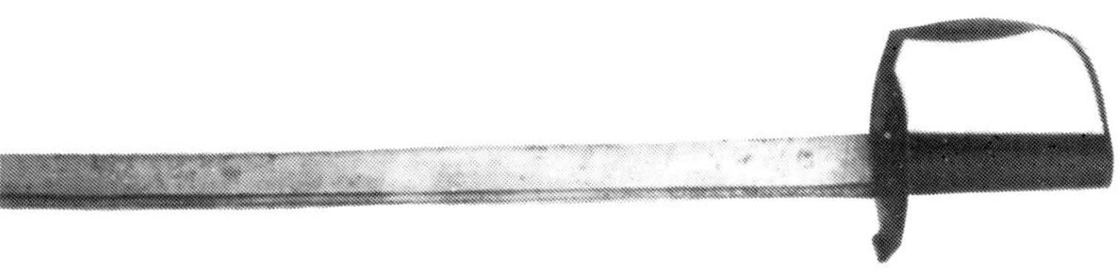

A late 18th century 'figure-of-eight' Naval boarding cutlass, single edged blade 28in., narrow back fuller, blackened iron guard and cylindrical grip. $155 £65

A late 18th century 'figure-of-eight' Naval boarding cutlass, single edged blade 29in., with narrow back fuller, iron hilt and cylindrical grip, with addition of two side loops. $155 £65

A Prussian mid 19th century Naval cutlass, single edged blade 26in., Beehive Maker's Trademark at forte, blackened iron hilt with solid half basket guard, ribbed grip, in its brass mounted leather scabbard. $150 £70

A mid 19th century Belgian folding cutlass, broad, clipped-back blade 14in., folding into plain sheet steel frame, twin black horn grips, double bar guard into which the blade tip folds, side release catch, overall length (open) 30in. $170 £70

A Prussian mid 19th century Naval cutlass, slightly curved, single edged blade 26in., by 'Holler', iron half basket guard, ribbed iron grip, in its brass mounted leather scabbard. $175 £85

A scarce French pattern 1833 Naval boarding cutlass, curved, single edged, pointed blade 27in., with broad central fuller and faintly engraved with anchor, backstrap engraved 'Manufe Rle de Chatellerault Juin 1842' with inspector's stamps at forte, iron half basket guard, painted black octagonal iron grip and pommel. $190 £100

A Prussian 1865 pattern Naval cutlass, single edged, recessed blade 23in., with traces of maker 'Clemen & Jung', solid steel, half-bowl guard, ribbed iron grip. $270 £115

A French 1833 Model Naval boarding cutlass, slightly curved blade 26½in., engraved with anchor, engraved on backstrap, 'Manufre Rle de Chatellerault Sbr 1840', iron semi-basket solid guard with octagonal iron grip, in its brass mounted leather scabbard. $330 £140

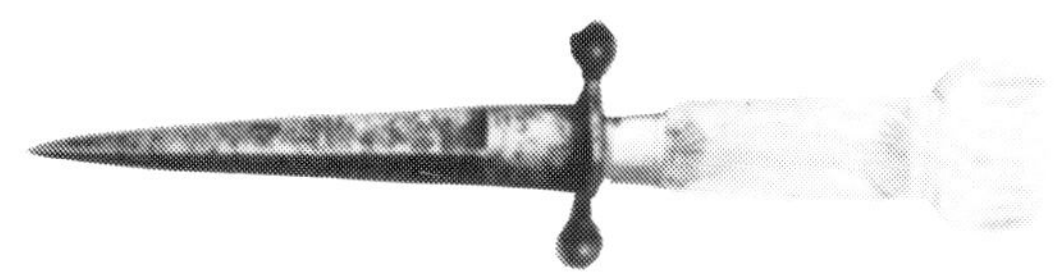

A Georgian stilletto dagger, straight diamond section tapering blade 4½in., small globular quillons to crosspiece, flattened ivory hilt with scallop patterns, eared, fluted pommel. $65 £26

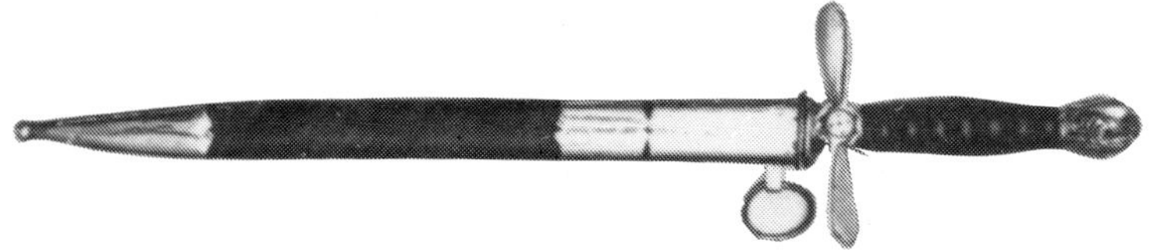

A Yugoslavian Air Force dress dagger, plated blade 9in., plated propeller crosspiece, cast scrolled pommel, wirebound black grip, in its leather covered metal sheath with plain plated mounts. $65 £30

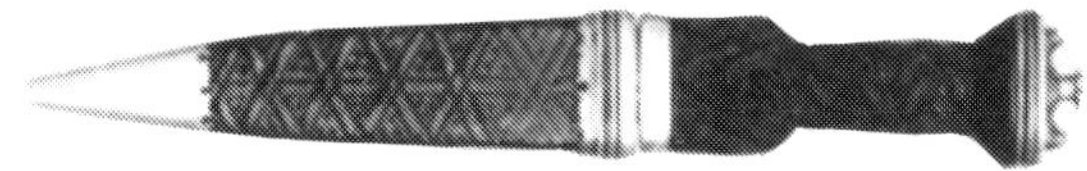

A silver mounted skean dhu, blade 4½in. with scallop back edge,fuller pierced with 3 holes, corded wood hilt, plate base mount and pommel mounts with conical mounts, in its blind tooled sheath with silver mounts, hallmarked Edinburgh 1917. $130 £55

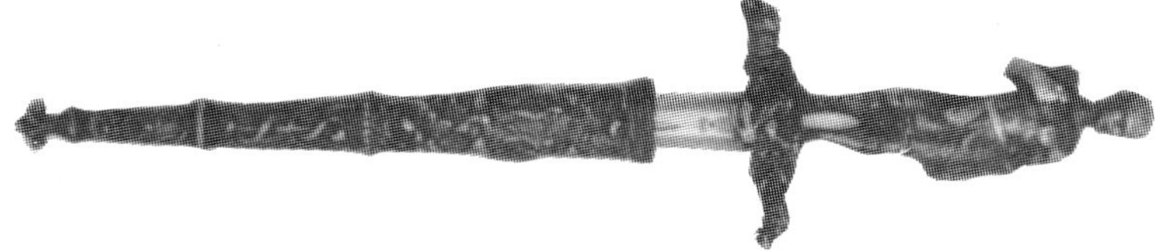

A Victorian hilted mystic dagger, double edged tapering blade 5in., of flattened diamond section with central fuller, by 'Geo. Wostenholm Sheffield', marked 'I.X.L.', the crosspiece with hounds' heads terminals, the hilt in the form of a standing native figure, 3½in. in its brass sheath with relief designs overall of fighting figures etc. $115 £60

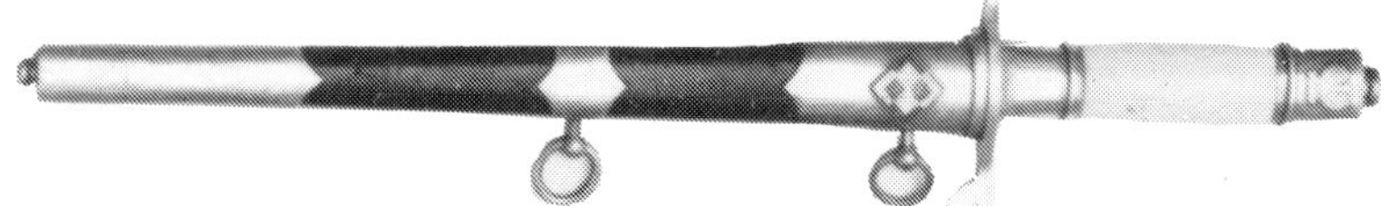

A Polish Air Force officer's dress dagger, blade 9in., plated reversed crossguard with spring catch, plated mounts, Polish Eagle on pommel, white celluloid grip, in its black leather covered metal sheath with 3 plated mounts. $125 £60

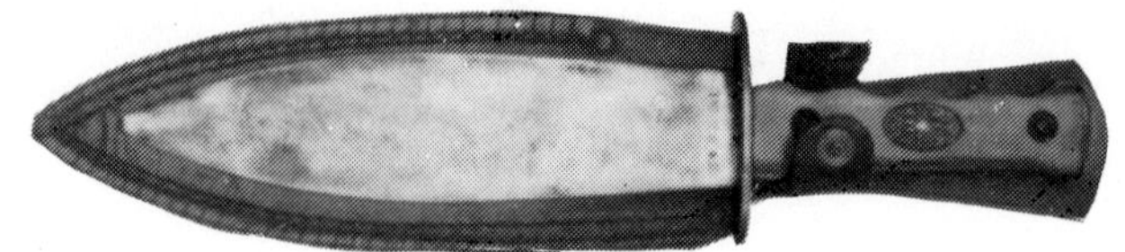

A 'Beaver Tail' type hunting dagger, broad double edged blade 7¼in., stamped at forte 'PC 2242', plain oval steel crosspiece, shaped hilt with horn panels, one inset with oval brass plaque with crowned Prussian type eagle, in its leather sheath with belt loop. $160 £75

A rare Australian or N.Z. World War II fighting knuckleduster dagger, double edged blade 8in., of flattened diamond section, hilt with much original khaki green paint. $210 £85

A Polish Air Force honour dagger, plated blade 9in. stamped at forte 'G. Borowski' and etched with foliate scrolls, Polish Eagle and 'Honor I Ojcyzna', in its black leather covered metal sheath with German silver mounts. $255 £115

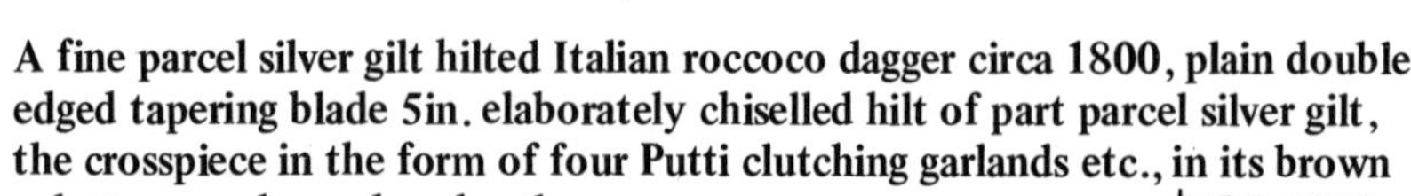

A fine parcel silver gilt hilted Italian roccoco dagger circa 1800, plain double edged tapering blade 5in. elaborately chiselled hilt of part parcel silver gilt, the crosspiece in the form of four Putti clutching garlands etc., in its brown velvet covered wooden sheath. $475 £220

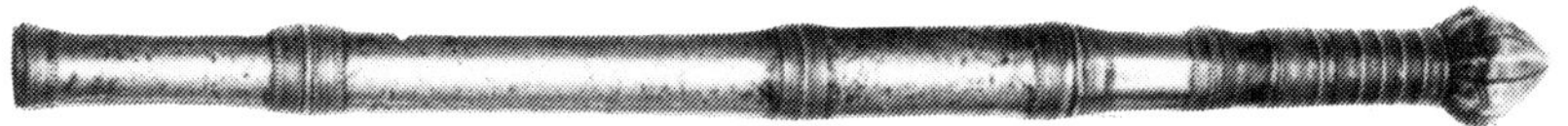

A silver mounted Burmese dha dagger, blade 10½in., the hilt covered in Eastern sheet and wire silver with Lotus pommel, central copper band, in its wooden sheath covered in Eastern sheet silver with filigree bands. $155 £75

A Burmese silver mounted dha dagger, slightly curved blade 8in., ivory hilt with Eastern sheet silver base mount, in its wooden sheath, with two Eastern sheet silver bands and wire mounts. $185 £80

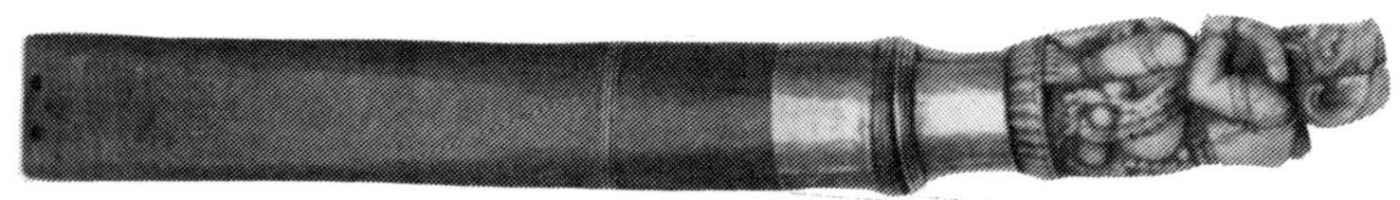

A Burmese dha dagger, single edged plain blade 9in., elaborate bone hilt carved in the form of a seated demon, 4in., with plain Eastern silver band, in its wooden sheath with 2 Eastern silver bands. $195 £85

A Burmese dagger dha, single edged blade 7½in., silver damascened with scrolls, silver ferrule, ivory hilt pierced and carved with demons inhabiting scrolls in various recumbant postures, in its wooden sheath. $300 £125

A Chillanum, curved blade 7in., iron hilt with straight crosspiece, baluster grip, crescent pommel, in its iron sheath with brass throat mount. $90 £45

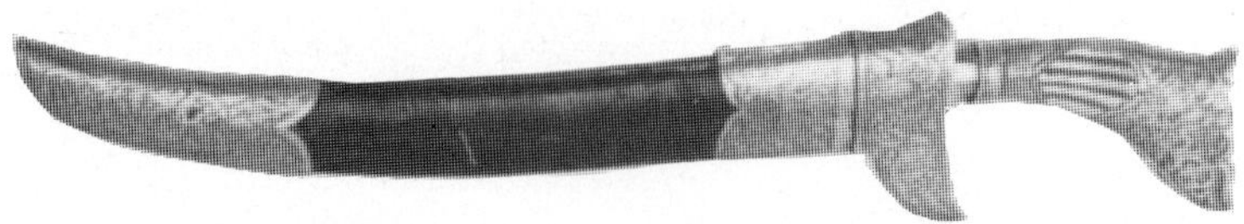

An unusual silver mounted Sumatran dagger of Sekin type, fullered single edged blade 9in., copper ferrule, foliate embossed and engraved silver hilt, in its leather sheath with well foliate engraved brass mounts en-suite with silver locket. $95 £50

A Celebes Golok of unusual form, steel, slim blade 12in., with broad, hooked tip, octagonal at forte, brass hilt with flattened knucklebow and rounded grip, black hair tuft to pommel. $120 £55

An old Indian silver mounted Bhuj (from Sind), clipped back blade 7in., mostly overlaid with foliate panels, issuing from chiselled elephant head, all metal hollow shaft similarly decorated overall with floral and foliate panels, and with screw-in concealed dagger, blade 5in with urn finial, overall 24½in. $205 £95

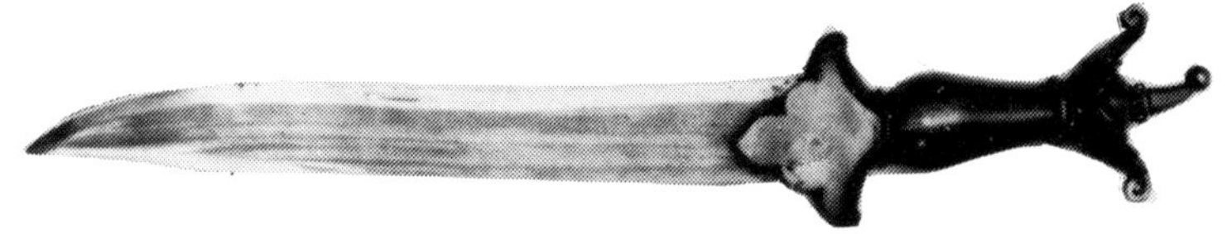

An Indian dagger, single edged watered steel blade 9½in. with multi-fullers clipped back tip and partly in-curving cutting edge, the hilt of solid copper with narrow guard and boat-style pommel. $230 £95

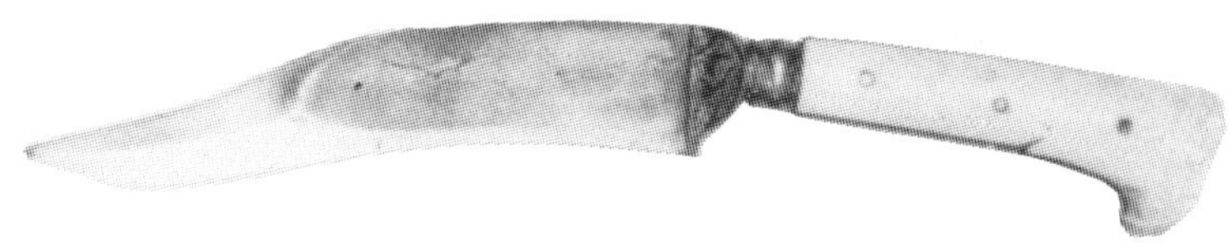

A 19th century Indian mail piercing dagger, slightly re-curved watered blade 5in. chiselled at forte with stylised birds, two piece ivory grips with ear shaped pommel, the backstrap pierced and inlaid with free moving steel balls, an allegory of 'the tears of the afflicted', in its leather covered sheath. $190 £100

An Indian dagger Khanjarli from Vizianagram, re-curved fullered double edged blade 7in., foliate chiselled and silver gilt overlaid at forte, 6 piece ivory grips with crescent shaped pommel retained by gold rivet heads, silver gilt backstrap, in its velvet covered sheath with copper gilt mounts. $230 £120

An Indian brass hilted dagger from Mysore, wavy blade 8in., single knucklebow, rounded grip with monster head pommel. $260 £120

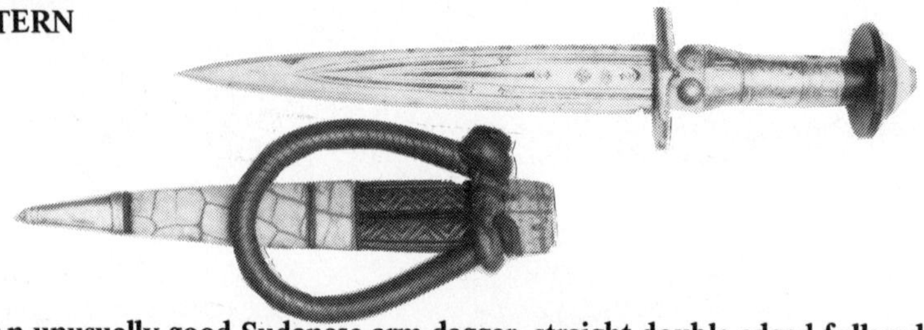

An unusually good Sudanese arm dagger, straight double edged fullered blade 9in., inlaid with brass plaque struck with Arabic devices, ebony and ivory hilt overlaid with gold and silver foil embossed with Arabic script, pique work to pommel, in its crocodile skin and leather mounted sheath. $270 £130

A Parang Latok, single edged blade 22in., Eastern sheet silver covered grip embossed with floral and foliate patterns, with iron fluted base, floral carved pommel, in its wooden sheath with suspension cord and part bound. $365 £170

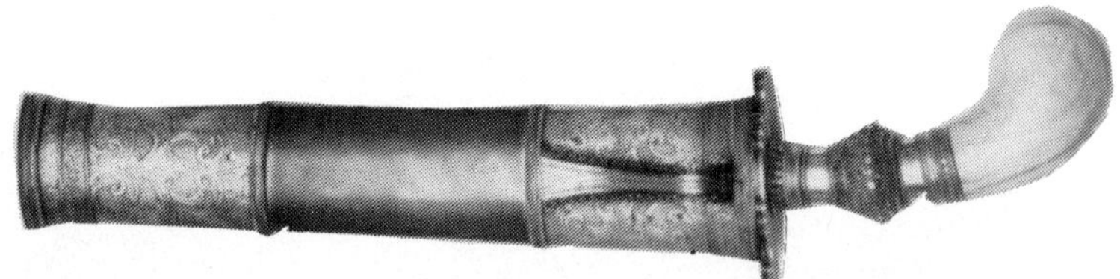

A fine and attractive Indonesian dagger, broad double edged shallow diamond section blade 10½in., two-piece copper gilt crosspiece engraved with foliage, round swollen ivory grip, in its copper gilt mounted sheath, large mounts foliate engraved with pierced silver gilt belt loop. $415 £180

A fine quality silver mounted Turkish dagger, single edged blade 8¼ inch etched with foliate spray, eared ivory grip, fluted pommel cap inset with stone concealing a pair of tweezers, in its wooden lined sheath of solid Eastern silver. $455 £210

A Nazi 1st pattern Luftwaffe officer's dagger, plated blade by Robert Klaas, plated mounts wirebound, blue leather covered grip, in its blue leather covered metal sheath with plated mounts, hanging chains and belt clip. $160 £65

A Nazi 1st pattern Luftwaffe officer's dagger, by SMF, plated blade, stamped '42' at forte, German silver mounts, wirebound black leather covered grip, in its black leather covered metal scabbard with plated mounts and original hanging straps and belt clip. $165 £80

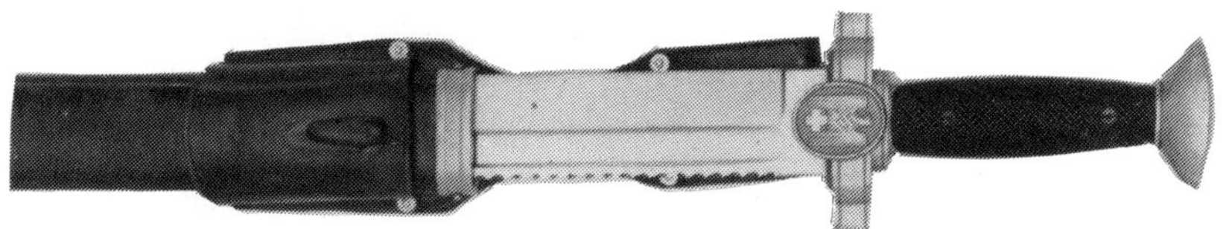

A Nazi Red Cross man's dagger, the blade retaining all original polish, and stamped at forte 'Ges Geschuzt', plated mounts, in its black painted metal sheath, with plated mounts and leather frog. $170 £90

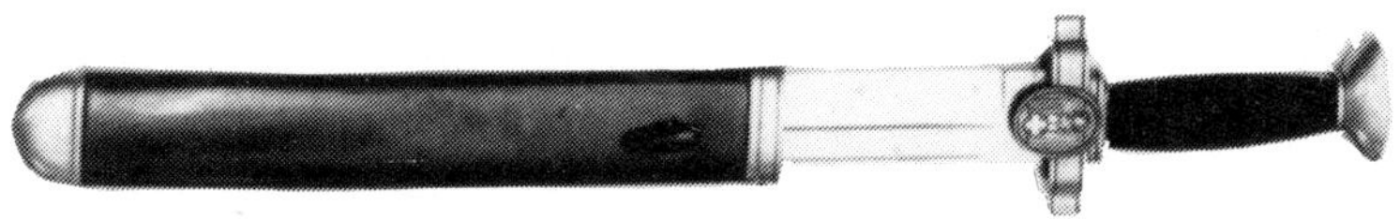

A Nazi Red Cross man's dagger, blade retaining all original polish, marked 'Ges Geschuzt', plated mounts, in its sheath with plated mounts. $230 £95

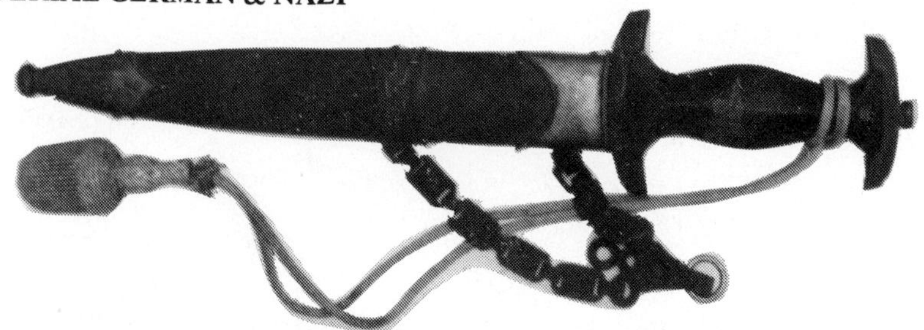

An original Nazi S.S. 1936 model officer's dagger, the blade retaining most original polish, German silver mounts, in its metal sheath with German silver chape and locket, the central mount originally plated, with original suspension chains and belt clip. $230 £95

A Nazi S.S. 1933 pattern dagger, by Gottlieb Hammesfahr, German silver mounts, in its metal sheath with German silver mounts. $190 £100

A Nazi Army officer's dagger, by Robt. Klaas, plated mounts, in its plated sheath. $295 £120

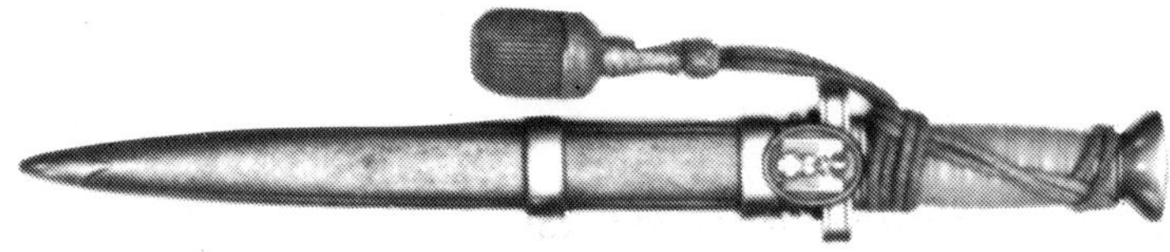

A Nazi Red Cross officer's dagger, plated mounts, yellow ivorine grip, in its metal sheath with bullion dress knot. $320 £130

A Luftwaffe officer's 2nd pattern dagger, by SMF, the blade with Luftwaffe control stamp and retaining all original polish, grey metal mounts, wirebound orange grip, bullion dress knot, in its grey metal sheath with original hanging straps and belt clip. $320 £130

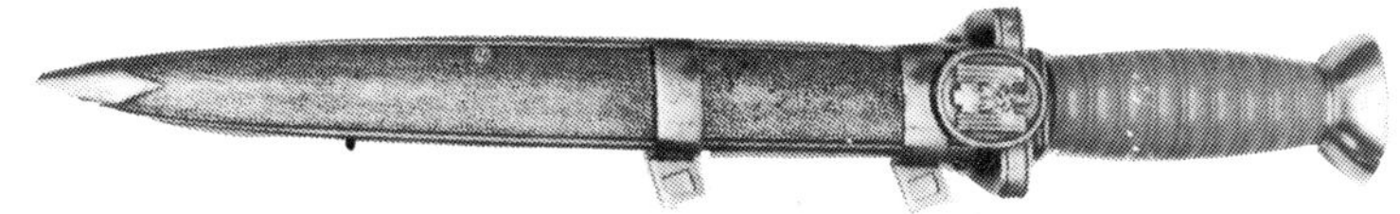

A Nazi Red Cross officer's dagger, blade retaining most original polish, plated mounts, orange grip, in its plated sheath. $325 £135

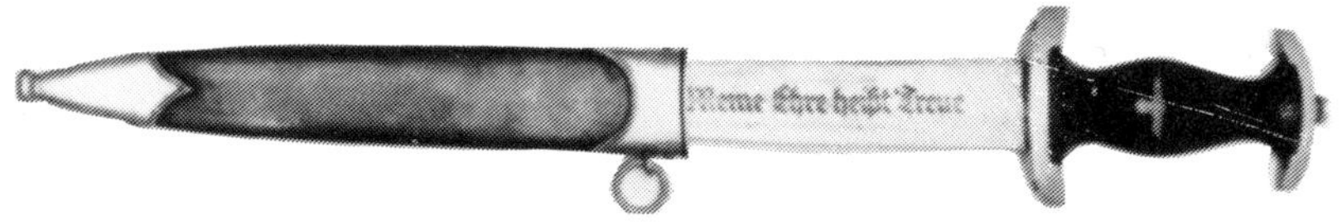

A Nazi model 1933 S.S. dagger, by Gottlieb Hammesfahr, German silver mounts, in its metal sheath with German silver mounts. $365 £150

A Nazi goverment official's dagger, by Alcoso, plated mounts, mother of pearl grips, in its plated sheath. $1,100 £450

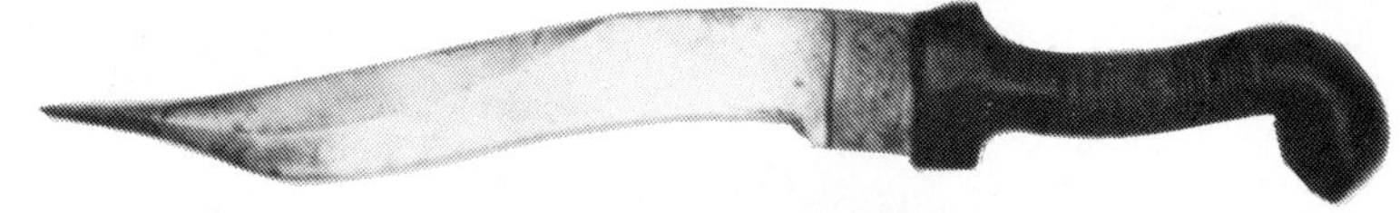

An unusual Eastern jambiya, re-curving blade 9in., with clipped back edge and re-enforced tip, etched at forte with inscription in Eastern script, re-curving ribbed bone hilt, in its leather covered wooden sheath. $55 £26

An Arab (waha Bite) jambiya, curved blade 19in. wooden hilt with white metal rosette mounts, the pommel with conical mounts, in its leather covered wooden sheath with large white metal mounts decorated with scaled and embossed foliate patterns. $140 £60

An Indo-Persian all steel jambiya, slightly curved blade 11in., chiselled at forte with foliage, the hilt chiselled overall with animals and birds within foliage, in its wooden lined steel sheath. $155 £70

An Arab silver mounted jambiya, curved blade 7in., with central rib, horn hilt with Eastern silver mounts with filigree patterns, domed caps to pommel, in its cloth covered leather sheath with large filigree decorated Eastern silver chape and locket. $140 £75

An Arab dagger jambiya, curved double edged blade 7in., with central rib, hilt and sheath mounts of intricate silver filigree work with bullion belt and large silver rings bound to sheath. $190 £81

A silver mounted Arab jambiya, curved blade 9½in. with central rib, traces of watered steel pattern, horn hilt, with Eastern silver domed studded mounts, in its wooden lined sheath of solid Eastern silver, with beaded patterns and band pattern tip. $205 £100

A Persian jambiya, curved blade 9in. with raised rib, horn hilt chiselled with embossed figures, a hand, and with Eastern inscription at base, in its fluted leather covered wooden sheath. $235 £125

An Indo-Persian jambiya, curved blade 9¼in., retaining most original finish, and with raised central rib and re-enforced tip, the iron hilt covered in gold, damascene, floral and foliate patterns, in its green velvet covered wooden sheath. $330 £150

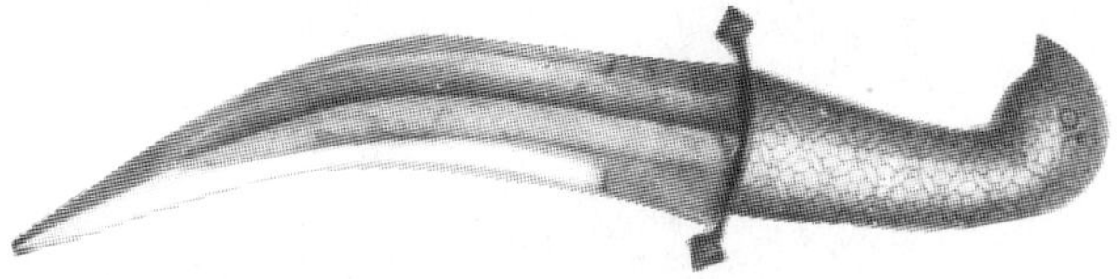

An Indo-Persian jambiya, curved, double fullered blade 9in., with traces of watered steel finish, iron hilt with 'Bird's Head' pommel, covered overall with gold floral and foliate damascene patterns, down curved 'pyramid' terminal short crossguard. $365 £170

An Arab silver mounted jambiya, curved blade 8in. with central rib, horn hilt partly overlaid with Eastern sheet silver and with beaded and filigree mounts, in its leather and cloth covered wooden sheath. $410 £200

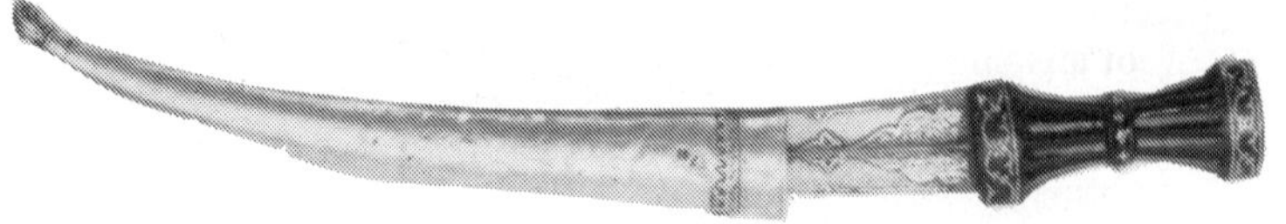

An Indo-Persian jambiya, curved, watered steel blade, 12in., with central rib, decorated at forte with gold damascened foliate patterns, fluted dark green stone hilt with gold inlaid foliate patterns, in its Eastern sheet silver covered wooden lined sheath. $930 £490

A kard, watered steel single edged blade 9¾in., traces of gold damascene at forte, bone grip, in its Eastern silver, wooden lined sheath. $130 £55

An attractive 19th century dagger kard, single edged watered blade 13in., gold damascened at forte with script and diaper pattern, two piece ivory grip, gold damascened grip strap. $165 £70

An Indian kard, blade 6½in., with gold and silver damascene decoration at forte, mutton fat jade rounded hilt, in its solid Eastern silver sheath.$190 £100

KHANJAR

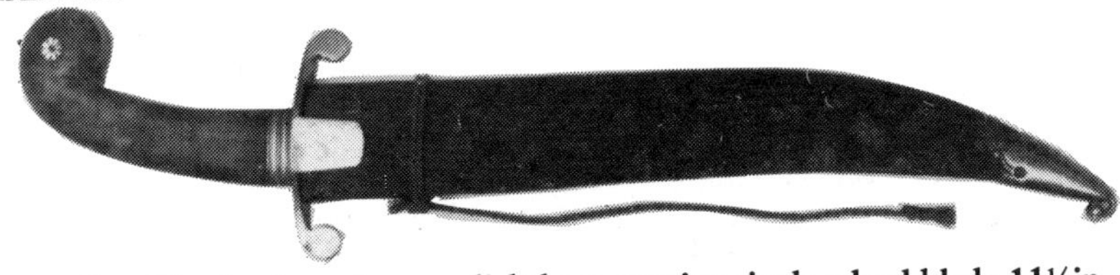

An Indian Khanjar type dagger, slightly re-curving single edged blade 11½in., with central fuller,steel crosspiece, the hilt of green jade stone, in its brocaded wooden sheath with silver tip. $280 £130

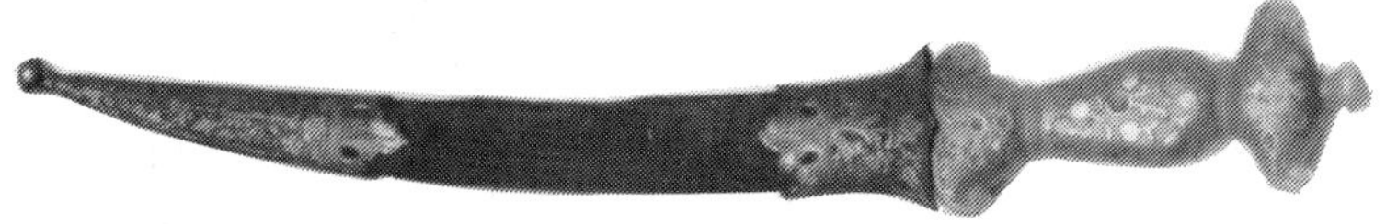

A scarce 18th century Indo-Persian jade hilted dagger khanjar, slender curved double edged blade 9¼in., pale green coloured jade hilt carved with foliate scrolls at root and pommel with ribs at grip, in its copper gilt mounted sheath. $345 £150

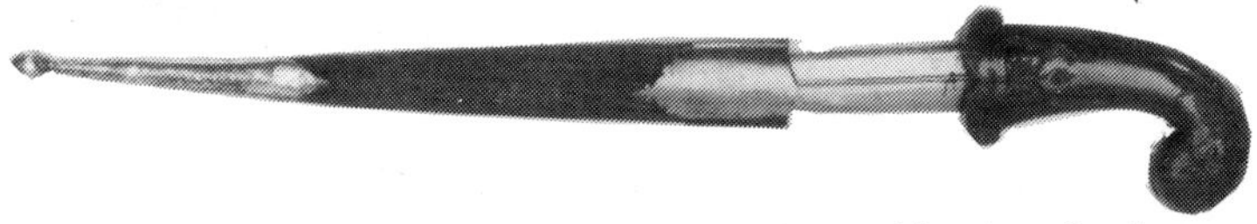

A well carved green jade 18th century Indian dagger khanjar, slender curved double edged blade 10½in. with central ribs, large heavy hilt carved with foliage , in its velvet covered copper mounted sheath. $760 £400

An old Indian katar, double edged blade 8in., reinforced point, multi-fullered at forte, plain iron guard with 5 bar grip, foliate gold damascened overall, in its red and green velvet sheath with ornate Eastern silver chape. $95 £40

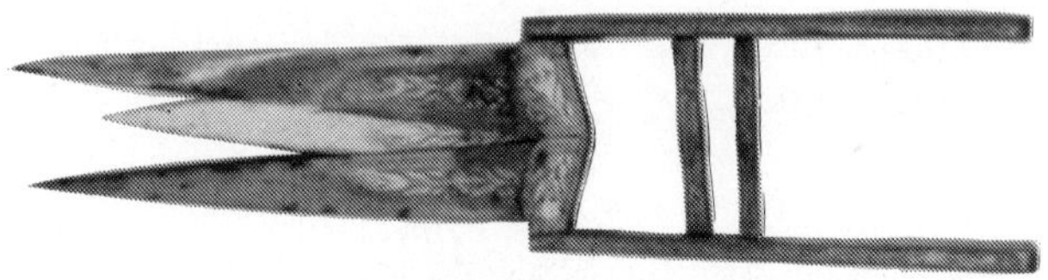

An Indian thrusting dagger 'scissors' katar, 17in. blades 8½in. hinged and hollow which separate to expose 7½in. inside blade, in its leather covered sheath. $85 £45

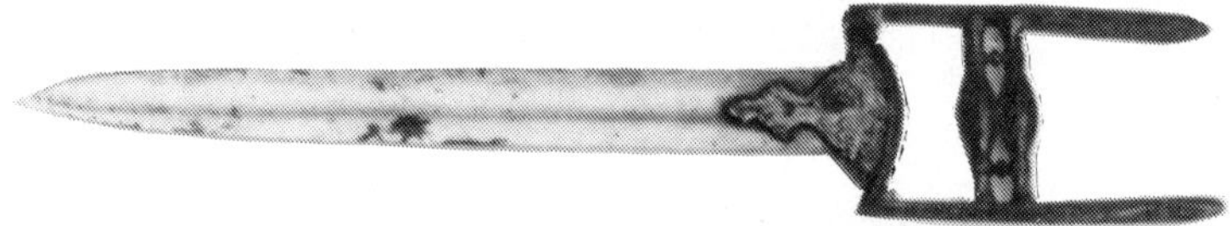

An 18th century Indian shi'ite thrusting dagger katar, straight double edged single fullered blade 12¾in., steel hilt well chiselled in relief and silvered overall with foliage and Arabic script, swollen octagonal grips, foliate finialed blade mount. $105 £45

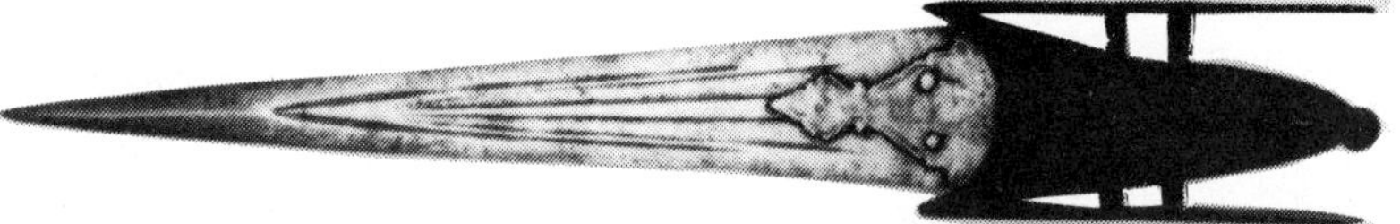

A Southern Indian katar, fluted double edged tapering blade 14½in., with re-enforced tip, iron hilt with re-curving sheet steel guard with foliate engraved decoration, grips of twin baluster form, incised side mounts. $130 £55

An all steel Indian thrusting dagger katar circa 1800, chevron fullered double edged blade 13in., with swollen point, foliate chiselled mount at forte, steel guard of patta form terminating in zoomorphic head with applied decorative borders, two swollen hemisperical grip bars. $265 £110

A Russian Artillery kindjal, curved, double edged double fullered blade 17in.. stamped with double headed Eagle mark at forte and d. '1915', wooden grips, brass mounts, in its brass mounted leather covered wooden sheath. $105 £50

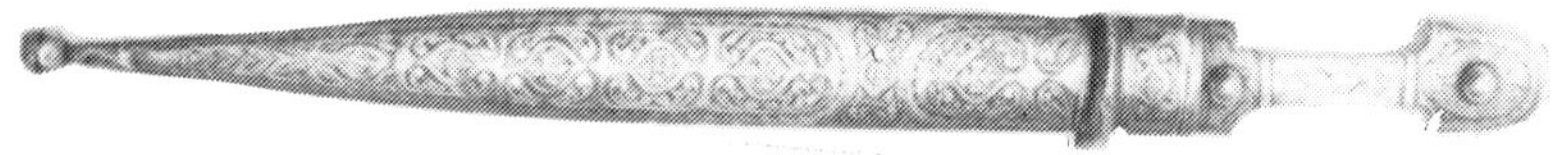

A Late 19th century Russian dagger kindjal, straight double edged single off-set fullered blade 14½in., white metal hilt and sheath decorated with chased foliage upon engraved ground within nielloed vignettes, button grip rivet heads and ball chape finial, locket band pierced for suspension. $125 £60

A good quality Caucasian dagger kindjal, multi-fullered double edged spear pointed blade 13in. etched at forte with Cyrillic script and date 1907, chiselled white metal and niello mounted horn hilt, with two embossed and chiselled rivet heads, in its leather covered wooden sheath. $205 £95

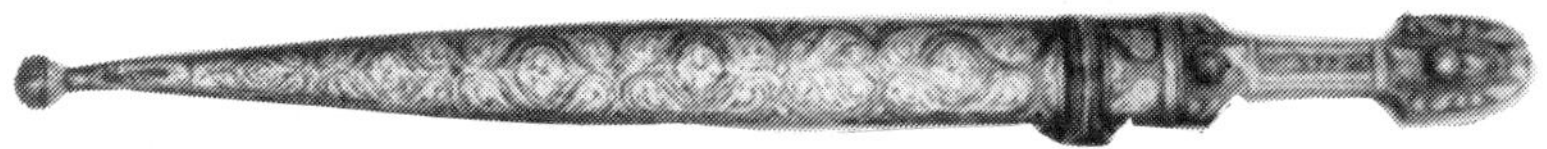

A Cossack kindjal, plain double edged blade, 12½in. with central fuller, the hilt and sheath covered overall with white metal decorated with chiselled foliate scrolls heightened with niello and gilt. $230 £95

A Caucasian dagger kindjal, straight tri-fullered double edged blade 15½in. etched with scrolls, 2 piece polished horn grips, silver inlaid and gold damascened rivet heads en-suite with hanging band and button chape, in its black leather sheath. $290 £120

A Madura kris, wavy, watered steel blade 14in., elaborately foliate carved bone hilt, silver cup base mount, in its wooden sheath, the blade housing covered in white metal sheet. $55 £30

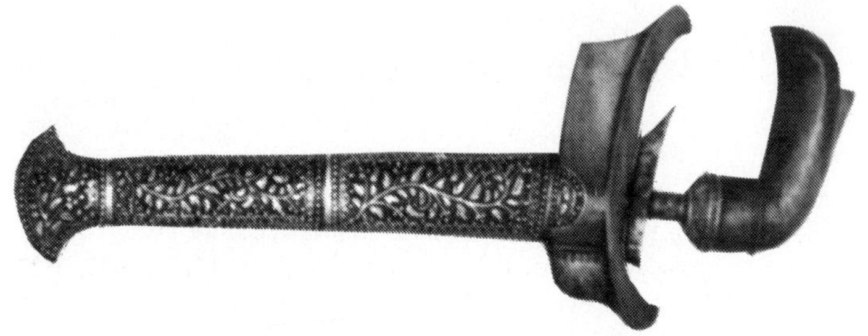

A Sumatran kris, wavy blade 9in., stylised carved wood garuda hilt, with white metal filigree cup mount, in its wooden sheath, the blade section covered in Eastern sheet silver embossed with beaded and foliate patterns. $135 £55

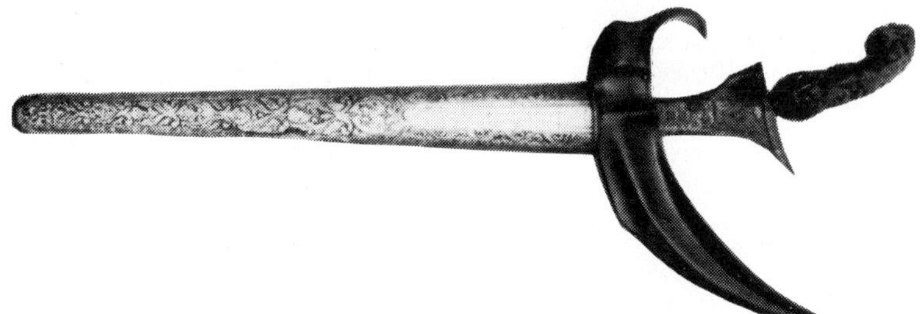

A Java kris, slightly wavy watered steel blade 13½in., the hilt of old ivory elaborately carved with scrolls, etc., with filigree Eastern silver base cup mount, in its wooden sheath. $145 £60

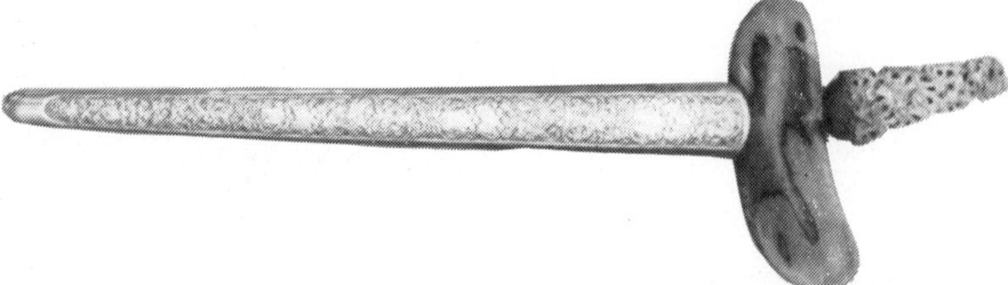

A Madura kris, wavy, watered steel blade 12in., old bone hilt pierced and carved with foliate patterns, in its wooden sheath, the blade housing sheathed in sheet white metal embossed with foliate patterns. $155 £70

A good Malayan dagger kris, shallow waved laminated blade 14¼in., inlaid with magical script and numbers in silver on both sides, brass cup, carved ivory garuda hilt, in its wooden sheath with figured top. $190 £80

A Java 'Kingfisher' kris, straight blade 9¾in., wooden hilt carved with stylised 'Kingfisher', in its wooden sheath. $195 £80

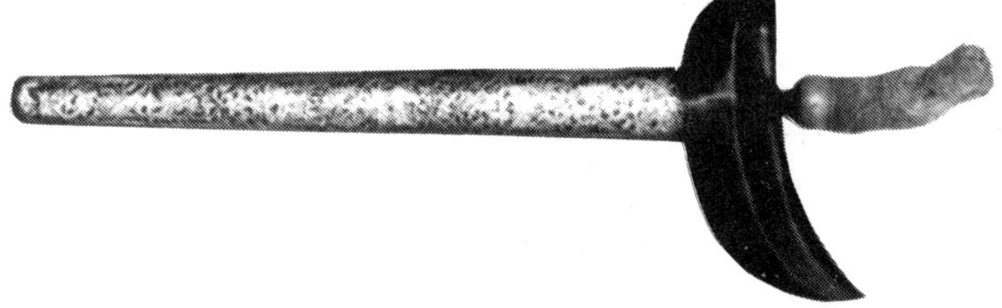

A good Malay kris, wavy, watered steel blade 13in., the bone hilt finely carved with foliate pattern in the form of a stylised figure of Raksha, beaded silver cup mount, in its wooded sheath, the blade section encased in Eastern sheet silver, the front panel decorated overall with embossed foliate patterns. $195 £82

An embossed Eastern silver mounted Balinese dagger kris, 4-waved blade 11¾in. sheet silver covered hilt and sheath embossed with foliage and scrollwork with geometric borders. $185 £90

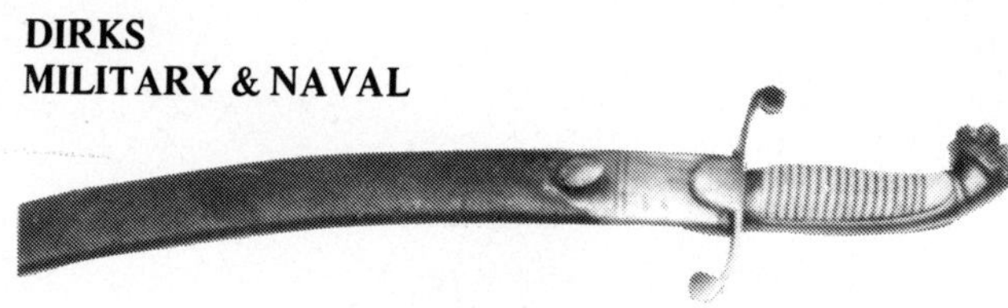

A Naval officer's dirk circa 1840 plain curved, single edged blade 14½in. with narrow back fuller, plain brass hilt with 'S' crosspiece, chiselled Lion's head pommel, wirebound ribbed bone grip, in its brass mounted leather sheath. $90 £42

An early 19th century Spanish Naval officer's dirk, straight double edged tapering blade 15½in.etched with military trophies and foliage, copper crosspiece with quatrefoil terminals, anchor in oval panel to centre, traces of gilt, spiral fluted black horn hilt, fluted copper pommel cap. $155 £65

A Nazi Naval officer's dirk, by Eickhorn, etched with fouled anchor, entwined dolphins etc., gilt mounts, wirebound white grip, in its gilt sheath with bullion dress knot. $160 £65

A good post-1902 Naval officer's dirk, blade 17½in., by 'J. R. Gaunt Late Edward Thurkle, London', retaining virtually all original polish, and well etched fouled anchor, Royal Arms and foliage. Copper mounts, in its brass mounted leather sheath. $240 £100

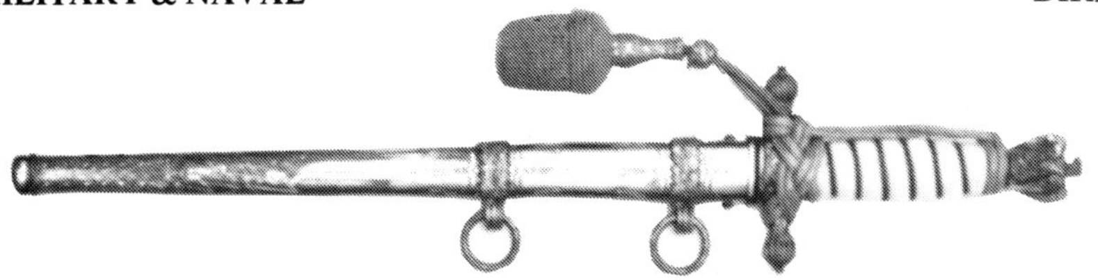

A Nazi Naval officer's dirk, by F. W. Holler, blade retaining most original polish, etched with sailing ships, fouled anchor and foliage, gilt mounts, wirebound white celluloid grip, in its gilt sheath, with bullion dress knot. $240 £110

A Nazi Naval officer's dirk, by Eickhorn, blade retaining virtually all original polish, etched with fouled anchor, entwined dolphins and foliage, gilt hilt, wirebound white grip, in its gilt sheath, retaining virtually all original gilding. $265 £110

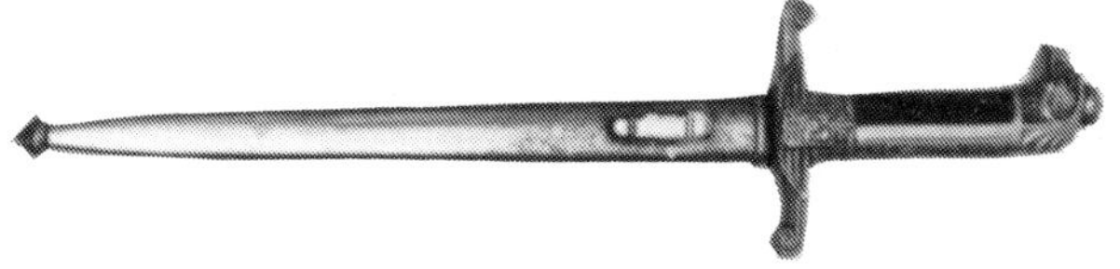

A Rumanian officer's dress dirk, plated blade 6in. by Holler with spear point, etched with royal arms, entwined crowned 'C' (for Carol) and foliate scrolls, brass hilt with crosspiece with royal arms, the backstrap with crowned cypher and oval vignette of King Carol, in its plated sheath. $355 £150

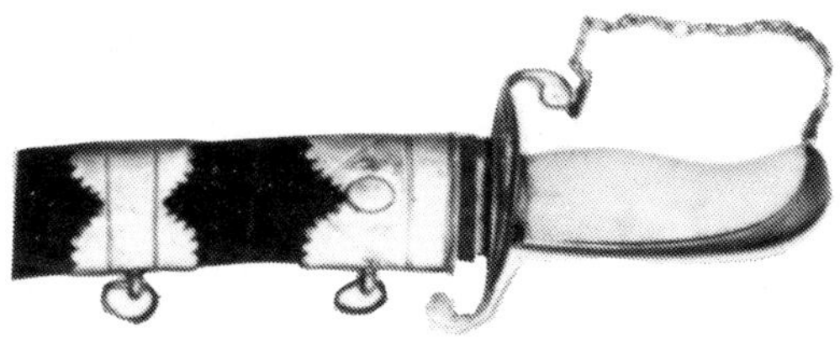

A scarce Georgian 'Nile Club' Naval officer's dirk, circa 1800, plain curved clipped back blade 16in., copper gilt hilt with side loop enclosing a chiselled design of a crocodile, plain copper backstrap, gilt chain guard, in its blind tooled leather sheath with three copper mounts. $365 £150

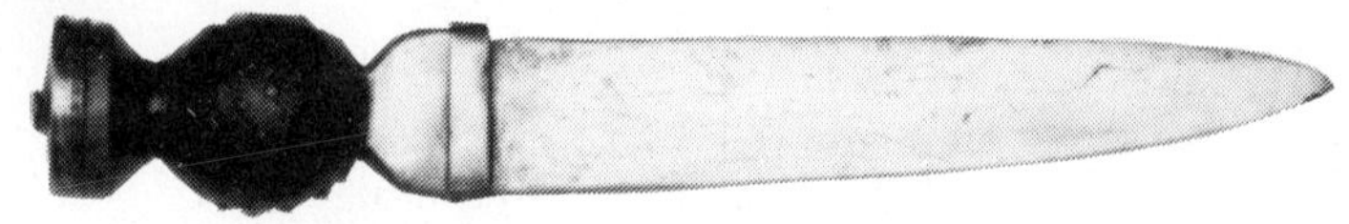

An early 19th century Scottish dirk, single edged tapering blade 9in., wooden swelling hilt decorated with brass studs, plain brass sheet circular pommel cap and base mount. $120 £50

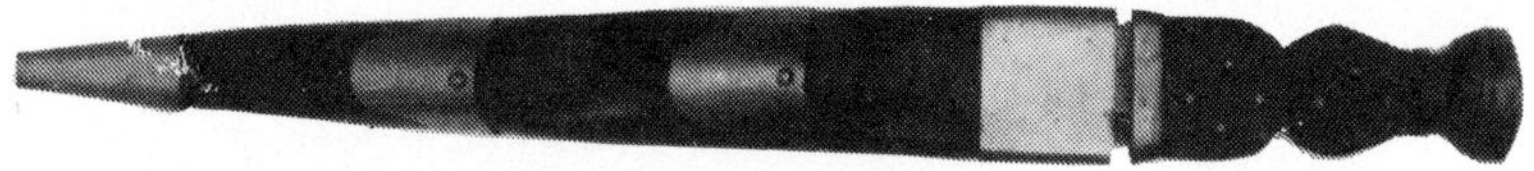

A late 18th century Scottish dirk, plain, single edged blade 12in., with single narrow back fullers, corded wood hilt, plain brass base mounts and pommel cap, in its leather sheath. Provision for companion knife and fork. $200 £90

A Georgian Scottish presentation highland dirk, single edged fullered blade 11½in. with scalloped back, strapwork carved wooden hilt with brass pique-work, pommel engraved 'Given from the Dunkeld for Philbrochs, CHFS, June 24th 1824', in its brass mounted leather sheath. $470 £200

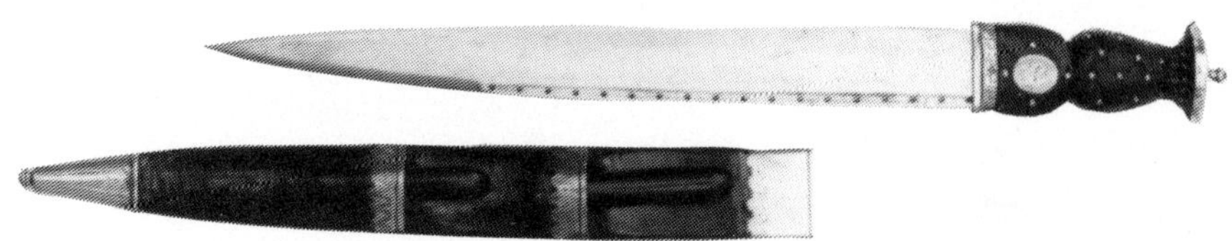

A Georgian silver mounted Scottish dirk set, single edged blade 13in., with clipped back spear point, corded wooden hilt mounted with silver studded decoration, motto 'Deus Altime' and initials 'F. W.', the circular pommel bearing hallmark for 1805, in its patent leather covered sheath. $540 £250

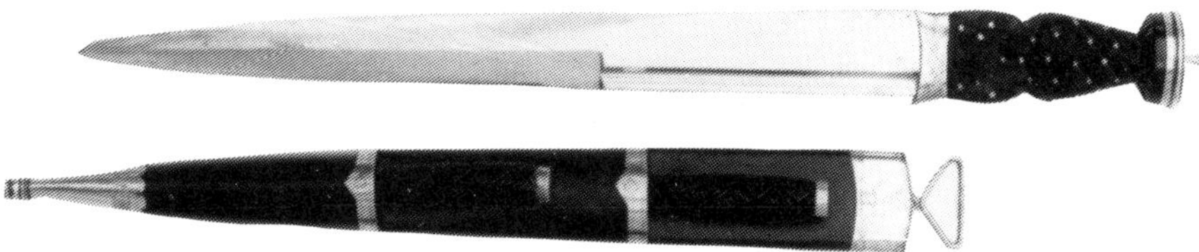

A 19th century silver mounted Scottish dirk set, plain single edged blade 14½in., with long clipped back top, corded wood hilt mounted with silver studs, in its black patent leather covered wooden sheath with four silver mounts, together with companion knife and fork. $625 £290

A Georgian silver mounted Scottish highland dirk, single edged fullered blade 13¼in. with false edge, stamped 'Paten Inverness', strapwork carved wooden grip with silver pique work, in its silver mounted leather sheath, with companion knife and fork en suite. $885 £375

A late Victorian Scottish officer's dress dirk set of The Highland Light Infantry, scallop back blade 11½in., well etched with many battle honours to 'Central India' within scrolls, Regimental Badge, 'V.R.', Elephant and 'Assaye' Honour. $950 £440

An officer's Scottish Victorian dirk of The 78th (Ross-shire Buffs) Highlanders, straight single edged bi-fullered blade with false edge 12in. etched and polished with Victorian crown, in its leather covered sheath with copper gilt mounts with St. Andrew and thistles applied. $1,000 £425

A 17th century German hanger, curved, single edged blade 28½in., with narrow back fuller with 'running wolf' mark, iron hilt with solid double shell guard, with large thumb ring and solid panel struck with a wheel mark, plain single knucklebow, wirebound grip, ovoid pommel. $105 £45

A late 18th century English military hanger, slightly curved single edged blade 24½in., with narrow back fuller, stamped 'Harvey' within 'Running Fox' mark, stamped at forte with ordnance mark, plain steel knucklebow and single side-loop, ovoid pommel, steel wire and copper band bound grip. $130 £60

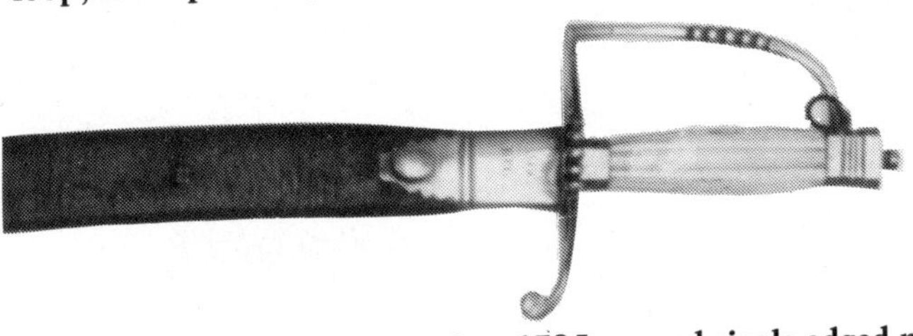

A Georgian officer's hanger circa 1785, curved single edged multi-fullered blade 25in., German silver hilt, with side-loop and knucklebow incorporating '5 Ball' design, fluted ivory grip, octagonal pommel engraved '95th Regt.' in its leather scabbard, the locket of German silver also engraved '95th Regt', and pricker engraved 'Knubley No. 7 Charing Cross, London', steel chape. $170 £70

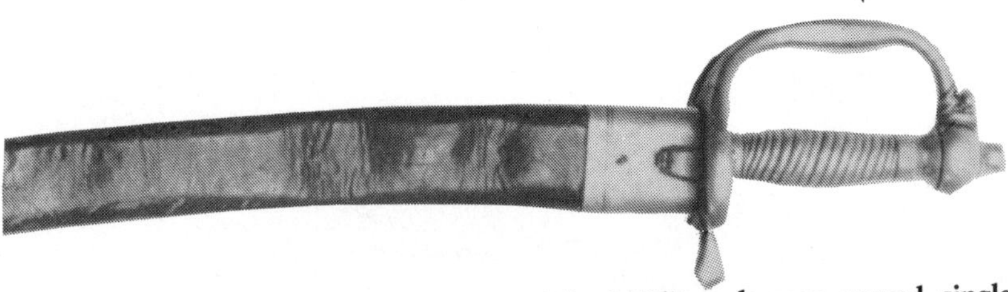

A mid 18th century Scandinavian brass hilted Military hanger, curved, single edged blade 25in., stamped at forte with 'P' and with heart-shaped guard, plain knucklebow, spiral grip, flattened pommel, in its brass mounted leather scabbard. $165 £90

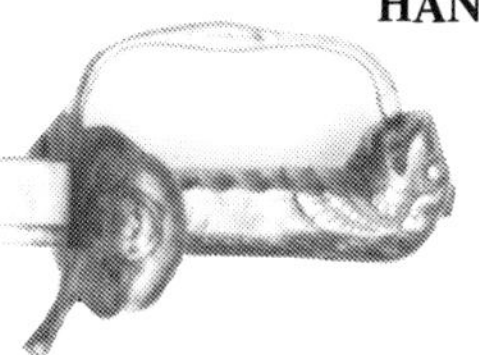

An English brass hilted hanger circa 1700, plain single edged, slightly curved blade 27in. with narrow back fuller, and struck with 3 Star Mark, small up-turned shell guard, and side ditto, single plain knucklebow, Gargoyle head pommel, ribbed shaped grip. $240 £110

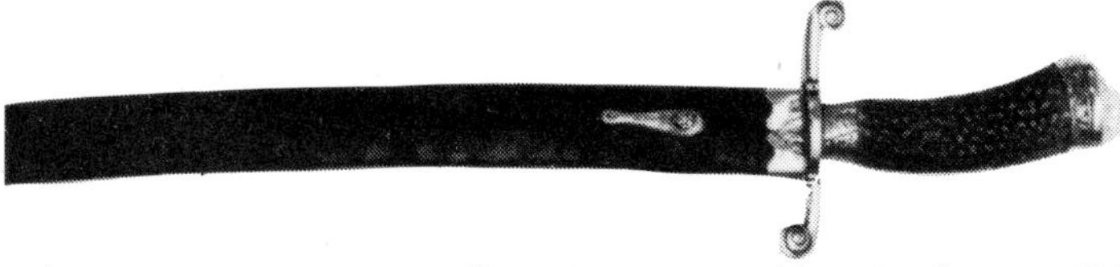

A scarce Charles II hallmarked silver mounted hunting hanger, slightly curved single edged blade 19in. with false edge, inlaid with 3 copper,comet shaped marks, reversed crosspiece with whorl quillon terminals, struck with maker's marks T.H. Staghorn grip, ferrule with lion assay mark, punched and engraved with 2 lion's heads within foliage, pommel struck with maker's mark G. S., in its original silver mounted leather scabbard. $320 £145

An English hanger, circa 1660, single edged blade 23in., iron chiselled hilt, with down-turned shell guard pierced with monster head, foliate scrolls, etc., and with a small mask to edge, smaller upturned shell guard, single knucklebow, spiral carved bone grip, iron pommel. $275 £150

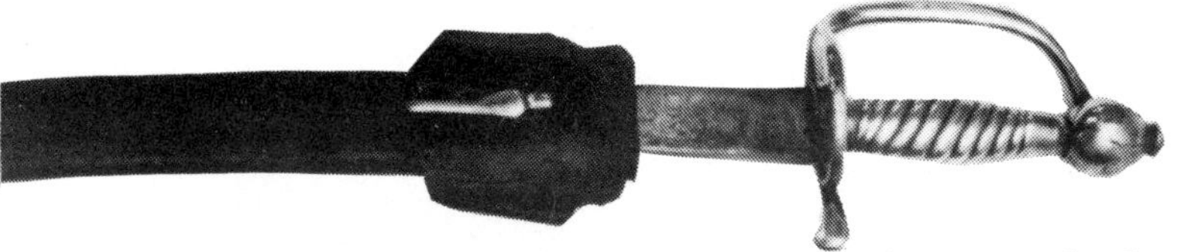

A scarce brass hilted early 19th century Danish military hanger, single edged curved blade 23½in., etched with crowned 'C.7' (i.e. for Christian 7th), and d. '1805' brass hilt with half-heart shaped guard stamped 'F.R.G.C. 36' the small back quillon stamped '1705 BGC', single knucklebow stamped '4 K.R.B. -2C-22' spiral grip, ovoid pommel, in leather scabbard with brass frog lug. $375 £170

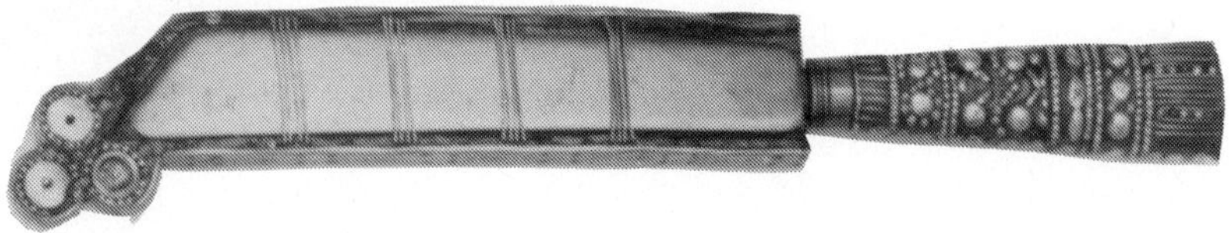

A Tibetan knife, single edged blade 7in., with hatchet tip, wooden hilt with white metal studded decoration, in its openwork wooden sheath with brass sheet and studded decoration at tip. $20 £10

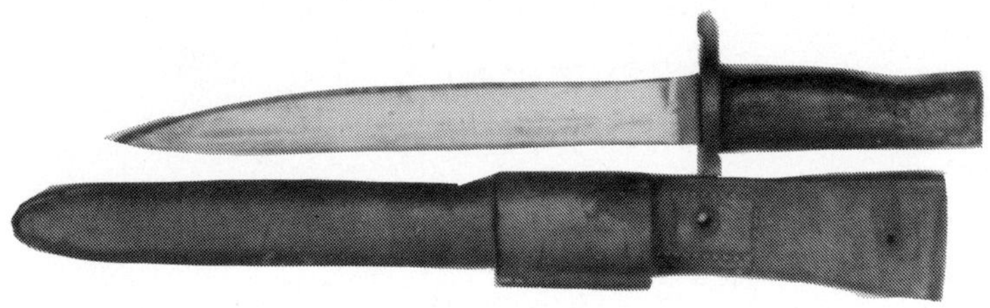

An interesting World War I trench knife made from a Ross rifle bayonet, blade 9¾in., with spear point, muzzle ring removed, leather covered grip, in its Ross rifle leather covered scabbard with integral frog. $45 £24

A silver mounted South American Gaucho knife, single edged tapering blade, 8½in., by Mailhos Montevideo, the hilt of round form of South American silver with simple decoration, in its leather sheath with silver chape and locket, simple decoration. $120 £50

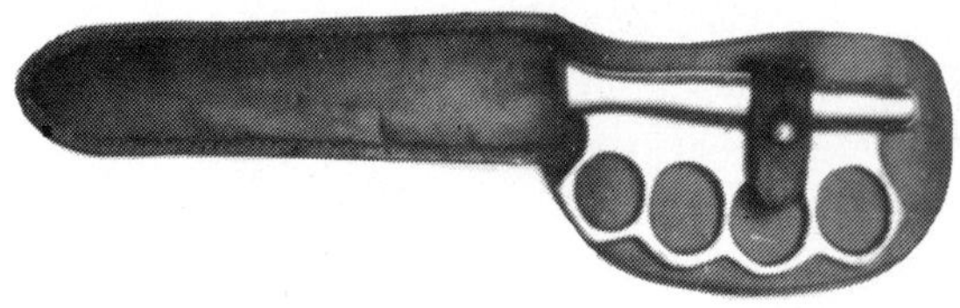

An interesting knuckleduster fighting knife, single edged blade 6in., with slightly clipped back tip, plated brass hilt with flattened knuckleduster grip, in its leather sheath, with belt loop and flap. $130 £58

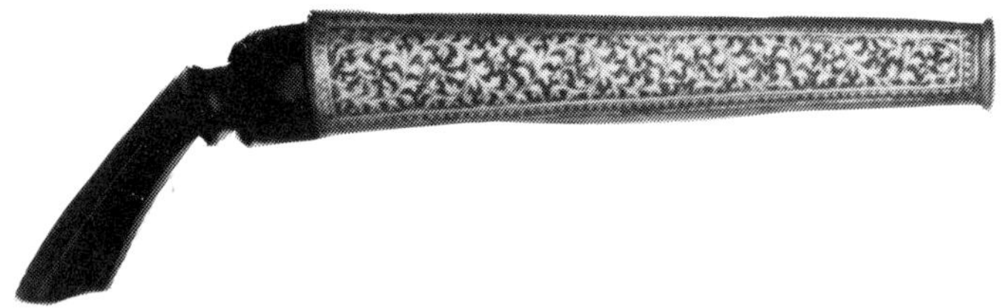

A bade-bade, blade 7¾in., black wood hilt with decoration, in its wooden sheath, covered in Eastern sheet silver embossed with geometric and foliate patterns. $110 £45

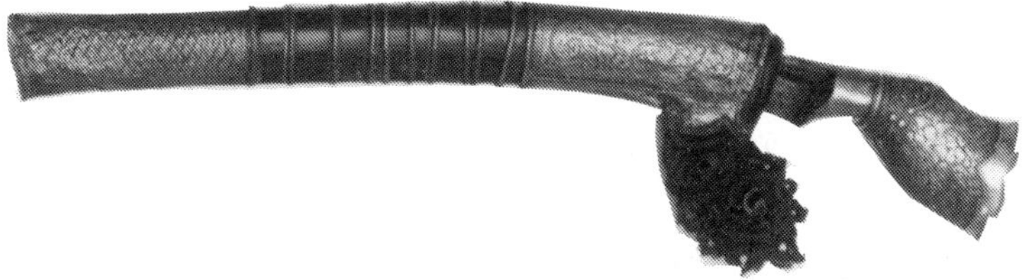

A silver mounted bade-bade blade 11in., tulip hilt overlaid with Eastern sheet silver with filigree base and gilt pommel, decorated with floral and foliate pattern, in its wooden sheath with long Eastern silver chape embossed with foliate scrolls. $100 £50

A silver mounted bade-bade, blade 7¾in., tulip hilt covered in Eastern sheet silver, embossed with foliate and beaded patterns, in its wooden sheath with 2 long Eastern silver chapes embossed with fish, foliage etc. $120 £50

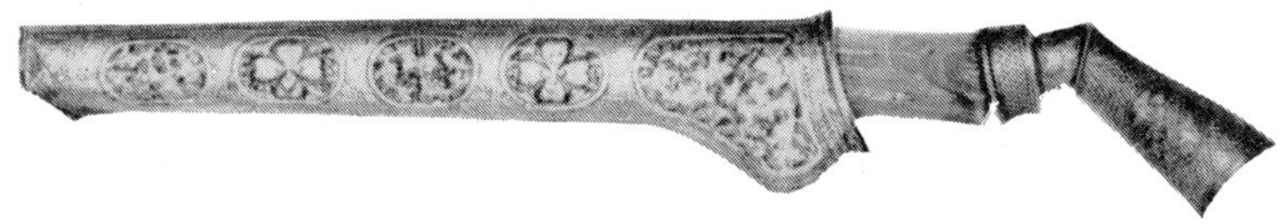

A silver mounted Malayan knife bade-bade, straight, laminated, single edged blade 8½in., Eastern silver covered hilt and sheath well embossed with foliate vignettes. $225 £100

A folding Bowie dagger, double edged tapering blade 6¼in., German silver crosspiece with quillons in form of cannon, mother of pearl grip, decorated with scrolls, thumb release catch, German silver panel pommel mounts embossed with a mask. $50 £22

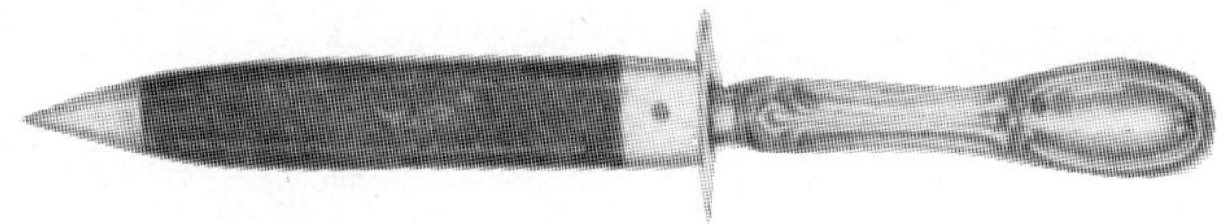

A Victorian Bowie dagger, double edged blade, 5in., by Henry Hobson, with faint etching 'Self protector', white metal embossed hilt and oval crosspiece, in its red leather covered sheath with white metal mounts. $50 £26

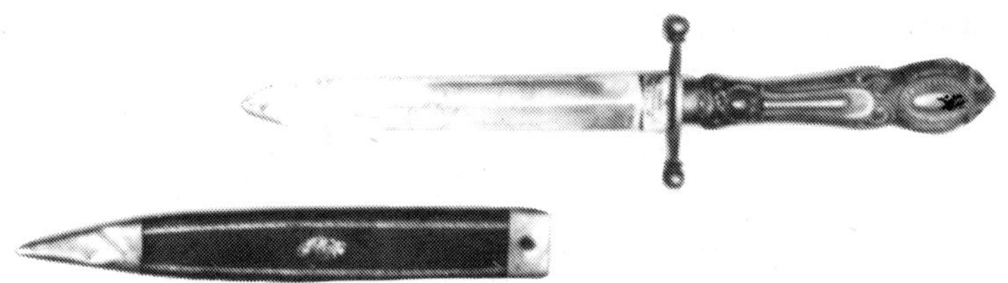

A 19th century Bowie knife, double edged spear pointed blade 6¼in., etched 'Never Draw Me Without Reason Nor Sheath Me Without Honour' amid scrolls, stamped 'Manson Sheffield' at forte, in its red leather tooled sheath. $70 £30

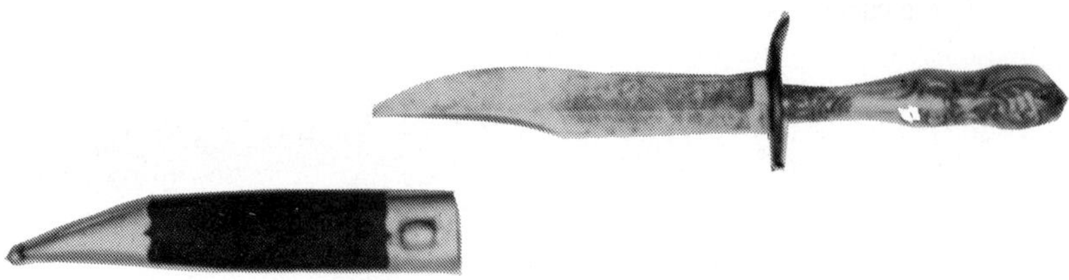

A Victorian Bowie knife, clipped back blade 6in., etched with bear, stag, and foliate scrolls, plated scrolled hilt, small steel crosspiece, in its white metal mounted leather sheath. $75 £40

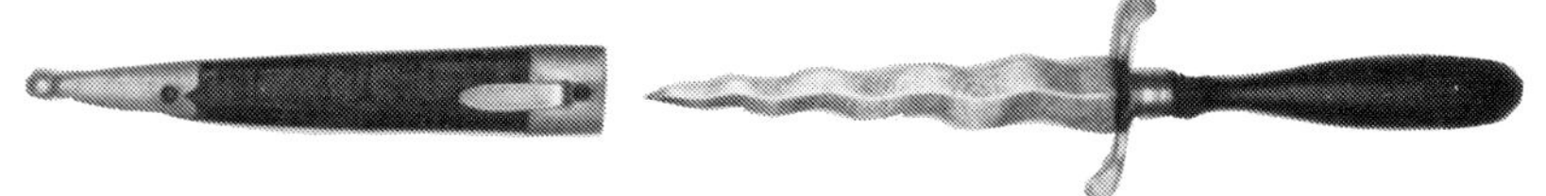

A Victorian flamboyant Bowie knife, wavy double edged blade 5in., etched with foliage sprays and flowers in vase, iron recurved crossguard, white metal mounted ebony hilt with fluted pommel, in its white metal mounted leather sheath. $85 £40

A Victorian white metal mounted Bowie knife, double edged spatulate blade 7½in., stamped 'S.M. Hill, Sheffield Patent', small turned white metal crosspiece, nobbled cowhorn hilt with mother of pearl inlays and white metal pommel cap, in blind tooled white metal mounted leather sheath. $95 £40

A good quality early Victorian Bowie type dagger, shallow diamond sectioned blade 5in., with stepped diamond quillon block, steel crosspiece, bone hilt with foliate carved pommel, in its white metal mounted leather sheath. $90 £42

A Victorian Bowie knife, clipped back blade 9½in. by 'William Rodgers Celebrated Dirk Knife', with trace of crown stamp, grey metal hilt, with lozenge crosspiece with hatched decoration, shaped hilt decorated with foliate scrolls. $135 £70

A folding Bowie knife, pronounced clipped back blade 7½in., by 'Wilkinson Sheffield'with award labels, white metal crosspiece, diced black grips. $135 £70

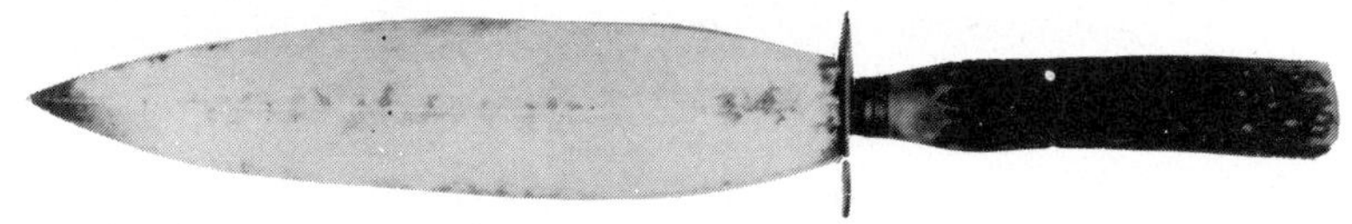

An unusual old Bowie knife, broad, double edged, spear shaped blade 9in., faintly etched 'California Bowie', white metal oval crosspiece, stag horn hilt with white metal mounts, in its red cloth re-covered sheath. $175 £85

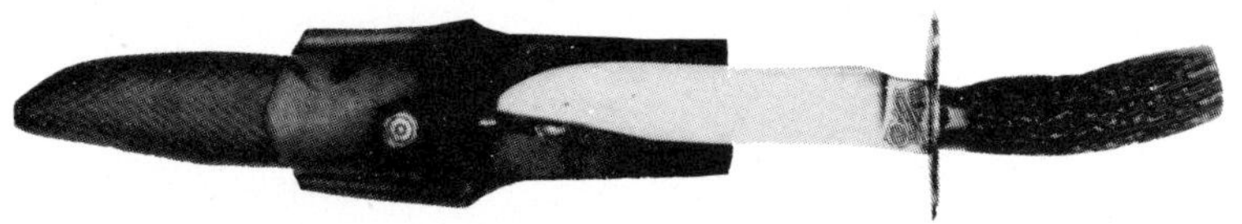

A Bowie knife, clipped back blade 7in., by 'Wilkinson, Pall Mall, London', etched 'R.B.D. Hunting Knife No. 1', steel crosspiece, staghorn hilt, in its diced leather covered, wooden sheath, with leather frog and spring catch. $185 £90

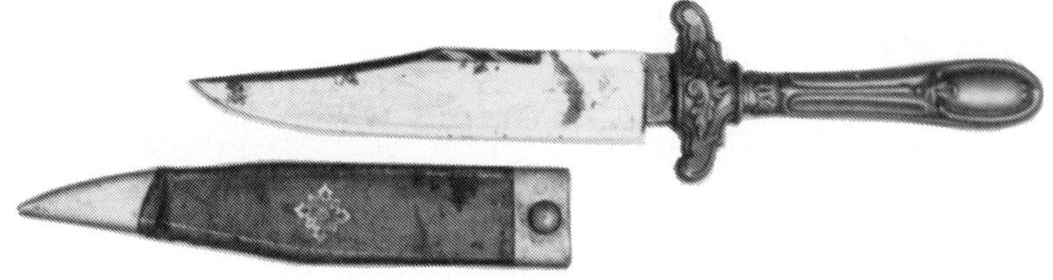

A 19th century Bowie knife, polished blade 6¾in., stamped 'Eyre Ward & Co. Sheaf Works' within oval band at forte, foliate embossed fluted white metal hilt with integral crosspiece, in its gilt tooled white metal mounted red morocco leather sheath. $185 £90

A most unusual 19th century Bowie knife, blade 8¾in. stamped 'Mazeppa C. Hancock & Son Pea Croft Works Sheffield', foliate embossed white metal crosspiece, white metal pommel embossed with eagle feeding young, ribbed leather covering to grip en-suite with ribbed leather sheath. $205 £100

A Victorian Bowie knife, single edged blade 7in., with spear point, stamped at forte 'Dobby', small German silver crosspiece with 'Ball' terminals, the hilt with German silver panels embossed with vase of fruit and flowers and foliage, in its leather covered sheath. $355 £155

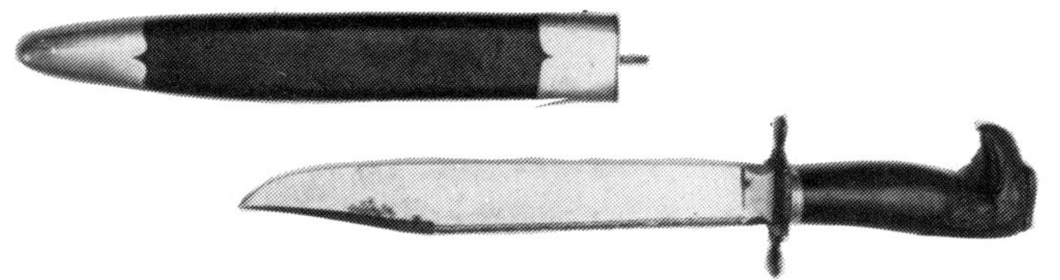

A Victorian Bowie knife, clipped back blade 10in., with roped backstrap, stamped at forte with crown 'VR', Thornhill, London', small steel crosspiece, black horn hilt with eagle's head pommel, in its leather covered sheath with white metal chape and locket and spring clip. $370 £180

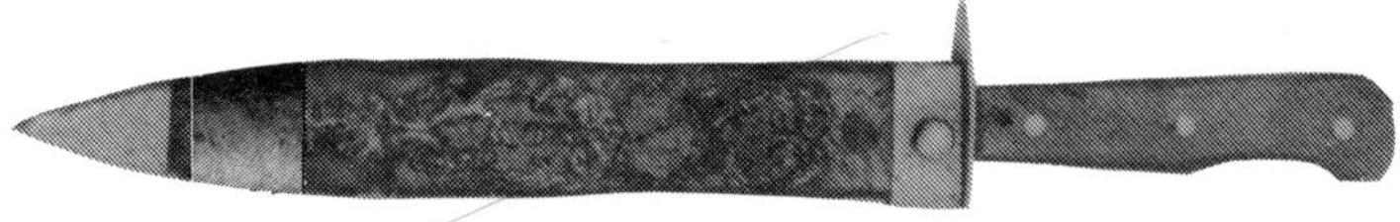

An English Bowie knife, circa 1850, made for the American market by S. C. Wragg, Sheaf Island Works, Sheffield, broad, single edged blade 8¾in., etched with foliate scrolls and 'Camp White'. One piece rosewood grip, white metal crosspiece and rivet heads, in its white metal mounted red morocco covered sheath gilt tooled with scrolls. $440 £240

A German World War I fighting knife, double edged blade 5in., by Anton Wingen Jr etched at forte with German soldier advancing with drawn sword, narrow crosspiece, staghorn hilt, in its black painted steel sheath with leather suspension strap and loop. $30 £16

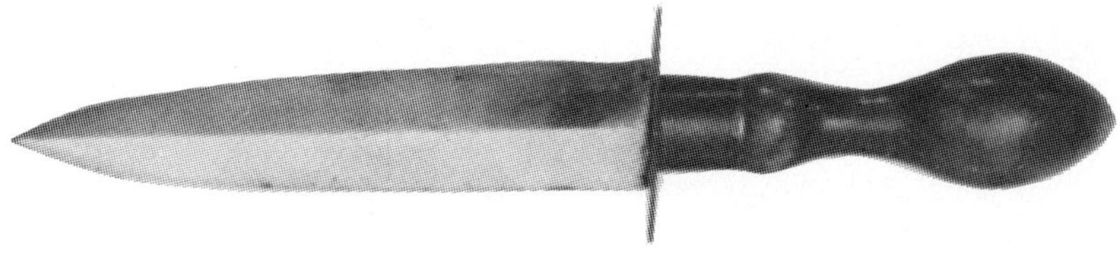

A good World War I fighting knife, burnished shallow diamond section double edged blade 7in. diamond shaped brass guard, turned bulbous walnut grip with brass collar, in its leather sheath. $45 £24

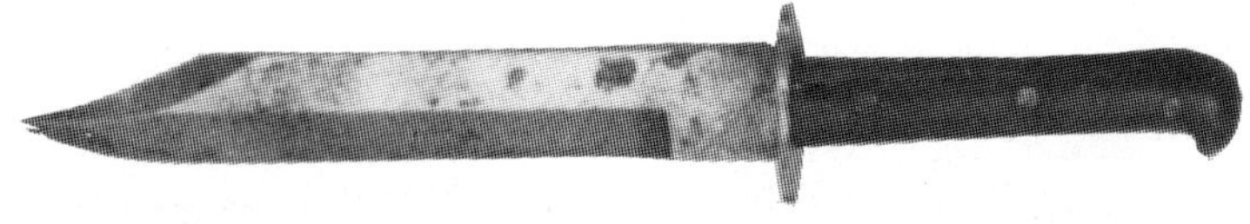

A World War II combat knife as made for allied troops in the pacific theatre of war, single edged, clipped back blade 7in., plain small oval steel guard, plain wood grips secured with 3 rivets, in its leather sheath. $60 £32

A World War II allied pacific theatre fighting knife, clipped back single edged blade 7¼in., German silver oval crosspiece, wooden grips secured by 3 steel rivets, in its leather sheath with flap and loop. $80 £42

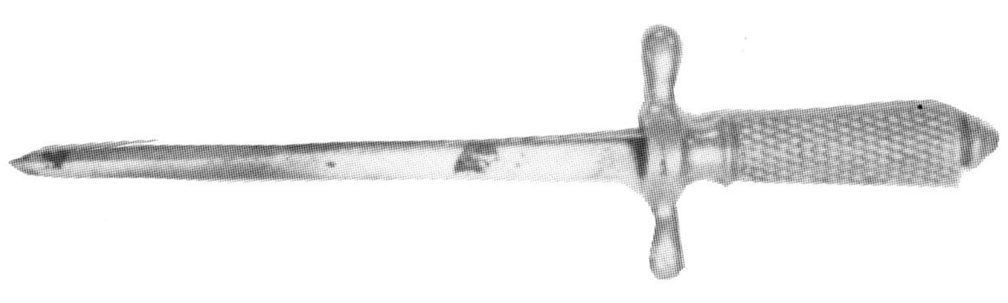

A French aluminium hilted trench knife, slender T section blade 8in., one piece hilt, diced grips, crossguard stamped 'Brevete' and 'Manufacture Francaise, Arms et Cycles, St. Etienne'. $125 £65

An officer's military style fighting knife based on the Indian Khyber knife, single edged, spear pointed blade 10in., retaining all original polish, finely chequered eared horn grips, steel mounts, in its leather covered wooden sheath with brass tip. $155 £82

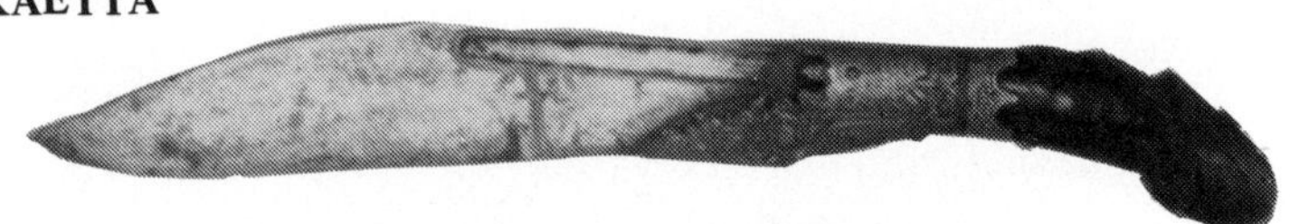

A Ceylonese knife pia kaetta, single edged blade 7in. with short fuller and engraved decoration, two piece scroll carved black horn grips, finely scroll chiselled brass ferrule, silver pommel, collar and gripstrap foliate scroll embossed and engraved. $75 £40

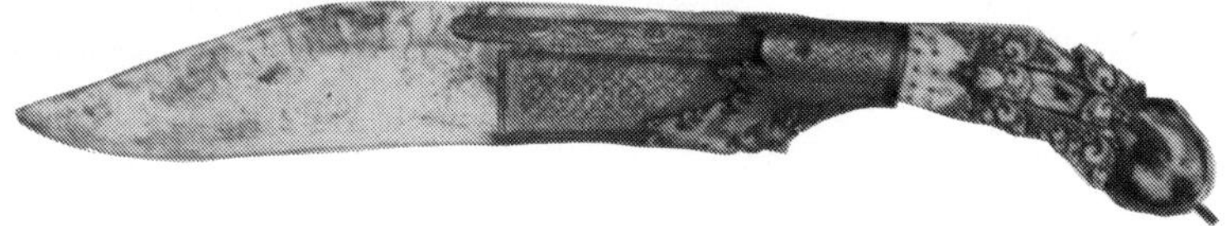

A Ceylonese knife pia kaetta, single edged blade 7½in. inlaid with scroll and geometric engraved brass sheets at forte, scroll chiselled ferrule, scroll carved 2 piece ivory grips with brass gripstrap and scroll embossed silver pommel. $95 £50

A Singalese dagger pia kaetta, iron blade 7in., partly sheathed in brass, bone carved hilt with brass scroll decorated base, silver sheet embossed pommel cap. $210 £90

A good Ceylonese knife pia kaetta, curved single edged blade 8in., inlaid with brass and silver, foliate chased, two piece foliate carved ivory grips with foliate embossed silver pommel, in its fluted wooden sheath with silver top. $210 £90

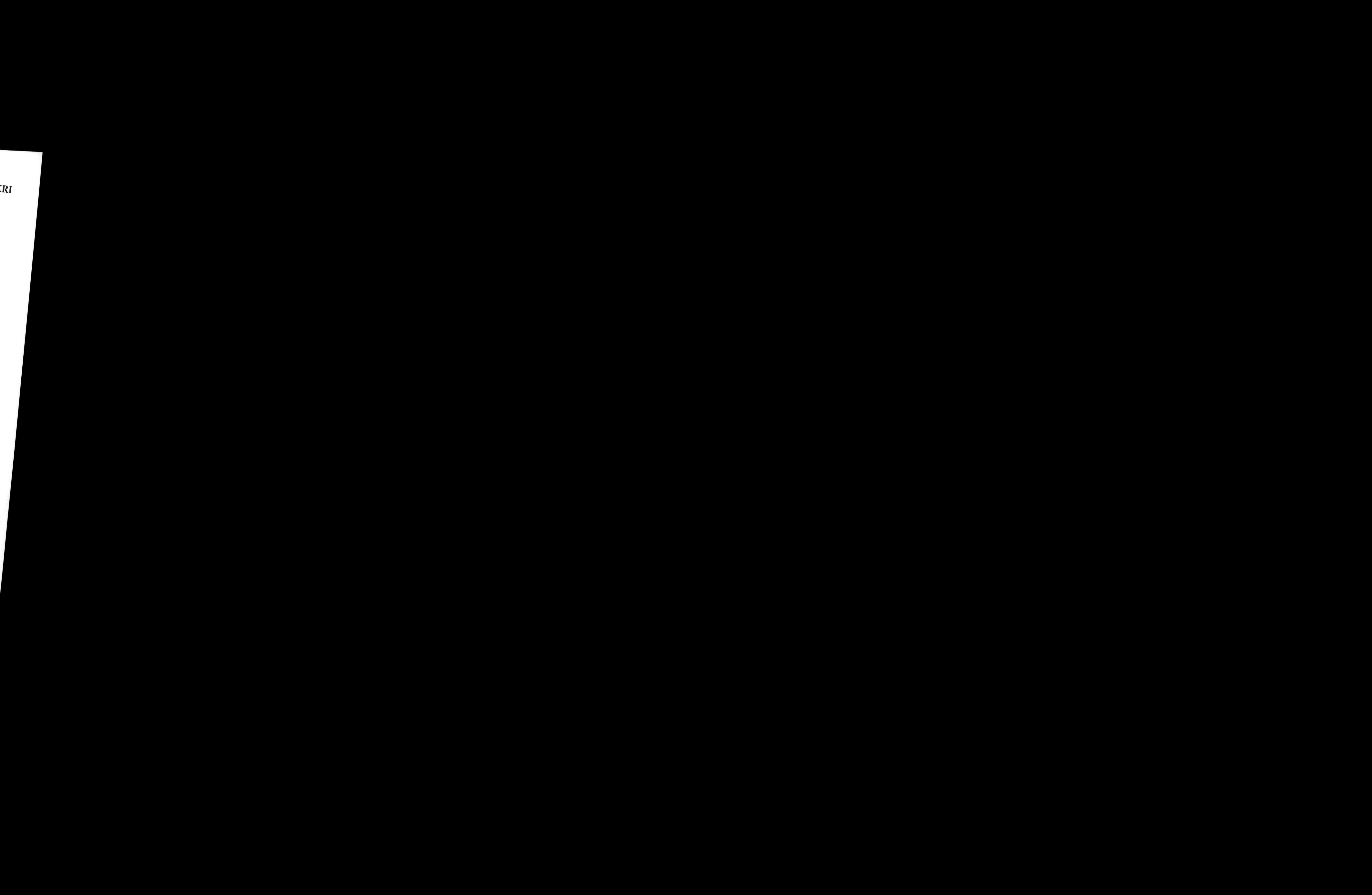

A rare Elizabethan staff head circa 1560, 4¾in. overall, pierced head with foliate arms, central radial device of bowed cherub's heads chiselled in relief, baluster turned socket, etched overall with foliage and flowers. $215 £90

An interesting 18th century sergeant's halberd, the head of conventional form, but the blade pierced with large 'E', secured to its original haft by long tangs, the the haft with copper shoe. $270 £110

An 18th century European spontoon, flattened steel spear shaped head, 9½in., etched with arms (possibly of one of the German States) of crowned shield with vertical bar bearing three crosses supported by two lions, on its wooden haft with steel base mount. $265 £120

An 18th century spontoon, steel double edged flattened spear shaped head 11in., engraved with crest ot a unicorn, straight steel crosspiece, steel haft mount, overall length 15½in., on restored wooden haft, overall 7ft. $290 £120

An early 18th century French ceremonial partizan, ribbed steel head, 10½in., with reversed crescent lugs, of plain form, on restored wooden haft, overall 6ft.10in. $280 £130

A Japanese polearm yari, blade 13½cm., signed Kodzuke Kiyokuni, narrow straight hamon, with its crinkle carved red lacquered cover, wooden pole with brass mounts and mother of pearl section inlaid top. $320 £145

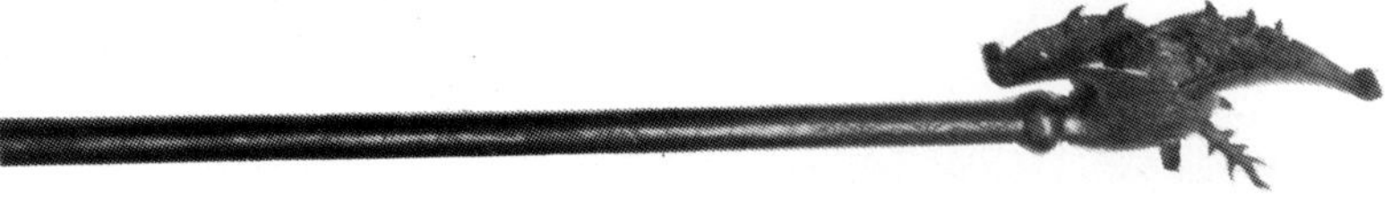

An interesting Indian all steel ceremonial mace, the head in the form of a dragon with open mouth, containing a painted face, with antlers, ears, and chiselled overall with mounted figures in combat within foliage rounded haft, overall 30in. $310 £150

A 16th century German halberd, steel head 25in., including long square section top spike, pierced backspike, pierced crescent blade 7in., integral steel straps, on its octagonal beechwood haft with woven and knotted silver bullion and green silk tassels. $435 £190

A 16th century German halberd, steel head 25in. including long square section top spike, pierced backspike with thickened point, pierced crescent blade 9½in. with thickened points, integral steel straps, on its long octagonal beechwood haft with woven and knotted bullion and green silk tassels.
$440 £190

A scarce 17th century linstock, the head 17in. overall formed of two scrolled arms terminating in serpents' heads, with slender diamond section spike between, and with octagonal socket, on its original haft with iron shoe.
$490 £200

An unusually long Japanese polearm yari, blade 67cm., signed 'Soshu ......' (rest unclear), massive broad deep brown painted full length hi, with its crinkle carved black lacquered cover, on its red lacquered haft with black painted mounts. $680 £310

A Japanese polearm yari, 3 pronged head 17½cm., signed Yamashiro Nokami Fujiwara Kunishige, with inscription 'second generation' and several other characters, with its crinkle carved black lacquered cover, on its wooden haft with brass mounted mother of pearl section decorated top. $485 £220

A Spanish early 18th century cup hilted rapier, double edged blade 38in. of flattened diamond section, marked at forte 'In Tol', steel bowl guard engraved with simple foliate decoration within panels, plain rounded straight cross-piece and plain knucklebow, wire bound grip. $265 £140

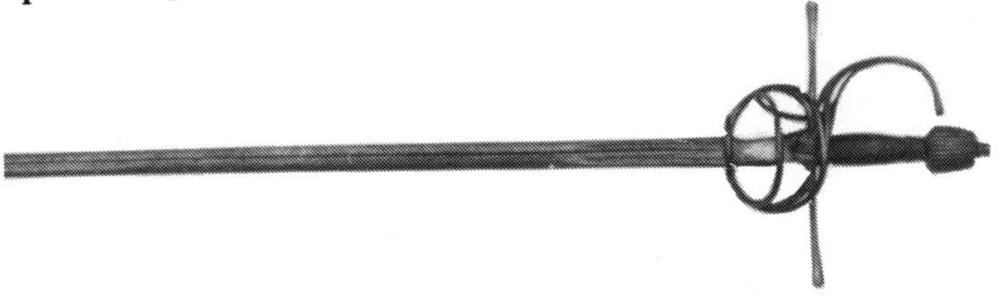

A good 17th century swept hilt rapier, double edged fullered blade 42½in. to ricasso, stamped 'Wilhelm Wirsserch Solingen' in fullers on each side at forte, multi-bar swept hilt, steel wirebound grip with steel 'Turk's Heads.' $1,600 £700

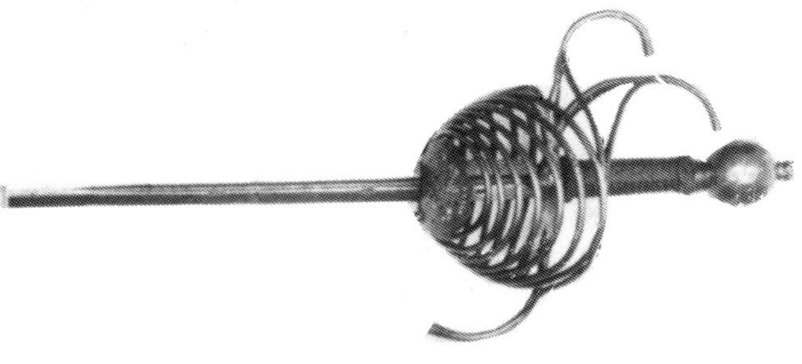

An Italian multi-bar swept hilted rapier circa 1620, shallow diamond sectioned blade 46¼in. fullered at forte and struck with crowned maker's mark (indistinct), hilt composed of 7 concentric rings, bulbous facetted pommel, woven steel wirebound grip with woven 'Turk's Heads'. $1,830 £890

A Georgian Light Infantry officer's sabre, circa 1800, Eastern style plain single edged blade 28½in., copper gilt hilt, with oval langets with applied strung bugle devices, squared knucklebow with twist engraved pattern, copper wirebound fishskin covered grip. $100 £40

A mid 19th century continental Cavalry trooper's sabre (of French pattern), plain curved blade 35½in., retaining all original polish broad and narrow fullers, no visible markings, triple bar brass guard, ribbed, leather covered grip, in its steel scabbard. $110 £50

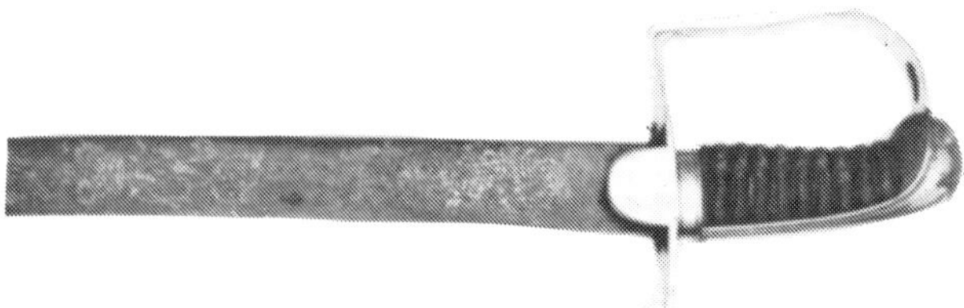

A Georgian officer's sabre, curved, single edged blade 29½in., with clipped back tip retaining some original blueing and gilding, and etched crown 'GR', plain copper gilt hilt with stirrup guard, retaining most original gilding, copper wirebound fishskin covered grip. $155 £70

A late 18th century Napoleonic era continental Cavalry sabre (possibly Spanish), curved single edged blade 38in., etched on both sides in large lettering 'No Me Saques Sin Raison, No Me Encaines in Honour', brass hilt, oval langets brass wirebound leather covered grip. $165 £75

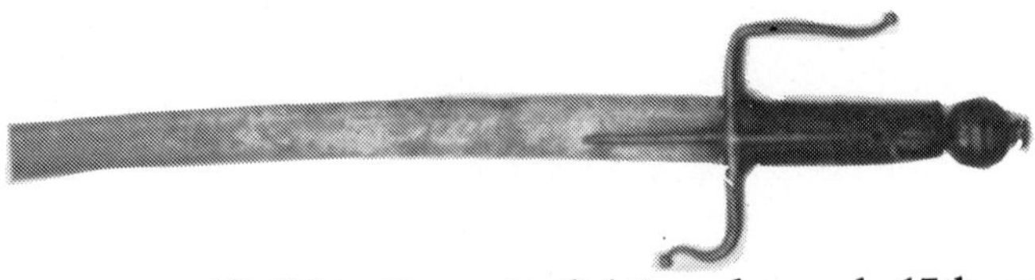

An unusual Polish or Hungarian fighting sabre, early 17th century, single edged broad curved single fullered blade 26in., octagonal section iron crosspiece integral with recurved quillons forming knucklebow with swollen bud shaped terminals, ribbed leather covered grip. $185 £80

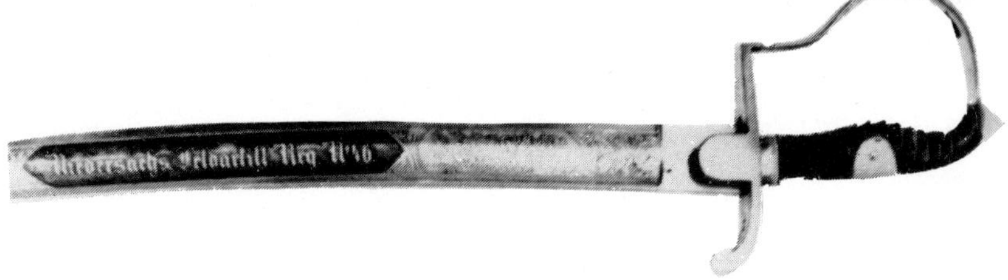

A Prussian Artillery officer's sabre, plated, curved blade 29½in., etched with Regiment 'Niedersachs Feldartill Reg. No 46' on blued panel, also with Prussian Eagle and foliate scrolls and military trophies, plated guard with plain stirrup guard, leather covered ribbed grip. $185 £85

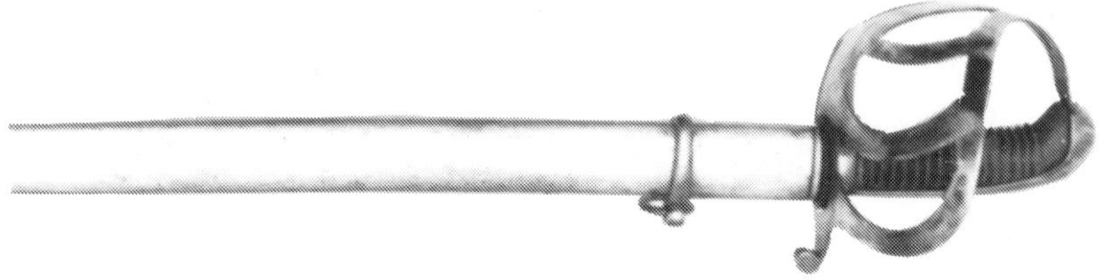

A Dutch mid 19th century Cavalry officer's sabre, plain curved blade 34in., with single fuller, etched within scrolls 'Yzer Houwer Frans Pauwels Gravenhage', steel semi-basket looped hilt, ribbed fishskin covered grip, in its steel scabbard. $185 £90

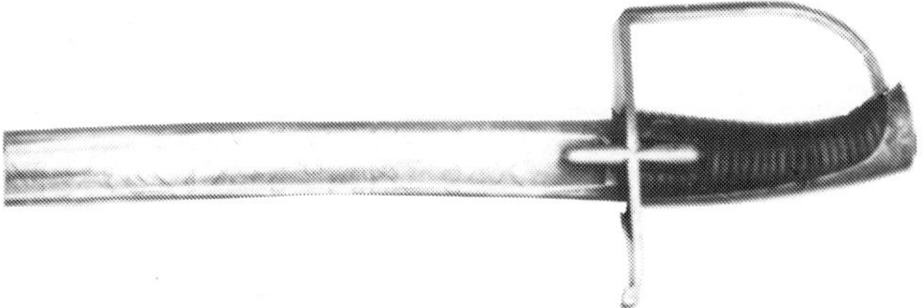

A 1788 pattern Light Cavalry trooper's sabre, curved single edged blade 33½in., narrow back fuller, stamped 'DGG' on backstrap, etched with mounted Hussar, talisman symbols, etc., plain steel hilt and guard, long langets, ribbed leather covered grip. $200 £90

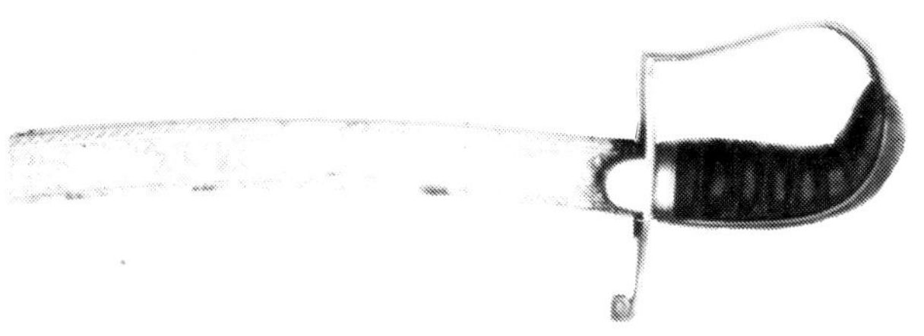

A good Georgian Light Company Infantry officer's sabre, circa 1805, curved blade 28in., well frost etched with: angel, standing figure of Britannia, foliage crown, 'GR', pineapple, 1801-16 royal arms, with gilt wash background (much remains), black leather covered grip, in its leather scabbard. $210 £90

A rare American revolutionary period horseman's sabre, flat single edged curved blade 33½in. with pronounced clipped back point, iron recurving 4-slot stirrup guard, deep iron domed pommel with raised button capstan, wooden spiralled fishskin covered grip. $220 £90

A French 1822 pattern Light Cavalry trooper's sabre, curved blade 38in. with broad and narrow fullers, engraved on backstrap: 'Manufre Rale de Klingenthal Julliet 1826' brass triple bar hilt, ordnance stamps to knucklebow, ribbed leather covered grip, in its steel scabbard. $220 £100

A scarce French Napoleonic period officer's sabre, broad single edged fullered curved blade 27¼in., etched with military trophies, foliate and floral devices, and retaining approx. 40 per cent blued and gilt decoration, brass stirrup hilt with ribbed borders, integral langets, stepped pommel. $240 £110

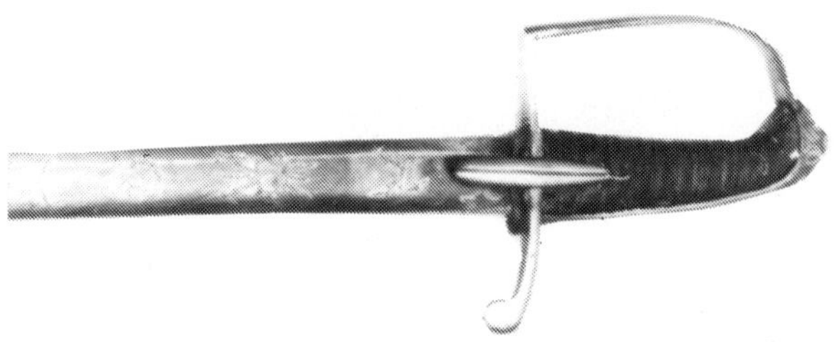

A Napoleonic period French officer's sabre, curved single edged blade 34in., retaining much original blued and gilt etched decoration of sun-in-splendour, makers initials at forte of 'C. W. T.', brass hilt with fluted single knucklebow, brass wirebound leather covered grip. $240 £210

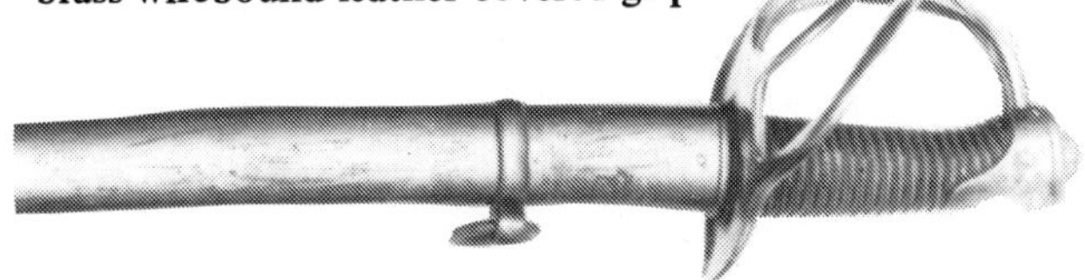

A good French Light Cavalry troopers 1822 model sabre, curved blade 36in., engraved on backstrap 'mre.D'armes de Chatt. Mai 1875. Cavrie Lre. Mle. 1822', triple bar brass guard, brass wirebound leather covered grip, in its steel scabbard. $245 £120

A Russian 1826 pattern Cavalry trooper's sabre, single edged curved blade 34½in., engraved on backstrap with Russian script and '1827' stamped at forte 'BAG', brass triple bar guard, plain brass mounts, ribbed leather covered grip, in its steel scabbard.. $295 £135

A French revolutionary period officer's sabre, broad, curved blade 31in., etched with figure of Justice holding scrolls inscribed 'La Nation', foliate scrolls officers bust within oval panel, 'La Loi', and with some traces of blueing and gilding, copper hilt, wirebound, leather covered grip. $290 £140

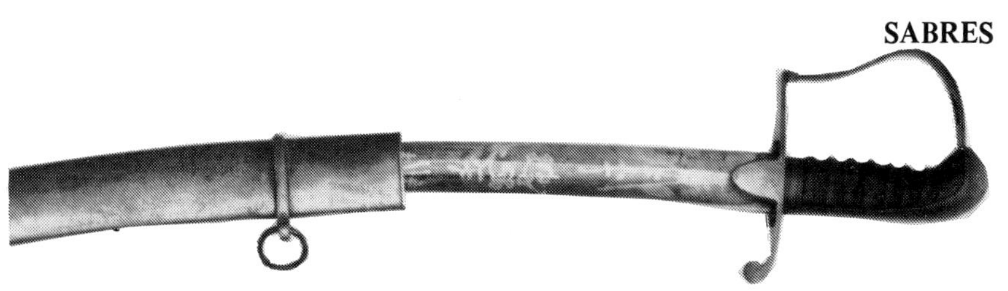

A 1796 pattern Light Cavalry officer's sabre, curved, single edged blade 27in., retaining much original blued and gilt etched decoration of military trophies, cavalry helmet and standard, plain steel hilt with stirrup guard, wirebound ribbed fishskin covered grip, in its steel scabbard. $365 £150

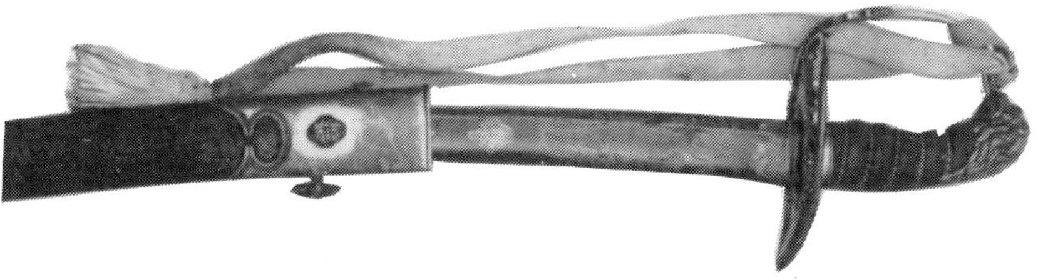

A Georgian 1803 pattern general officer's sabre, curved single edged blade 33in. engraved on the backstrap 'J.J. Runkel Solingen' and retaining most original blued and gilt etched decoration, 1801-16 Royal Arms, original wash leather dress knot and tassel, in its copper mounted leather scabbard. $340 £180

A late 18th century silver mounted Eastern European officer's sabre (possibly Polish or Hungarian), plain, curved single edged blade 32½in., with narrow back fuller, the hilt covered in Eastern silver, in its leather scabbard with 3 Eastern silver mounts, decorated en suite with the hilt. $460 £200

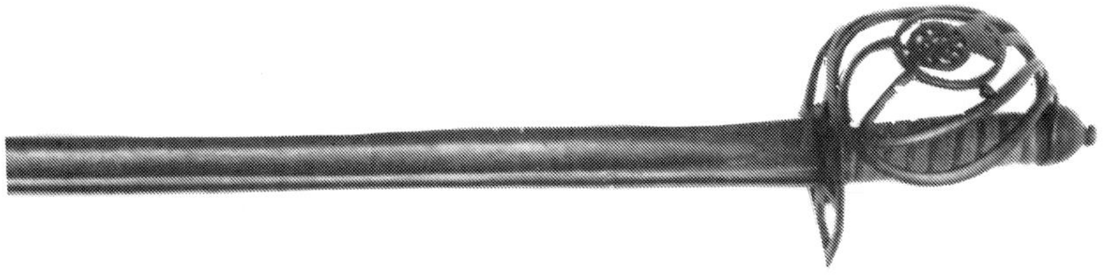

A continental Napoleonic era officer's sabre, curved single edged blade 33in., etched with Trophies-of-Arms, brass wirebound leather covered grip, in its steel scabbard with brass throat mount and ring bands, stamped at throat 'G.T.F.2.' $475 £230

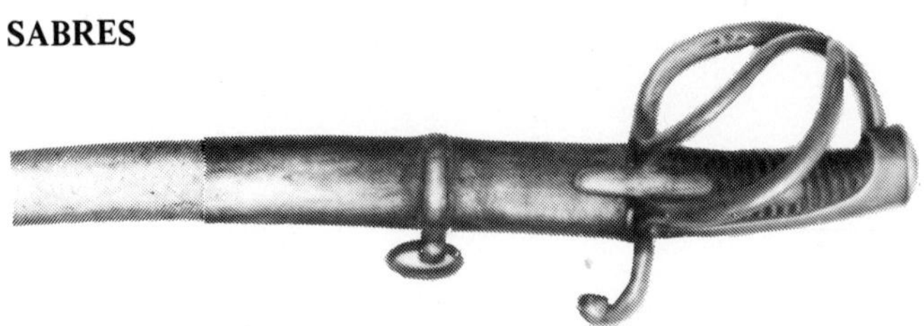

A French AN II Light Cavalry trooper's sabre, curved fullered blade 34in., engraved on backstrap 'Mfture Imple du Klingenthal, Juillet 1813', triple bar brass guard, leather grip, inspector's stamps etc. to forte and guard, in its steel scabbard. $625 £260

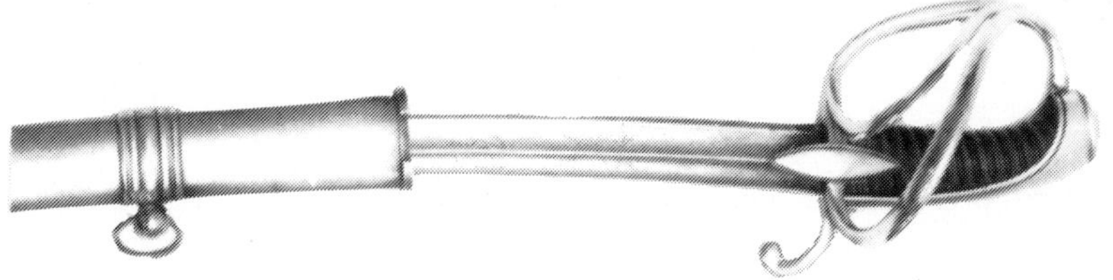

A scarce French Napoleonic era Cavalry officer's sabre, curved, single edged blade 32½in. with double fullers, etched with crossed standards, bugle horn, floral sprays etc., copper wirebound leather covered grip, the back quillon stamped 'DUC'. in its steel scabbard. $670 £280

A good 1796 Light Cavalry officer's sabre, curved, single edged blade 32in., with traces of maker on backstrap 'Woolley & Sargent' and retaining approx. 80 per cent original blued and gilt etched decoration of crown, 'GR' Mounted Trooper, in its steel scabbard. $590 £310

A good continental Napoleonic era officer's sabre, curved blade 31½in., etched at forte 'P. Knecht a Solingen', retaining virtually all original blued and gilt etched decoration of miltary trophies and foliate sprays, in its steel mounted scabbard with brass suspension rings and band mounts. $850 £360

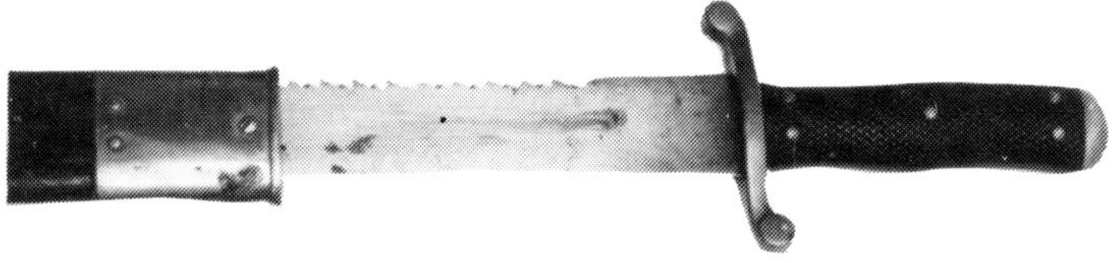

A scarce Swiss Pioneer sidearm, saw-backed blade 19½in., by Weyersberg Kirschbaum with Swiss cross stamp at forte, reversed brass crosspiece, diced grips, brass mounts, in its brass mounted leather scabbard. $160 £65

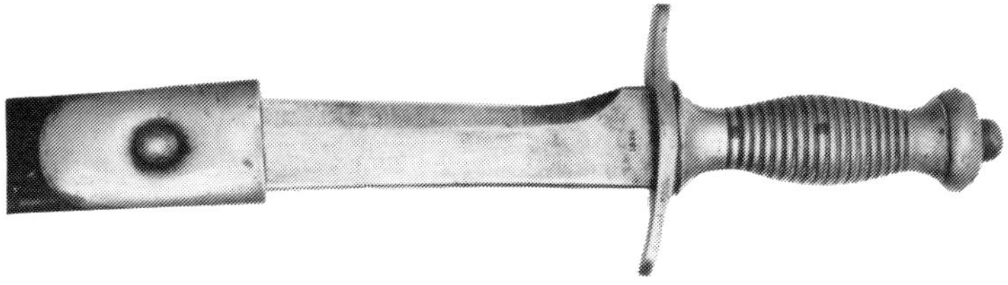

An unusual continental mid 19th century brass hilted sidearm (possibly Scandinavian), plain single edged curved blade 19¾in., swelling towards tip, by 'S. & K', d. '1859' at forte, slightly reversed crosspiece, ribbed brass hilt, in its leather scabbard with brass locket. $160 £65

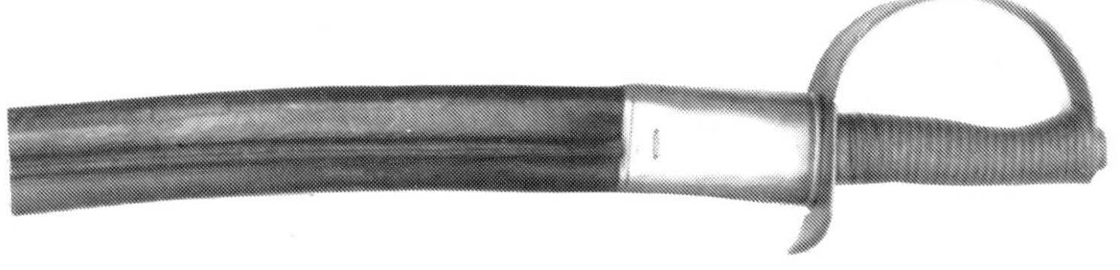

A scarce 1896 pattern Mountain Artillery sidearm, curved single edged blade 30½in., stamped on backstrap with W.D. arrow 'I' and 'Mole', 'I' with W.D. arrow at forte, narrow sheet steel guard, ribbed iron grip, in its brass mounted leather scabbard stamped '1918'. $195 £90

A good quality Georgian hunting sidearm, pierced bi-fullered late 17th century blade 15in., etched with foliage, brass arme and sun-in-splendour, traces of gilding, fluted pommel, diced ivory grip, in its sharkskin covered sheath, foliate engraved pierced steel locket. $240 £110

SPADROONS

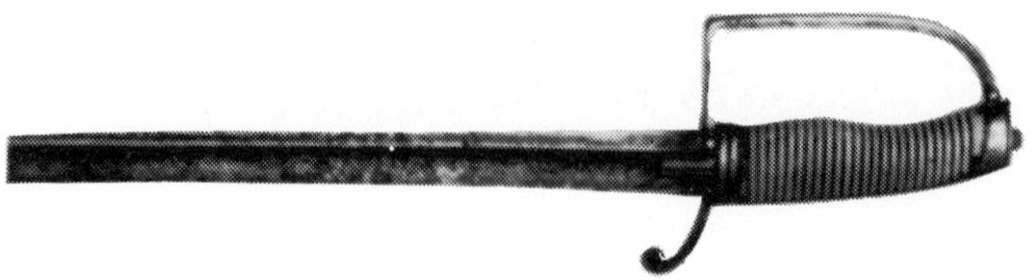

A Georgian officer's spadroon, circa 1780, straight single edged blade 32in., etched with pre-1800 royal arms, plain steel hilt with single squared knucklebow, plain steel mounts, small 'feathered' langets, ribbed ivory grip.
$110 £46

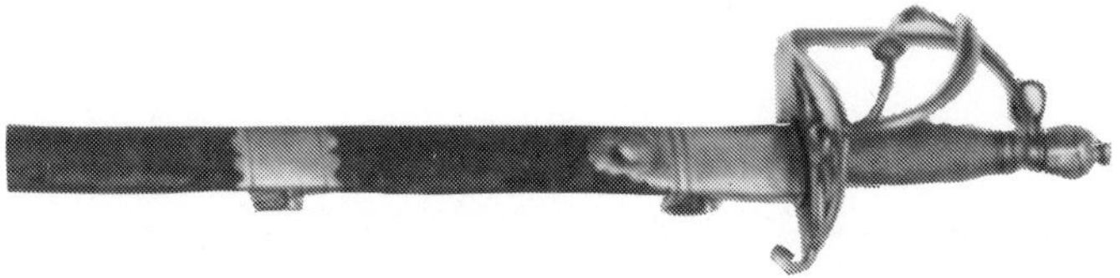

A Georgian officer's spadroon circa 1796 of a Grenadier company, plain, single edged blade 32in., copper, semi basket hilt, with side-loop incorporating flaming grenade, plain knucklebow with double side-loop, the bottom loop also incorporating 2 flaming grenades, in its patent leather covered scabbard.
$270 £125

SWORDS

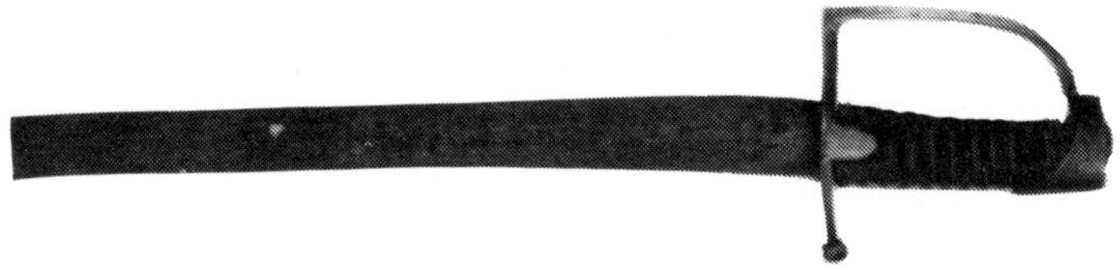

An 18th century Russian sword, plain curved blade, 26½in., stamped 'A' at forte, brass plain hilt with single knucklebow bearing a cyrillic letter stamp, cyrillic letters to top of back quillon, brass wirebound ribbed leather covered grip.
$130 £55

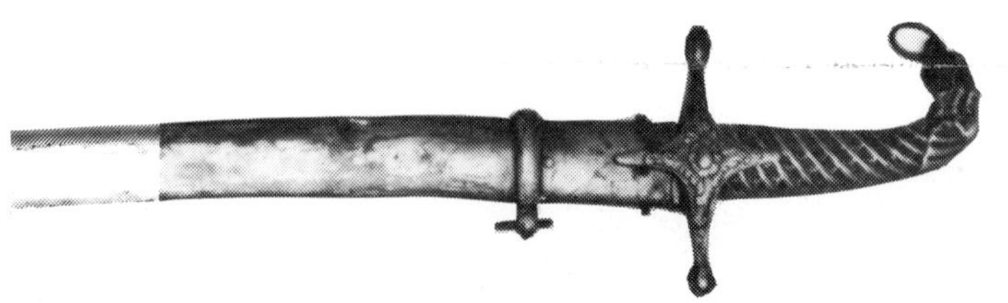

A band sword circa 1820, plain curved blade 27in. by 'Hamburger Rogers, 30, King St., Covt. Gardn., London' brass hilt with crosspiece with central floral panel, twist grip with scallop pattern, man's head pommel with ring in the mouth, in its brass scabbard. $155 £70

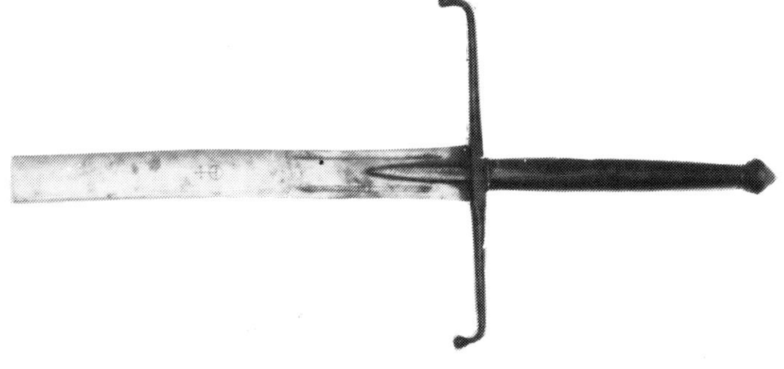

A good copy of a Scottish 16th century 'Lowland' two-handed sword, double edged, slightly tapering blade 32in., with orb and cross mark, plain quillons with down-turned terminals, iron ovoid pommel, wooden grip. $240 £110

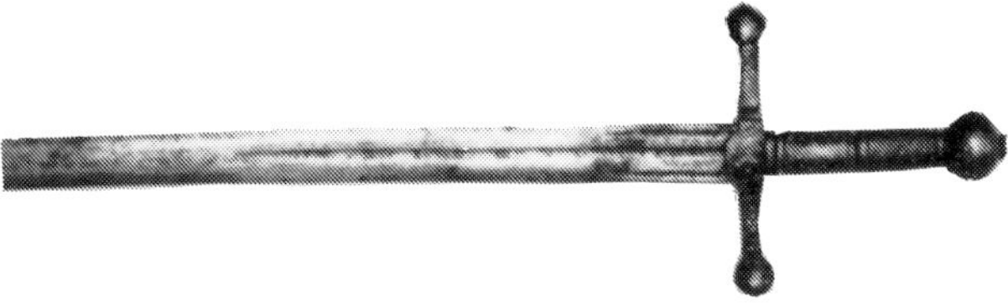

A 17th century German pillow sword, straight double edged blade 23in., with single part fuller signed 'Andrea Ferrara', iron cruciform hilt, with reversed straight crossguard with globular terminals, recessed grip, flattened pommel, the hilt inlaid overall with brass picquet studs. $380 £155

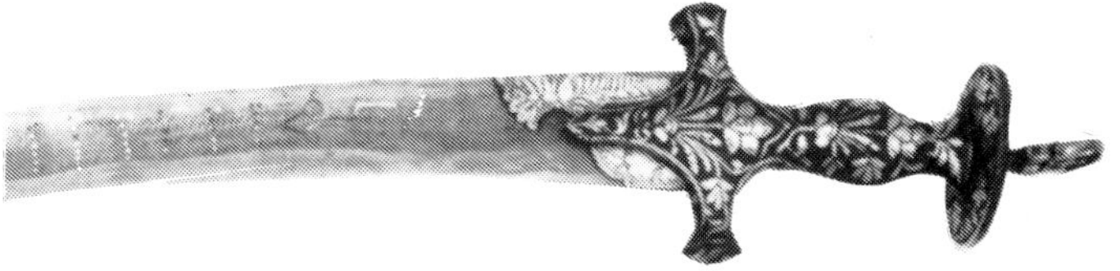

An Indian sword, Sosun Pattah, slightly curved single edged yataghan type blade, 24in. of watered steel, one side inlaid with dots and stylised inscription in script in silver, with gold foliate damascene at forte, iron hilt of tulwar form chiselled overall with floral and foliate patterns damascened overall in gold.

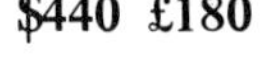
$440 £180

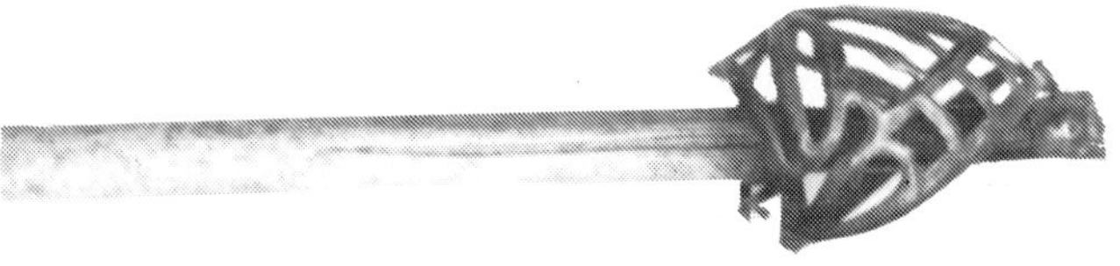

A 17th century basket hilted Venetian sword Schiavona, straight double edged blade 27in., short single fullers at forte, basket hilt composed of ladder and radial wrought designs with integral thumb scroll and tear drop finial. Square shaped pommel with swollen sides, leather covered grip. $430 £200

A 17th century Hispano Moresque sword, straight, double edged tapering blade 34½in., of flattened diamond section, etched at forte with scrolls with inscription within oval panel 'Ceci Faciet Do Me Insum Fines', down-turned flattened quillons, broad side loop, flattened re-curving knucklebow, octagonal iron grip, conical octagonal pommel. $730 £300

A French late 18th century silver gilt hilted smallsword, slim, tapering, triangular hollow ground blade 30½in., with maker's name at forte 'P. Kregal en Solingen'. The hilt with oval guard intricately chiselled with urns, foliate sprays etc., the grip knucklebow and ovoid pommel decorated en suite. Paris hallmarks on Pas d'Ane rings and on grip for 1786. $756 £350

An 18th century German processional two-handed sword. Flamberge blade 52in., with brass inlaid stylised running wolf mark at forte. Down drooping projecting side lugs, leather covered ricasso, large iron flattened crossguard with side loops and scrolled scaled stylised fish decoration. Large mushroom iron pommel, original grip covering. $970 £450

An 18th century European processional two-handed sword, straight, broad double edged blade 50½in., projecting lugs below ricasso, iron down drooping crosspiece with scrolled terminals, double side loops, leather covered wooden grip, chiselled sexagonal pommel. $1,035 £450

An early 18th century English Cavalry backsword, tapering, single edged blade 35½in., with broad and narrow back fullers and long clipped back tip, iron basket guard with plain panels, the central panel with applied numeral '1', flattened circular pommel, leather covered spiral grip. $225 £110

An English short fight backsword, circa 1620, single edged full length tri-fullered blade 31½in., struck in the fullers 'Me Fecit Clemens Kevller Solingen' on each side. Semi-basket hilt with two circular devices of different sizes built integrally with guard, re-curved quillon terminals, faceted swollen pommel. Octagonal wooden grip with brass 'Turks' heads'. $470 £200

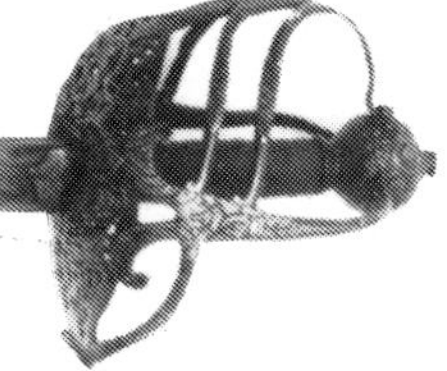

A mid 17th century Cromwellian basket hilted backsword of mortuary type, straight, single edged, single fullered blade 36in., stamped 'Andrea Ferrara' in fullers. Pierced basket type guard with scrolling foliage and 4 bust portraits supported by 2 pair of cherubs. Foliate chiselled pommel. $475 £230

A mid 17th century Cromwellian basket hilted mortuary backsword, straight, single edge, tri-fullered blade 31½in., stamped "*Mefecit*Sol*Lin*Gen* Mefecit*', pierced engraved foliate guard incorporating 2 stylised bust portraits of Charles I. Foliate chiselled pommel. $515 £250

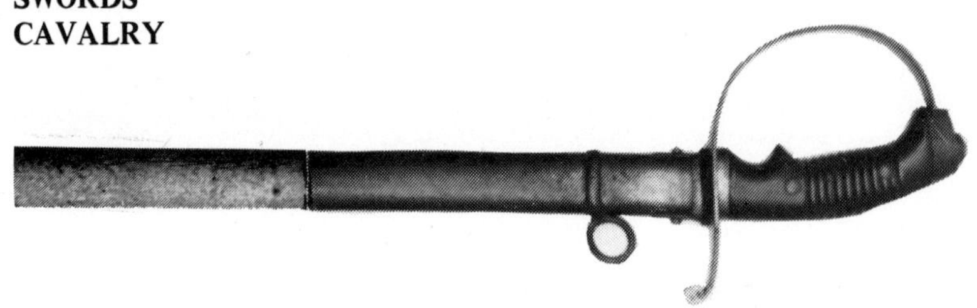

A Prussian Cavalry trooper's sword, plain, curved, single edged, pipe-backed blade 31in., with long, clipped back tip, by 'F. W. Holler', plain steel single knucklebow, ribbed composition grip, in its steel scabbard. $145 £60

A Bavarian Mounted Artillery trooper's sword, plain, single edged, curved blade 29½in., stamped on backstrap with crowned 'O' (for Otto) and '07', thick steel single knucklebow, plain steel mounts, ribbed leather covered grip, in its steel scabbard. $160 £65

A Victorian H.A.C. Light Cavalry officer's sword, slightly curved, single edged blade 35in., by 'Thurkle, 104 High Holborn', well etched with Regimental Crest and Title 'L.C.' (i.e. for Light Cavalry), triple bar steel guard and mounts, wire-bound, fishskin covered grip, in its leather scabbard with plated chape and locket. $190 £80

A Victorian 1821 pattern Light Cavalry officer's sword of The 3rd King's Own Hussars, single edged blade 34in., by 'Henry Wilkinson, Pall Mall', well etched with Regimental devices, crown, interlaced 'V.R.', Battle Honours in scrolls to 'Goojerat', Officers Crest and initials, steel hilt, triple bar guard, silver wire-bound, fishskin covered grip, in a brass Field officer's scabbard. $210 £95

A Light Cavalry trooper's sword, circa 1780, plain, straight, single edged blade 35in., with hatchet point, ordnance stamp at forte, plain brass hilt with single knucklebow, ribbed leather covered grip. $280 £130

A French Revolutionary period Cavalry officer's sword, slightly curved blade 29in., etched with 'Pour Le Salut De Ma Patrie Vivre Libre Ou Mourir', brass slotted hilt with additional fold-out side guard, retained with spring catch, brass mounts, copper wirebound grip. $450 £220

A Heavy Cavalry (possibly Household Cavalry) trooper's sword, circa 1808-18, single edged blade 34½in., with hatchet tip, ordnance stamp at forte, brass pierced guard of semi-basket form, ribbed leather covered grip. $540 £250

A Georgian hallmarked silver hilted 1796 pattern Heavy Cavalry officer's dress sword, double edged, tapering blade 33in., etched for entire length with 1801-16 Royal Arms, standing figure of Britannia, crown etc. and with presentation inscription: 'Presented by the Officers of the 2nd Battn. 44th Regt. to Colonel Robert Garden as a token of Their Sincere Esteem Jany. 1809' on gilt backing. $3,348 £1,550

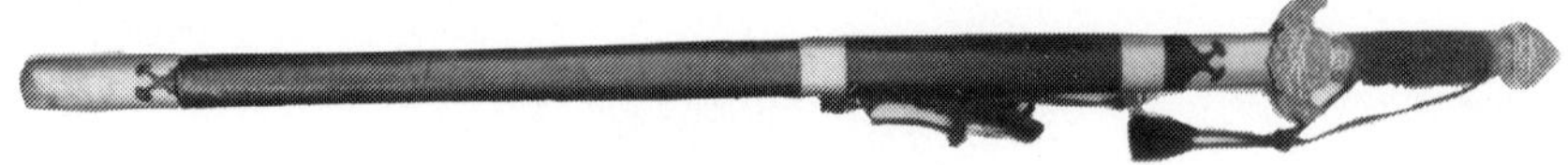

A Chinese sword, straight, double edged blade 30in., brass crossguard chiselled with demon mask and foliage, brass pommel and mounts chiselled with dragons etc. Cord bound grip with tassel mounts, suspension cords and brass belt clip. $185 £85

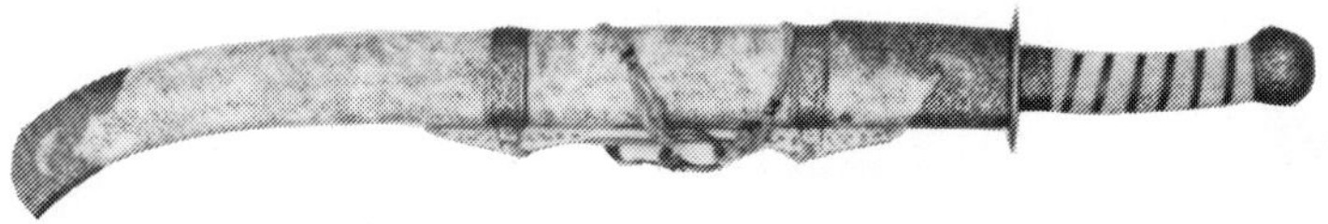

A Chinese sword, single edged blade 18in., with double fullers, brass oval guard and mounts decorated with traditional patterns, wirebound, white fishskin covered grip, in its fishskin covered wooden scabbard with brass mounts decorated in foliate sprays. $255 £105

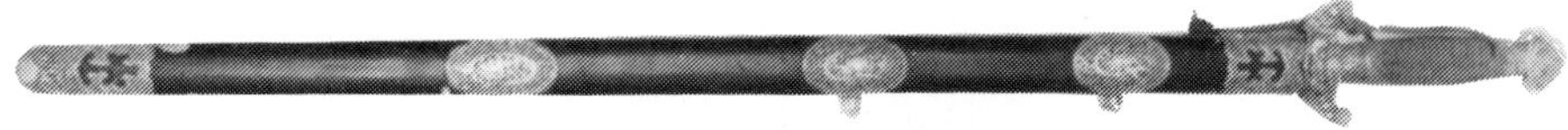

A Chinese sword, straight, double edged blade 29½in., inset with some brass studs, brass crosspiece chiselled with demon mask, brass pommel and mounts similarly chiselled with traditional patterns, cord bound grip, in its black lacquered wooden scabbard with 5 pierced brass mounts. $240 £110

A Chinese sword, curved blade 27in., with scrolled gilt sprays at forte, elaborately pierced oval gilt metal guard with designs of dragons within foliage, squared pommel and mounts similarly decorated, blue cord bound grip and blue tassel, in its vellum covered scabbard. $500 £250

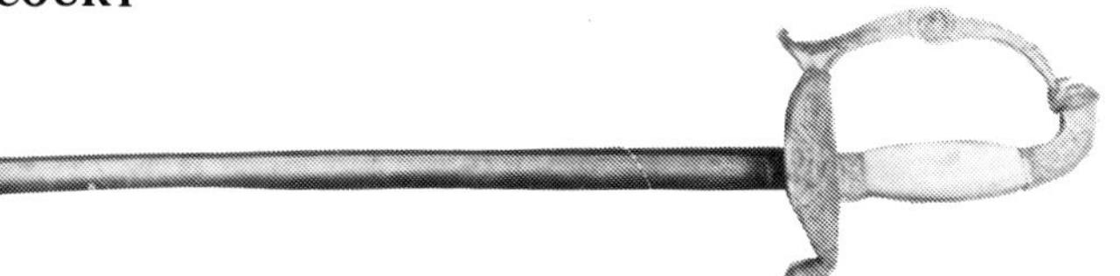

A mid 19th century French courtsword, slender fullered, single edged blade 32¾in., etched with small trophies and with initials IG.B. at forte. Copper gilt ormolu hilt, helmet centred flag trophy on guard, lions on knucklebow and lion's head pommel. Mother-of-pearl grips, laurel impressed grip straps, lion's head quillon terminal. $70 £35

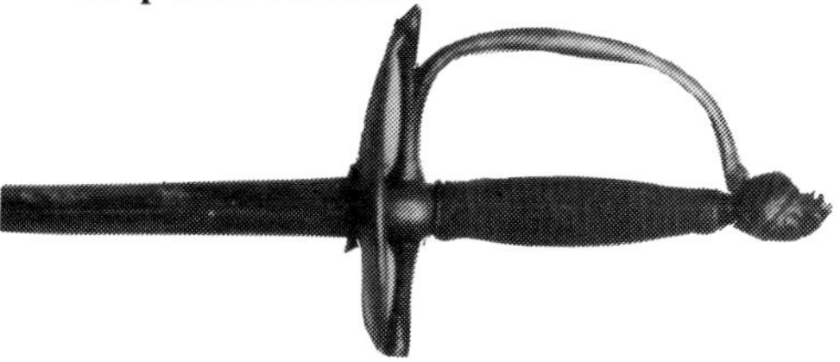

A French Napoleonic era dress courtsword, tapering, triangular, hollow ground blade 32in., etched with military trophies and foliage, gilt brass hilt with boat-shaped guard, plain knucklebow and rounded crosspiece, plumed helmet pommel, copper wirebound grip with 'Turk's head' finials. $110 £60

A Victorian cut steel hilted courtsword, triangular blade 31in. etched with foliage, arms trophies, scrolls and named 'Coote Conduit Street London', polished steel shell guard with grooved decoration and set with faceted steel rivets, hilt, knucklebow and urn pommel similarly decorated, in its polished steel mounted patent leather scabbard with velvet frog and webbing waist belt.

$185 £85

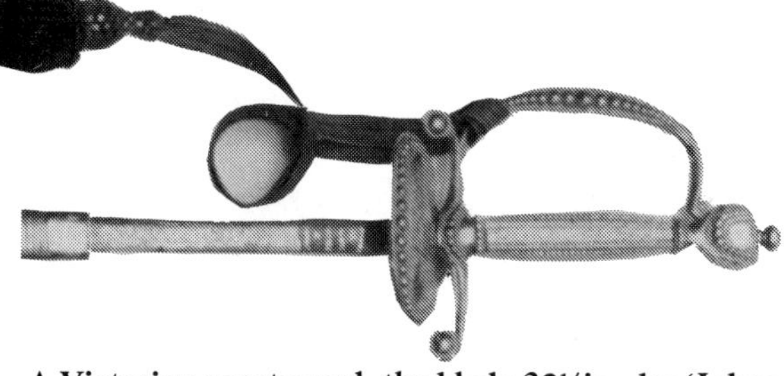

A Victorian courtsword, the blade 32½in., by 'Johnson & Folcard, Clifford St.', etched with crown, 'V.R.', crossed flags and foliage, gilt hilt with beaded decoration to shell guard, knucklebow and urn pommel, with original bullion dress knot, in its patent leather scabbard with gilt mounts. $245 £135

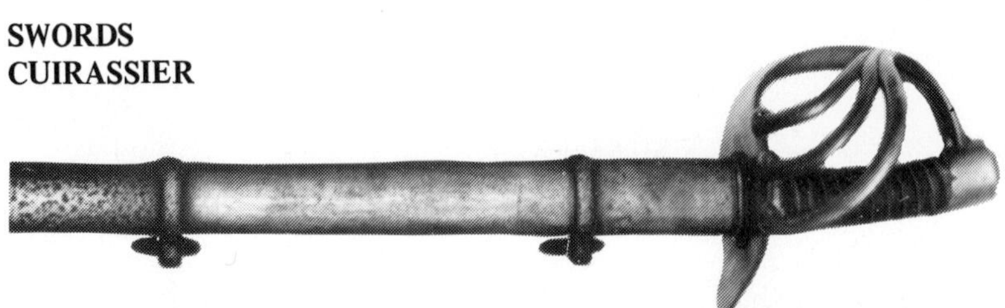

A French AN XI Cuirassier's sword, straight, doubled fullered blade 37in., with spear point and ordnance stamp at forte, backstrap with traces of engraved inscription 'Klingenthal Coulaux Freres', brass hilt with knucklebow and triple bar guard, brass wirebound leather covered grip, in its steel scabbard. $240 £100

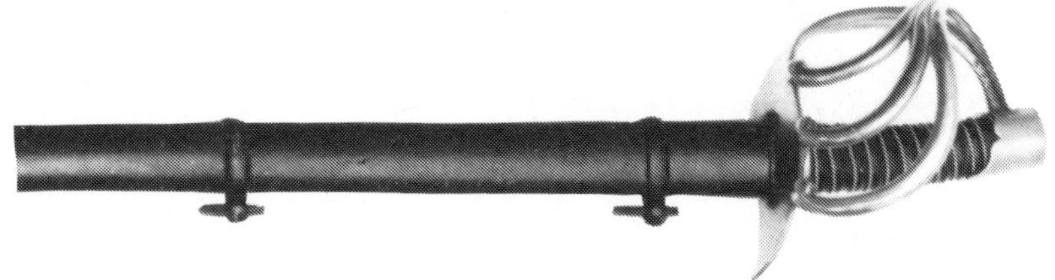

A French AN XI Cuirassier's sword, double fullered blade 36in., with spear point, engraved on backstrap 'Manufre Impale Du Klingenthal Juin 1812', brass knucklebow, mounts and triple bar brass guard, beak stamped 'Versailles', brass wirebound leather covered grip, in its black painted steel scabbard. $205 £100

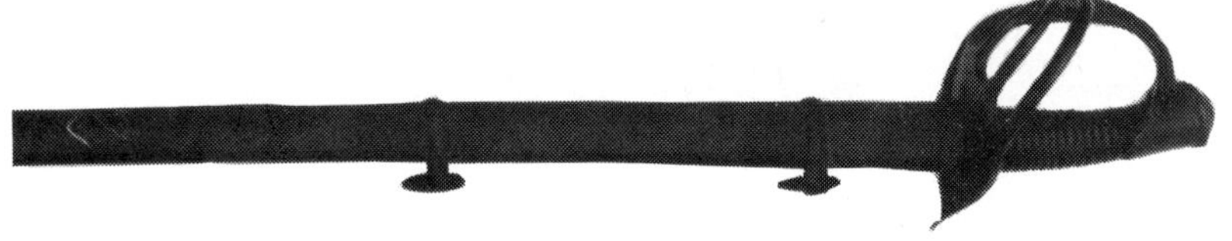

A French 1854 pattern Cuirassier trooper's sword, straight, pipe-backed, double fullered blade 38½in., with spear point, traces of engraving on backstrap, brass hilt with triple bar guard, ribbed, leather covered grip, in its steel scabbard. $240 £110

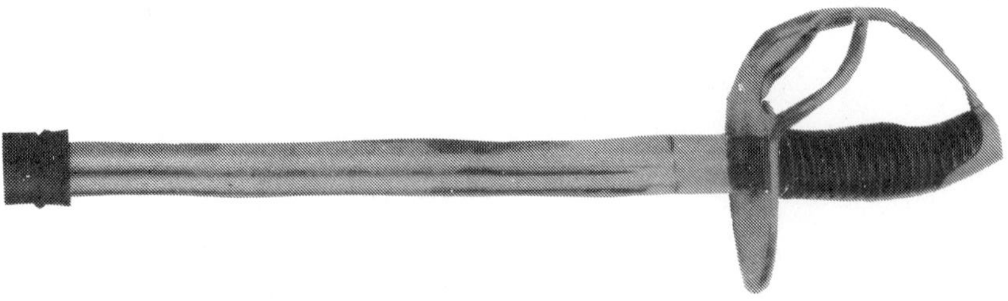

A Bavarian Cuirassier officer's sword, plated, double fullered blade 35in., etched with Bavarian motto in scroll, upon laurel spray, gilt triple bar guard, plain mounts, copper wirebound black grip, in its black painted scabbard. $420 £210

A French Naval Flag officer's dress sword, circa 1850, straight, double edged, tapering blade with raised central rib by 'Coulaux et Cie Klingenthal' etched with Stand-of-Arms, military trophies and foliage, gilt hilt the shell guard chiselled with crowned fouled anchor, the knucklebow chiselled with twisted rope and laurel sprays, ribbed mother-of-pearl grip, in its leather scabbard. $230 £95

A Georgian officer's dress sword, circa 1790, straight, double edged, tapering blade 32in., of flattened diamond section, etched with pre-1801 Royal Arms, crown, 'G.R.', foliage and 'Por Dios Por La Ley', copper boat-shaped guard, reversed crosspiece, single knucklebow, fluted pommel, copper band and wire-bound grip, in its leather scabbard. $345 £150

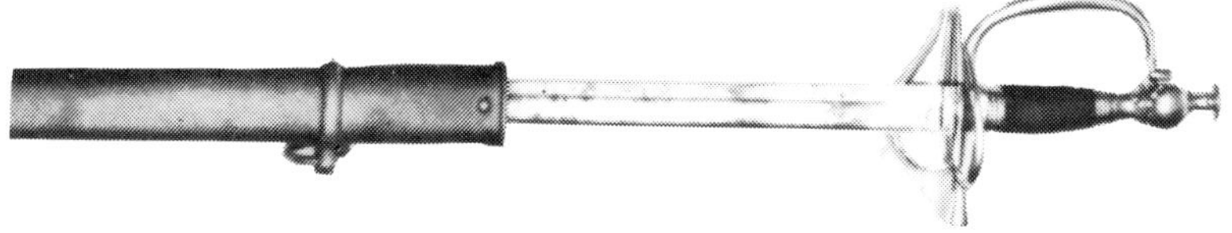

An officer's dress sword of The 2nd Life Guards, circa 1840, straight, single edged blade 34in., by 'Henry Wilkinson, Pall Mall', etched with crown above flaming grenade, gilt hilt with semi-boat-shaped guard, one folding, rounded knucklebow, ovoid pommel, copper wirebound grip, in leather scabbard. $680 £310

A Royal Horse Guards officer's dress sword, circa 1832, plain, single edged blade 38in., by 'Hamburger Rogers & Co., 30 King Street, Covent Garden, London', brass hilt with scrolled side guard and with crown on shell, rose motif on pommel cap, fishskin covered grip, in its steel scabbard. $912 £480

An old Borneo sea Dyak sword, Campilan, single edged blade 29in., pierced with holes at point, wooden hilt with some carved decoration and mounted with some hair tufts, with eared pommel. $65 £25

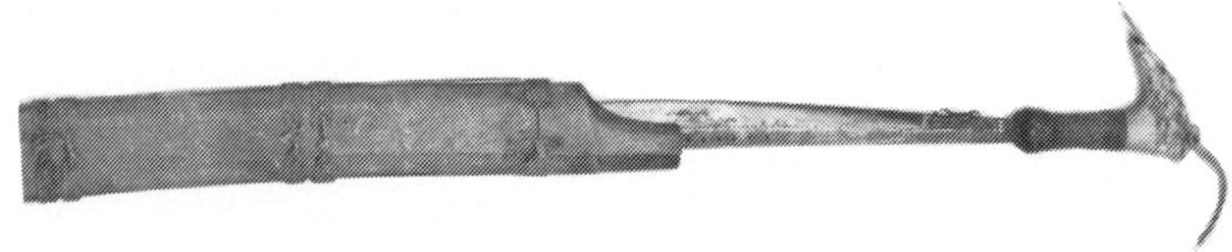

A Borneo head-hunter's sword, Mandau, blade 22in., with chiselled patterns and inlaid with brass studs, loops at forte to edge, rattan bound grip, elaborately carved bone pommel with traces of hair tufts, in its wooden sheath with carved panel and rattan bands. $90 £45

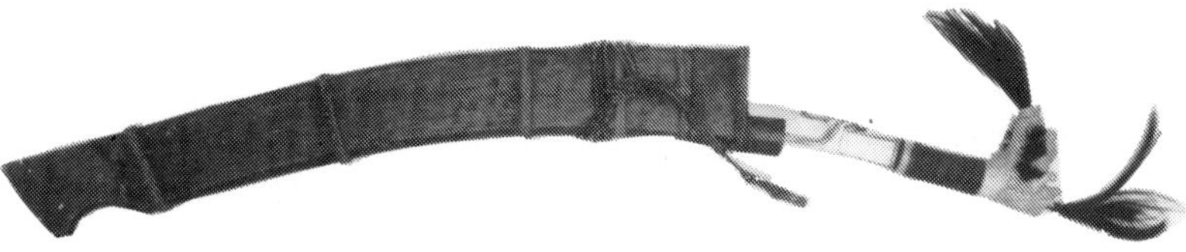

A Dyak head-hunter's sword, Mandau, curved blade 22in., bone hilt with rattan bound grip and carved with scrolls and loops, also mounted with hair tufts, in its wooden scabbard with rattan bands, and some carved decoration at the top. $125 £65

An old Dyak head-hunter's sword, Mandau, blade 19½in., with clipped back tip, and with incised foliate designs, carved bone hilt with white metal wire and rattan bound grip, hair tuft issuing from pommel, in its wooden scabbard. $175 £72

A Turkish sword, yataghan, single edged blade 24in., silver damascened with star and Arabic inscription. Two-piece large eared marine ivory grip with silver gilt grip strap decorated with pink corals and ornamental studs.
$152 £80

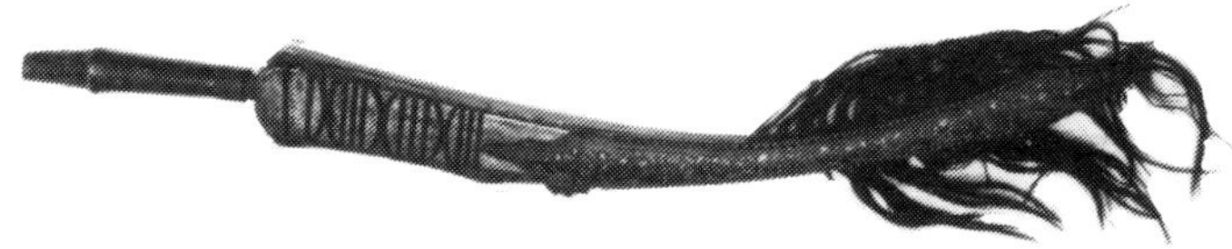

An old Formosan sword, slightly curved, single edged spear blade 14½in., wooden rounded hilt with some foliate and floral carving, in its wooden scabbard with openwork section at throat with iron lattice type mounts, the scabbard carved with similar patterns to the hilt. $195 £80

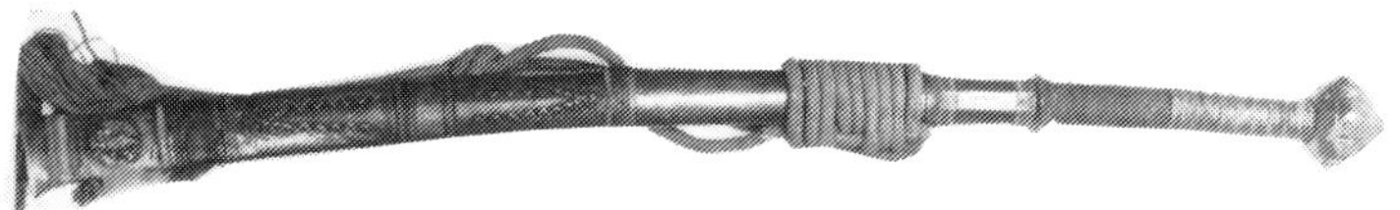

A silver mounted Burmese dha, single edged, curved blade 18½in., wooden hilt entirely overlaid by sheet Eastern silver and wire, part octagonal part round with some beaded decoration, with large silver bud pommel in its wooden sheath. $175 £85

A silver mounted Burmese dha, curved blade 24½in., with silver inlaid decoration of animals within foliate scrolls, bone grip with Eastern silver mounts embossed with floral and foliate patterns, conical pommel, in its green cloth covered wooden scabbard with Eastern silver mounts. $185 £85

An 18th century Turkish kilij, curved single edged blade 32in., multi-fullered at back edge, etched with Man-in-the Moon, Stars, Sun-in-Splendour, and foliate scrolls, plain rounded steel knucklebow, langets and back quillon, horn bulbous grips, in its leather covered wooden scabbard. $185 £85

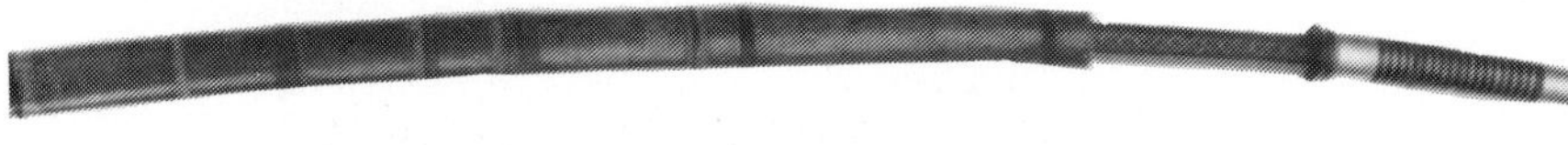

A silver mounted Burmese dha, slightly curved single edged blade, silver damascened against a stippled ground for entire length with scrolls etc., silver and copper mounted hilt with copper bands interspacing silver wire binding in its rattan bound wooden scabbard. $185 £85

A Ram dao, broad, single edged curved blade 19½in., with chiselled geometric and foliate patterns to top edge, with brass inlaid decoration, brass eye at tip, ribbed wooden grip with iron mounts and brass bands. $205 £95

An old Indian gauntlet sword, pata, double edged tapering blade 36in., with straps at forte, the hilt of brass, decorated with a mask, the guard with scrolled and other decoration. $230 £125

A silver mounted Singalese sword, kastane, curved, single edged blade 18in., the hilt with brass guard faced with Eastern silver, the langets and down-drooping quillons of brass similarly decorated and faced, the quillons terminating in monsters' heads, horn grip, 'monster head' pommel with red stone eyes, in its wooden lined scabbard. $190 £100

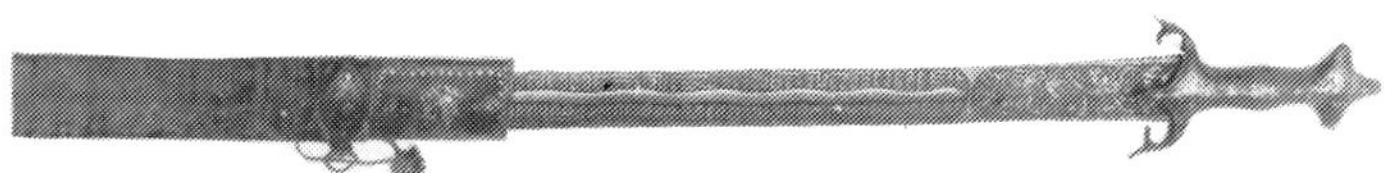

An Indo-Persian sword, straight, double edged blade 29in., etched for entire length with Mounted Warriors, Huntsmen, Band etc., Mooresque iron hilt with down-drooping quillons, eared pommel, in its velvet covered wooden scabbard with 4 iron mounts. $310 £150

A 19th century silver mounted Turkish sword shamshir, single edged finely watered Persian blade 32½in., silver fittings, strap work engraved crosspiece with swollen quillon terminals, silver chain knuckleguard, engraved silver grip-strap, translucent horn grip with silver rivet heads, in its black ass skin covered scabbard. $535 £260

A silver mounted Turkish yataghan, single edged blade 21in., issuing from Eastern silver gilt studded foliate mount and inlaid on both sides with gold foliate patterns, eared hilt of solid Eastern silver gilt and beaded filigree decoration set in foliate and floral sprays and coral stone centres, in its leather covered wooden scabbard. The chape of Eastern silver of Bichaq type. $864 £400

FALCHION

An early 17th century European falchion, broad, single edged curved blade 22in., with single fuller and clipped back point, scrolled decoration to back edge, reversed plain iron quillons and side loop, wirebound grip with 'Turk's head' finials, octagonal iron pommel. $526 £230

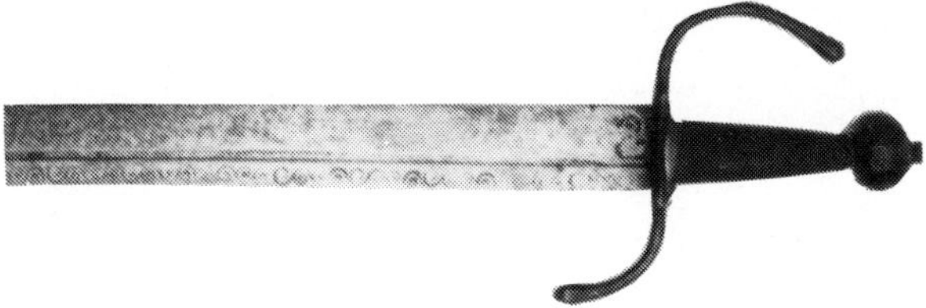

An early 17th century European falchion, broad, single edged, curved blade 22in., with single fuller and clipped back point, scrolled decoration to back edge, reversed plain iron quillons and side loop, wirebound grip with 'Turk's head' finials, octagonal iron pommel. $490 £200

HUNTING

A late 18th century German hunting sword, curved, single edged blade 24in., with crowned 'L.X.' cypher, above 'Hessen', the backstrap marked 'Schimmelbusch & Fils A Sohlingen 1790', plain brass squared crosspiece and mounts, staghorn grip. $145 £60

An early 19th century European hunting sword, straight, single edged blade 25in., etched with deer, hare, bugle, trophies and foliage, brass plain shell-guard, straight octagonal crosspiece, staghorn hilt with 2 oval brass lozenges, plain brass mounts. $140 £60

A mid 18th century European hunting sword, slightly curved, single edged blade 20in., with crescent-moon mark, brass knucklebow with central figure device, the back quillon with a crown, spiral horn grip, the knucklebow issuing from a negro head brass pommel button. $170 £70

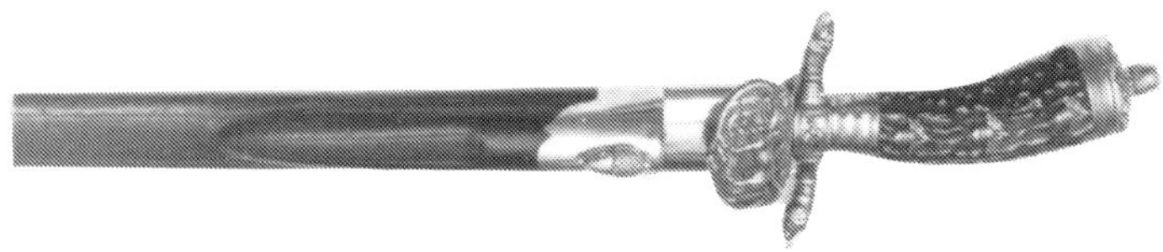

A late 19th century German dress hunting sword, straight, single edged blade 15½in., with Eickhorn double squirrel mark at forte, reversed crosspiece with hound's head finials, staghorn grip mounted with 3 brass acorns, foliate, chiselled pommel, in its brass mounted leather sheath. $150 £70

A mid 18th century European hunting sword, slightly curved blade 25in., with broad central fuller, etched at forte with foliate sprays, reversed brass short crosspiece, black horn grips mounted with 3 oval brass studs, brass mounts. $170 £70

A Russian mid 18th century dress hunting sword, single edged, clipped back blade 17½in. of watered steel, narrow double back fullers, etched at forte and silver overlaid with Imperial crowned Eagle and crowned cypher of Empress Elizabeth 1st (1741-62), octagonal agate hilt with white metal and silver mounts, in its leather covered wooden sheath with plain silver mounts. $475 £220

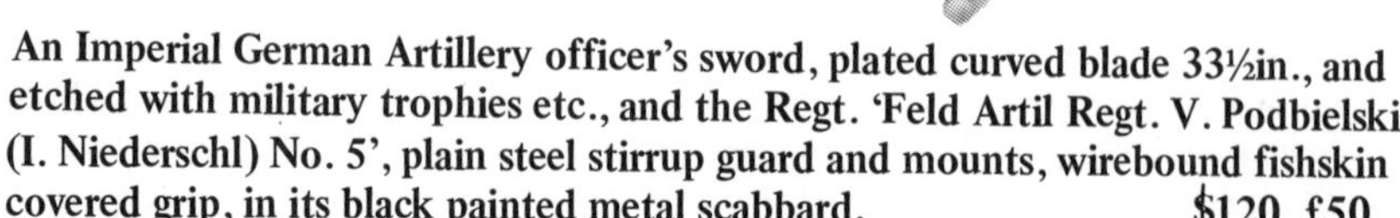

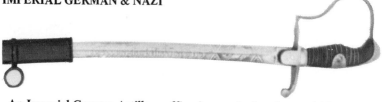

An Imperial German Artillery officer's sword, plated curved blade 33½in., and etched with military trophies etc., and the Regt. 'Feld Artil Regt. V. Podbielski (I. Niederschl) No. 5', plain steel stirrup guard and mounts, wirebound fishskin covered grip, in its black painted metal scabbard. $120 £50

A Nazi Army officer's sword, slightly curved, plated blade 29½in., by Horster, brass hilt, with stirrup guard chiselled with oak leaves, Nazi eagle to langet, lion's head pommel with red glass eyes, wirebound, ribbed black grip, in its black painted metal scabbard. $120 £50

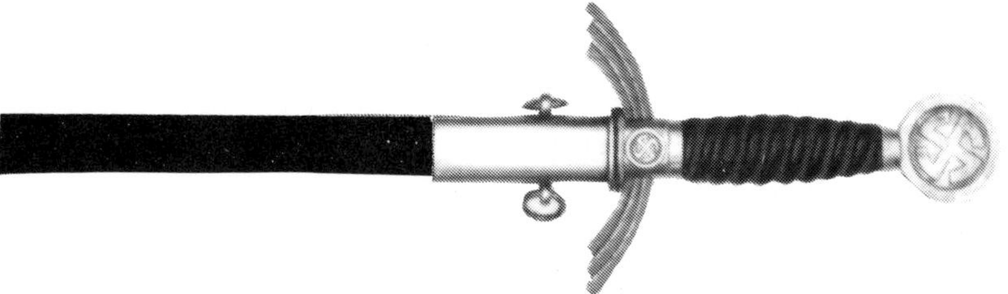

A Nazi Luftwaffe officer's sword, plated blade 28½in., with traces of maker's and proof marks, German silver mounts, wirebound blue leather covered grip, in its blue leather covered metal scabbard with German silver mounts. $135 £56

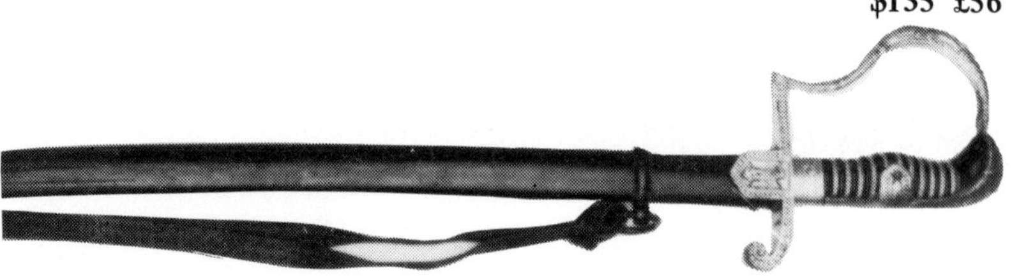

A Nazi Army officer's sword, slightly curved, plated blade 34in., by Eickhorn, gilt hilt with shield-shaped langet with Army Eagle, flattened stirrup knucklebar, the hilt with scrolled and oak-leaf pattern, wirebound black grip, in its black painted metal scabbard with dress knot. $130 £60

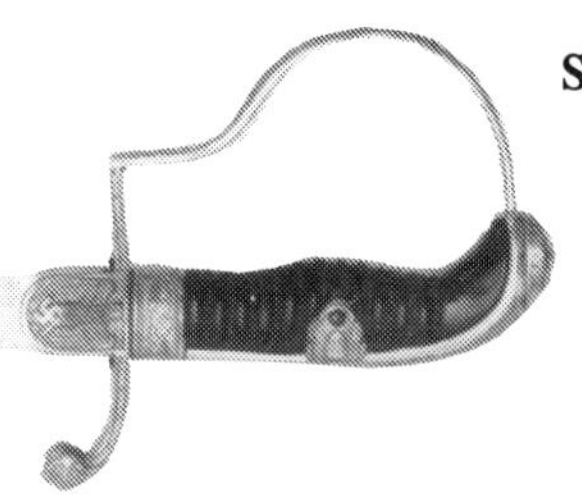

A Nazi Army officer's sword, plated, curved blade 29in. by W.K.C., gilt hilt with stirrup knucklebow decorated with oak leaves, Nazi Army Eagle on langet, mounts decorated with laurel and oak-leaf sprays, wirebound black ribbed grip, in its black painted steel scabbard. $125 £65

A Nazi Cavalry officer's sword, hilted officially to Imperial curved plated blade 32½in., by Weyersberg, well etched with Regt. '1 Pos. Feld Artill Regt No 20', mounted cavalry officer, etc., gilt hilt with stirrup guard, Nazi Eagle to langet, backstrap chiselled with oak leaves, wirebound, black ribbed grip, in its black painted metal scabbard. $170 £70

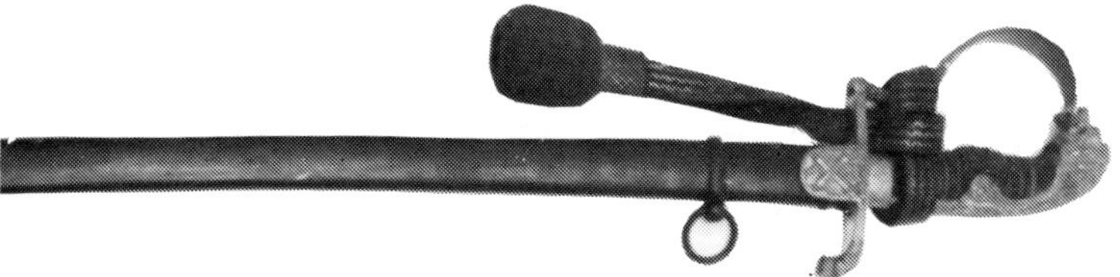

An Imperial German Artillery officer's sword, slightly curved blade 31½in., etched with military trophies etc., gilt chiselled hilt, oval langet with crossed cannon and oak-leaf spray, the stirrup guard with oak-leaf spray, lion's head pommel inset with red glass eye, wirebound, fishskin covered grip, in its metal scabbard. $180 £75

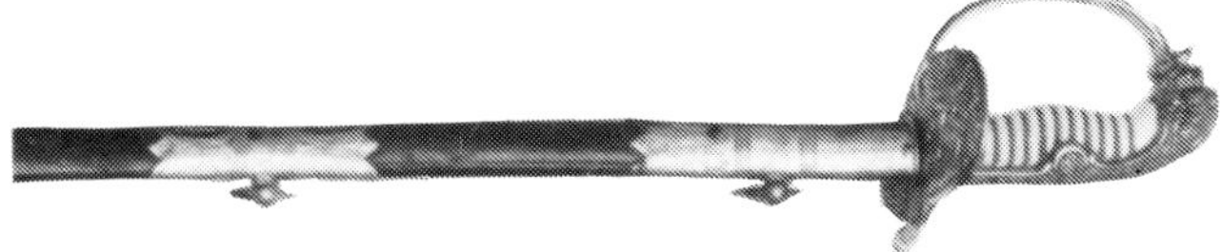

An Imperial German Naval officer's sword, curved blade 31in., with early Eickhorn trade mark at forte, bright metal hilt with large and small folding side guards, the large guard chiselled with crowned fouled anchor and oak leaves, lion's head pommel with red and green glass eyes, wirebound, celluloid covered, ribbed grip, in its leather scabbard with bright metal mounts. $165 £80

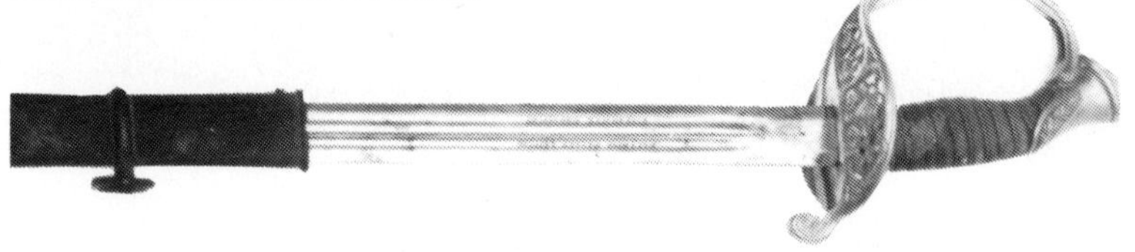

An Imperial German Saxony Army officer's sword, straight, multi-fullered blade 34in., by W.K.C. and etched in the fullers: 'Matthias Muller Leipzig Eisenhauer Garantirt', brass hilt with guard pierced with Saxony Royal Arms and foliate scrolls, wirebound, fishskin covered grip, in its steel scabbard. $235 £100

A Nazi Police officer's sword, blade 31in., by Krebs, plated guard and mounts, wirebound, ribbed black grip inset with Police badge, in its black painted metal scabbard, with plated mounts, the throat stamped with S.S. runes. $245 £100

A Nazi Luftwaffe officer's sword, blade 28in., by S.M.F., with Luftwaffe acceptance and inspection stamp, white alloy mounts, wirebound, blue leather covered grip, in its blue leather covered metal scabbard, with white alloy mounts, with belt clip. $260 £110

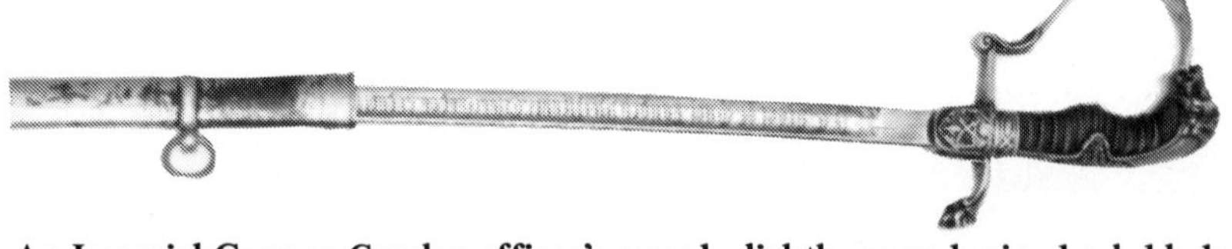

An Imperial German Cavalry officer's sword, slightly curved, pipe-back blade 32in., of watered steel, etched with military trophies, 'Damast Stahl Eisenhauer', and with presentation inscription of 'H. C. Frost S/L Gust Langen Jr. zur Freundl Erinnerung an August 1887', brass hilt with crossed swords on shield langet, lion's head pommel, white metal, wirebound, ribbed fishskin covered grip, in its plated scabbard with brass rings. $260 £140

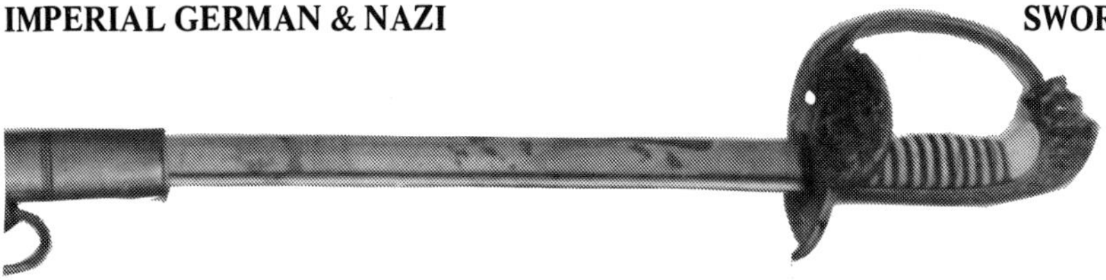

A Nazi Naval officer's sword, plain, curved, pipe-back, clipped back blade, 29in., by Alexander Coppel, brass hilt, folding shell and side guards, lion's head pommel, wirebound, white celluloid grip, the small folding side guard stamped with Eagle over 'M' and 'N.2283', in its brass mounted leather scabbard. $275 £145

An Imperial German Garde du Corps hunting sidearm, plated, single edged blade 16in., with central fuller, and etched with Garde Stars and 'Vive Le Roy et Ses Chasseurs', gilt metal hilt, with short, straight crossguard, the grip mounted with enamelled Garde Star, chiselled Eagle's head pommel with red glass eyes, in its leather sheath with gilt chape and locket. $410 £170

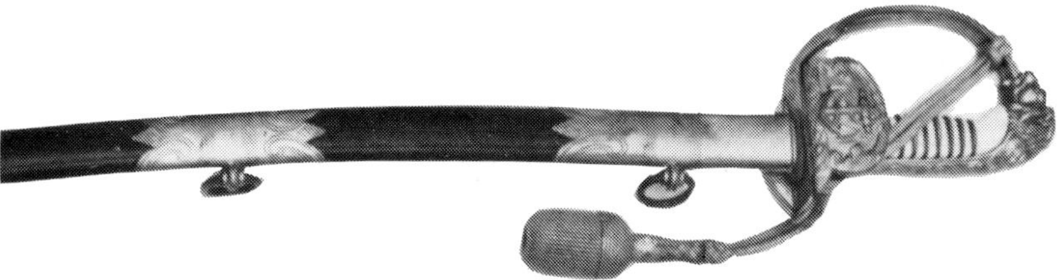

A Nazi Naval officer's sword, slightly curved, pipe-backed, clipped back blade 29in., by W.K.C., gilt hilt with large and small folding guards, lion's head pommel, wirebound, white ivorine grip, in its leather scabbard with three gilt mounts and with silver bullion dress knot. $575 £240

An Imperial German Artillery officer's sword, plain, pipe-back, clipped back blade 33in., chiselled gilt hilt, oval langets chiselled with oak leaves, crossed cannon etc., pierced stirrup guard, lion's head chiselled pommel inset with red stone eyes, ribbed ivory grip, in its plated scabbard. $625 £260

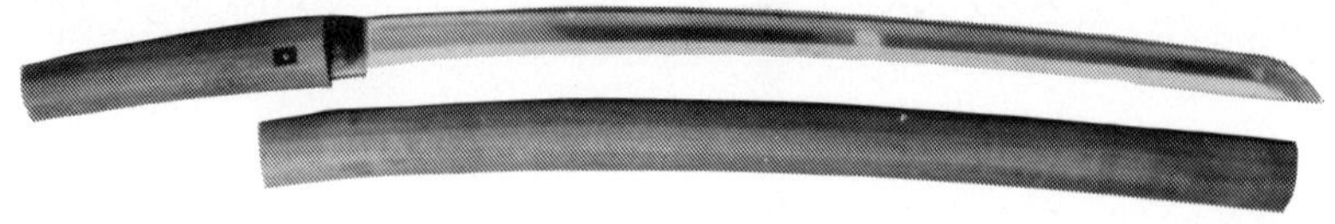

The blade from a Japanese sword katana, 60.8cm., signed 'Minamoto Kiyoshige Tsukuru', dated Keio 3rd year (1867 A.D.), one mekugi ana. Chu suguha hamon, broad nioi clusters, masame hado. $875 £350

A Japanese court sword ito-maki no tachi, blade 68.8cm., katana-mei-kuninaga, one mekugi ana, gunome hamon, muji hada. Tape bound tsuka, foliate engraved brass mounts, dragon menuki. Dai seppa Aoi tsuba, nashiji lacquered saya, with tape bound top and 2 ashi, leather obitori. $1,080 £450

A Japanese sword katana, blade 69.5cm., signed Kashu no ju Fujishima Tomoshige, one mekugi ana. Shallow tori, gunome hamon, broad nie line, itame hada. Tape bound tsuka, gilt foliate menuki, gilt fuchi kashira. Iron tsuba chiselled with sage and waves. In its black lacquered cloud designed saya with silver and gilt kojiri en suite. $1,380 £575

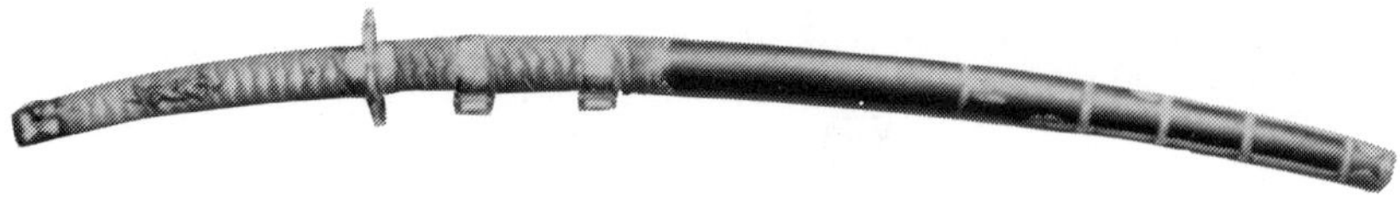

A Japanese sword ito-maki no tachi, blade 65.5cm., mumei, 4 mekugi ana, gunome hamon, mokume hada, fine nioi line. Tape bound tsuka, part tape bound nashiji lacquered saya. Foliate engraved brass fittings and tsuba all en suite. (Blade probably Shizu School, circa 1600 A.D.) $1,860 £775

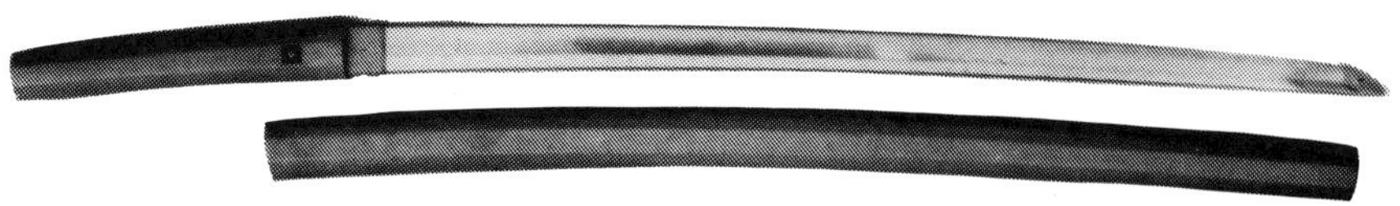

The blade from a Japanese sword katana, 65.7cm., mumei, one mekugi ana, kiri yasurime. Ko-choji hamon, broad nie line, itame hada. In shirasaya with NBTHK green paper and Kankeisho by Dr. Kashima, both attributing the blade to 'Uda Kunimune' Oei period (1394-1428 A.D.). $2,160 £900

A Japanese World War II Army officer's sword katana, blade 70.4cm., signed 'Bizen Kuni Osafune Yosazaemonjo Sukesada' dated 1504 A.D., 2 mekugi ana, gomobashi with two bonji characters as horimono. Hiro suguha hamon, broad nie clusters, masame hada. In shin gunto mounts with steel saya.
$2,424 £1,010

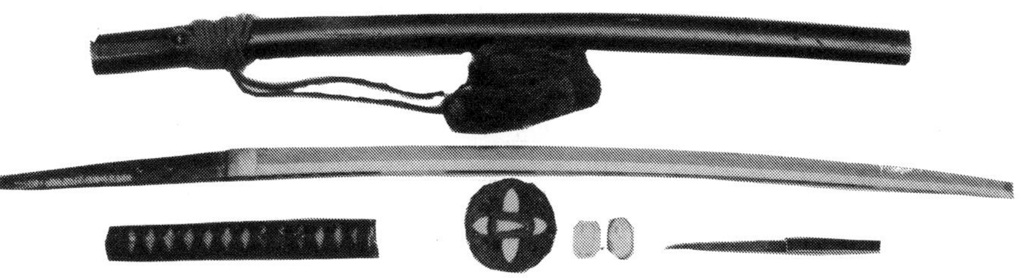

A Japanese sword katana, blade 73.5cm., signed Hoshu Takada No Ju Fujiwara No Sadayuki, 2 mekugi ana. Very tight itame hada, chu suguha hamon with broad nioi. Tape bound tsuka, shakudo fuchi kashira with gold nunome and shallow chiselling of Fuji and surround. Gin neko gake habaki, black lacquered saya with shakudo nanako kodzuka, 3 horses on relief, gilt detail.

$2,060 £1,125

A late 19th century Japanese sword tachi, blade 76.5cm., shinogi zukuri, signed 'Bishu Osafune Yokoyama Kaganosuke Fujiwara Sukenaga Saku Tomonari 56th Descendant'. Broad choji hamon. Silvered mounts en suite with shakudo mons of single cherry blossom flower head. Gold nashiji lacquered saya. $2,484 £1,150

A Japanese carved ivory mounted sword katana, blade 72cm., signed Bungonuju Yamato Fujiwara Tadayuki. Deep tori, broad straight hamon, O-kissaki. Tsuka, tsuba and saya made entirely from ivory sections, carved in high relief in the most minute detail. $3,180 £1,080

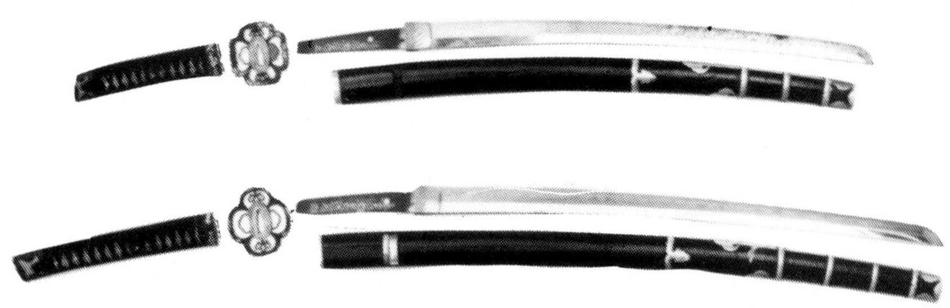

A pair of Japanese swords, daisho. Katana 57.5cm., signed Nagasone Okisato Niudo Kutetsu, dated Kwanbun 6th year (1666 A.D.). Gunome hamon, muji hada. Wakizashi 51cm., signed Nagasone Okimasa Kore Wo Saku, dated Genroku 3rd year (1681 A.D.). Gunome hamon, muji hada. Tape bound same tsukas, shakudo nanako fuchi kashira with gilt dragons en suite with menuki, pierced shakudo tsubas, katana tsuba with gilt dragons, Wakizashi tsuba with gold inlaid foliage. Silver mounted black lacquered sayas. $3,024 £1,400

A Japanese sword katana, broad blade 75.5cm., signed Hoki no Kami Taira no Ason Masayoshi of Satsuma, dated Bunkwan 4 (1807 A.D.). One mekugi ana. Bo-hi, kata-chiri hisaki agari, kaki-nagashi. Hiro gunome hamon, very large irregular nie clusters, mokume hada. Leather bound tsuka with iron fuchi kashira and tsuba with silver damascened Buddhist symbols. $7,440 £3,100

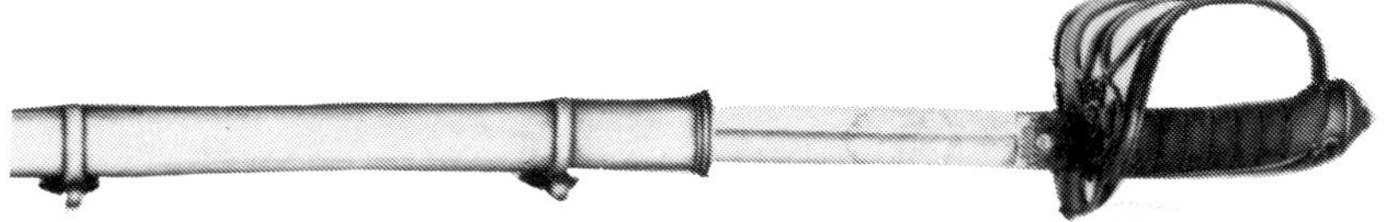

A Victorian 1822 pattern Infantry field officer's sword, slightly curved, fullered blade 32½in., by Henry Wilkinson, etched with 'V.R.' cypher amid scrolled panels and owner's crest and initials 'W.H.D.'., copper triple bar hilt, wirebound fishskin covered grip, in its brass scabbard. $75 £32

A Military sidearm offically adapted from Light Cavalry trooper's sword, circa 1780, straight, single edged blade 25in., clipped back point, ordnance stamp at forte, brass hilt with plain, single knuckelbow, leather covered ribbed grip. $85 £44

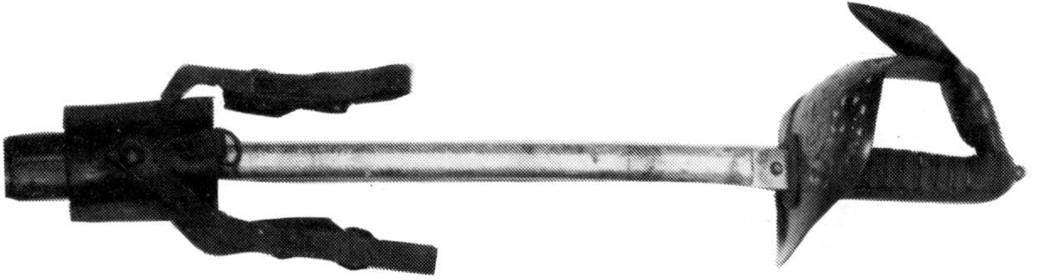

A Victorian Rifle Volunteer officer's sword, blade 32in., by Henry Wilkinson, Pall Mall, blade well etched with crown 'V.R.', foliate sprays, strung bugle, 'North York VI Rifle Volunteers', officially re-hilted with Edward VII pattern steel infantry hilt, wirebound, fishskin covered grip, in its leather covered Field Service scabbard with Sam Browne frog. $110 £46

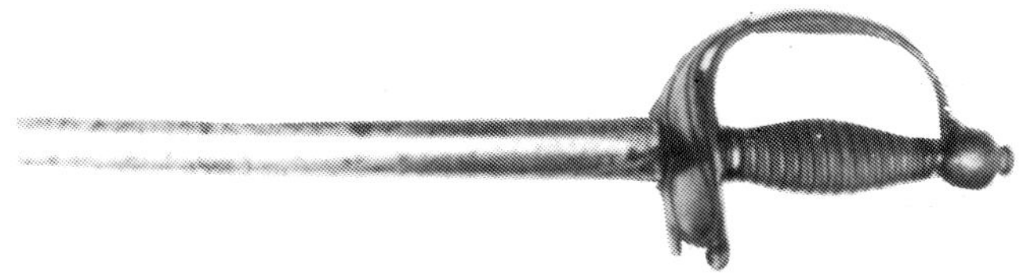

A late 18th century Georgian officer's sword, plain, single edged, tapering, straight blade 31in., plain steel boat-shaped guard, ovoid pommel, plain knucklebow, silver band and wirewound grip. $110 £50

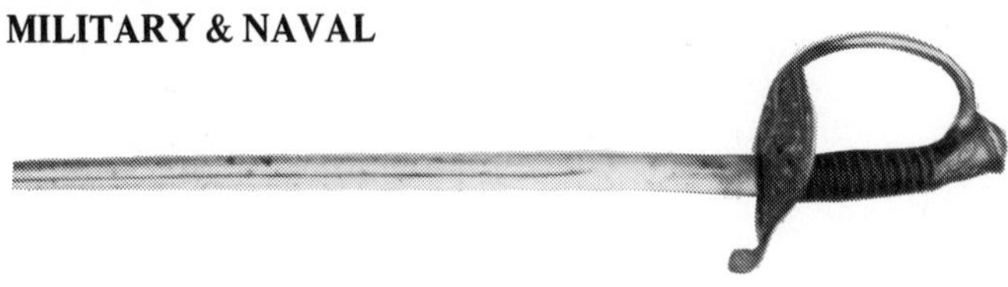

A Greek Artillery officer's sword, straight, double edged blade 30in., with single central fuller, by Eickhorn, brass hilt with floral and foliate pierced double shellguard, single knucklebow, the pommel with Greek Arms, wirebound, ribbed black grip, the reverse of guard with flaming grenade above cannon. $110 £50

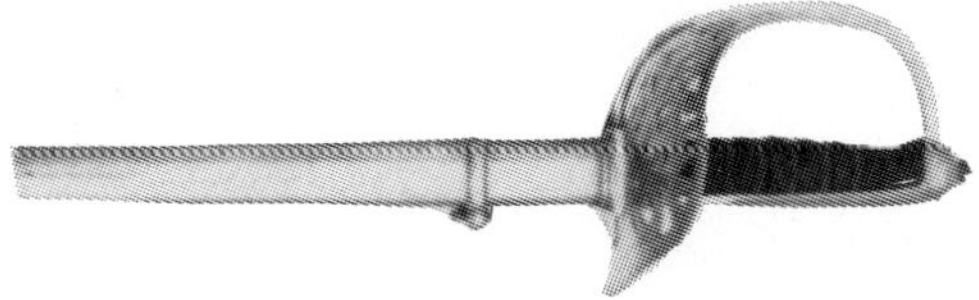

A George V 1897 pattern Light Infantry officer's sword, straight, slim blade 32½in., by Jones, Chalk & Co., etched with 'GVR' cypher and Royal Arms amid scrolled panels, plated steel guard, wirebound fishskin grip, in its plated scabbard. $120 £50

A Georgian 1827 pattern Naval officer's sword, plain, slightly curved pipe-backed blade 26in., with pronounced clipped back tip, silver plated knucklebow and hilt with folding shellguard, lion's head pommel, copper wirebound, white fishskin covered grip. $130 £55

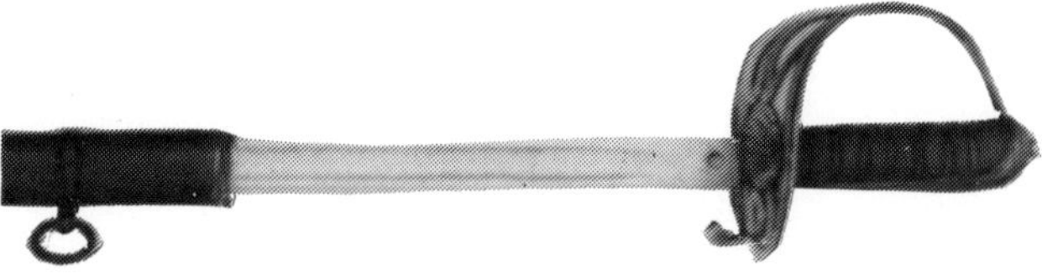

A Victorian 1822 pattern Egyptian Army officer's sword, blade 32in., by 'Hobson, Lexington St.', etched with Egyptian Emblem in panel, foliage, brass hilt with cartouche with Egyptian Arms, brass wirebound, fishskin covered grip, in its metal scabbard. $114 £60

A Prussian 1889 pattern Infantry officer's sword, straight, plated, double fullered blade 29½in., gilt hilt with folding guard, crowned 'WRII' cypher to wirebound, ribbed black grip, in its black painted scabbard with original dress knot. $145 £60

A late Victorian 1827 pattern Rifle officer's sword, straight 1892 type blade by Robert Mole & Sons, well etched with 'V.R.' cypher, stringed bugle and initials 'H.D.P.', within scrolled panels, plated triple bar guard, wirebound fishskin covered grip, black leather sword knot, in its plated scabbard and chamois lined oilskin cover. $145 £62

A late 18th century Military sword (possibly American Revolutionary period), plain, single edged, straight blade 28in. Iron hilt with side loop, plain knucklebow and single bar, ribbed wood grip. $155 £65

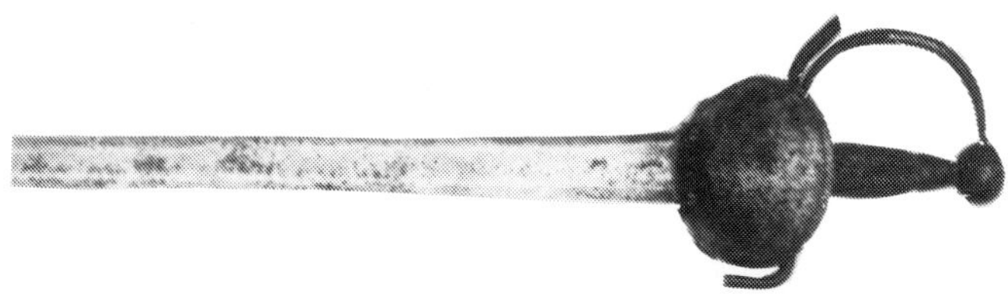

A Spanish 18th century Military 'Bilbo' sword, tapering, double edged blade 34in., stamped at forte with 'L' and another mark, steel double shell bowl guard, plain steel single knucklebow and reversed quillons, brass and copper wirebound grip, ovoid pommel. $155 £70

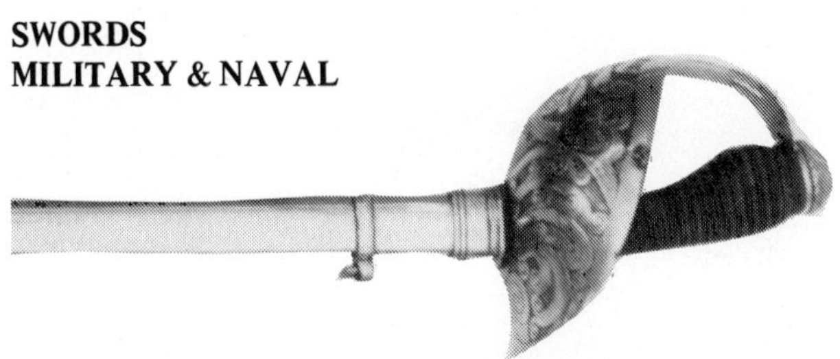

A George V 1912 Cavalry officer's sword, straight, slim blade 34in., by Henry Wilkinson, Pall Mall, etched with crown, Royal cypher and arms, foliage, and 'R.H.B. Arkwright, 12th Royal Lancers', plate bowl guard, wirebound, fishskin covered grip, in its plated scabbard. $165 £70

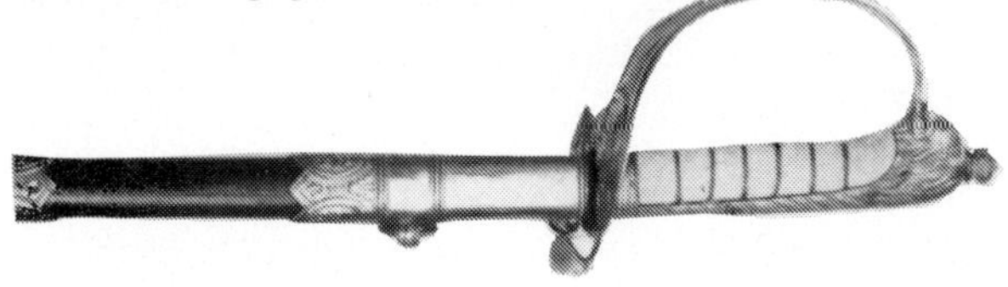

An Italian World War II Naval officer's sword, slim straight blade 31½in., etched with Italian Royal Arms, crown above fouled anchor bordered with laurel spray, etc., gilt solid half basket guard with crowned fouled anchor in cartouche, small folding locking side guard, lion's head with crown pommel button, wirebound, white fishskin covered grip, in its black patent leather covered metal scabbard. $170 £70

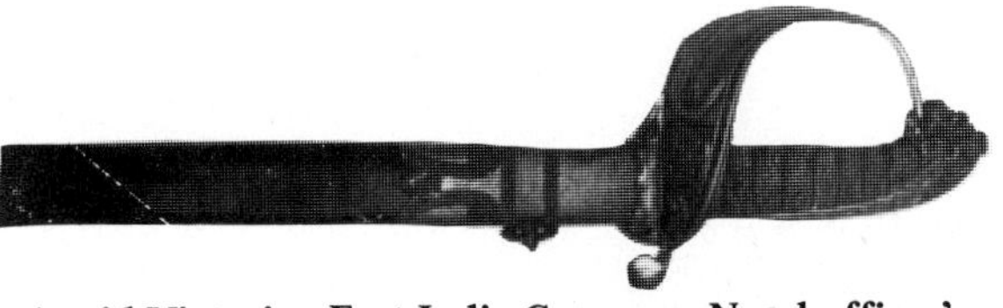

A mid Victorian East India Company Naval officer's sword, slightly curved blade 31in., by 'Hart, 26 Pall Mall, London', etched with East India Company lion, fouled anchor and foliage, copper gilt hilt, with folding side guard, cartouche with East India Company lion, chiselled lion's head pommel, copper wirebound, white fishskin covered grip, in its copper gilt mounted patent black leather scabbard. $180 £75

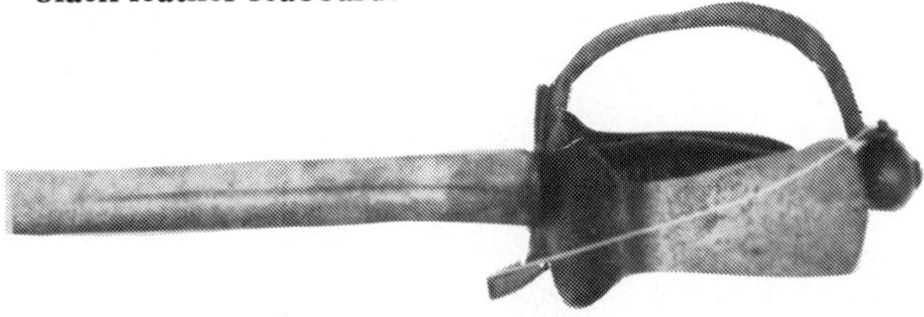

An early 17th century European sword, straight, tapering, double edged blade 29in., with running fox mark with 'H', engraved at forte 'C.C.F. No. 2', iron hilt with broad side plate guard and narrow tongue, simulated iron bound grip, rounded pommel, flattened single knucklebow. $150 £80

A Georgian 1796 pattern Heavy Cavalry officer's dress sword, straight, single edged blade 32in., engraved on backstrap 'J. J. Runkel Solingen' and gilt etched decoration of 1801-16 Royal Arms, crown 'G.R.', etc., copper gilt hilt with boat-shaped guard, silver wirebound grip, and original bullion dress knot, in a contemporary leather scabbard. $150 £80

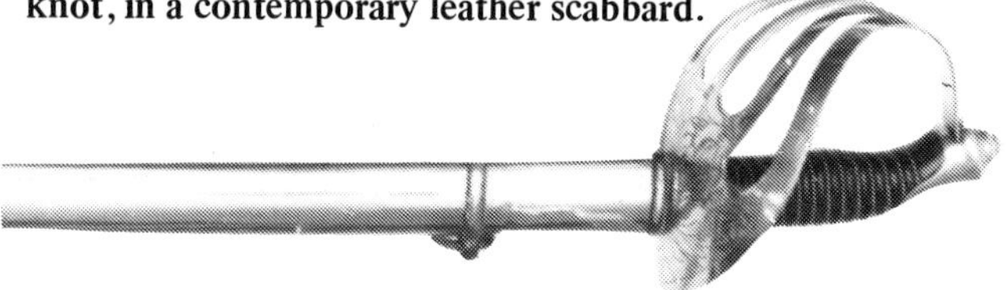

A Dutch Infantry officer's sword, single edged, pipe-back, clipped back blade 34in., etched within scrolls 'Erven Van Dyk Utrecht' and 'Yzerhower' plated semi-basket bowl guard, plated mounts, wirebound, black ribbed grip, in its plated scabbard. $165 £80

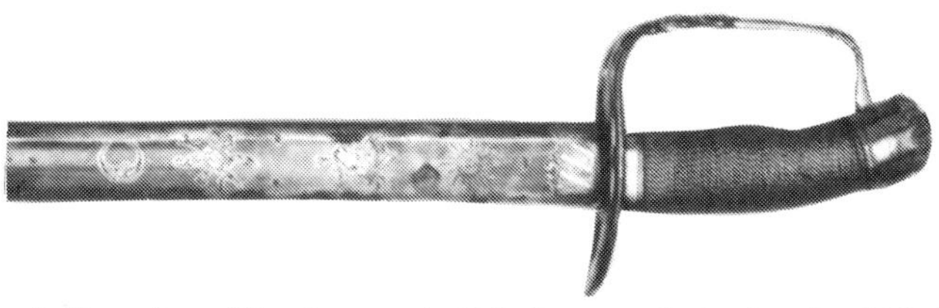

A Georgian officer's sword, slightly curved, single edged blade 32in., the back-strap engraved 'J. J. Runkel', the guard from an 1803 General officer's sword, copper gilt fluted pommel with foliate spray cap, silver wirebound grip, in its leather scabbard with three copper gilt mounts. $175 £80

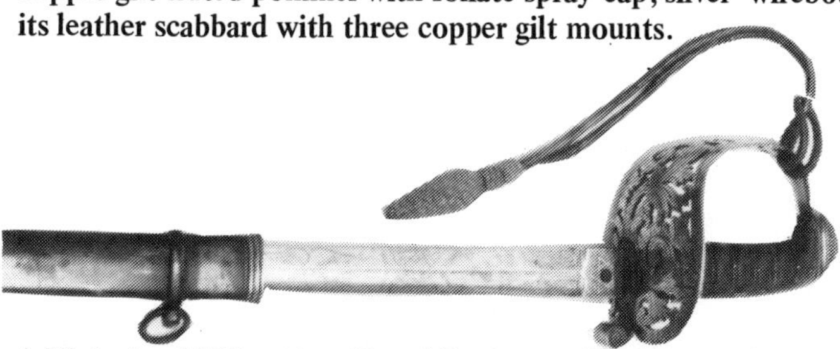

A Victorian 1857 pattern Royal Engineer officer's sword, blade 32in., by 'Pillin, London', etched with 'Royal Engineers', crown, 'V.R.', etc., brass hilt, copper wirebound, fishskin covered grip, bullion dress knot, in its steel scabbard. $190 £80

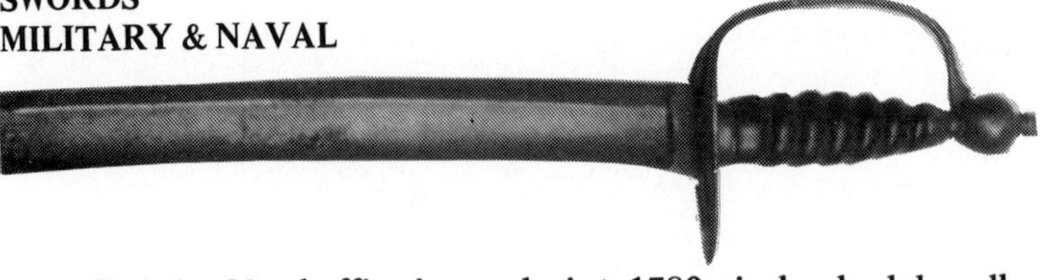

A Georgian Naval officer's sword, circa 1780, single edged, broadly fullered blade 29in., the white metal guard with 4 slot pattern and fluted knucklebow, rounded quillon, urn-shaped pommel engraved with fouled anchor. $150 £80

A Bavarian Artillery officer's sword, plated curved blade 32¾in., early Eickhorn trade mark at forte, etched with 'K.B.8 Feldart Regt', bust of King Otto etc., plain steel loop guard and plain steel mounts, ribbed black composition grip, in its black painted metal scabbard. $195 £80

An Edward VII Naval officer's sword, blade 31in., by 'Caffin, 13 Railway St., Chatham', etched with crown, fouled anchor, Royal cypher and foliage, gilt brass hilt, lion's head pommel, gilt backstrap, gilt wirebound, white fishskin covered grip, original bullion dress knot, in its brass mounted leather scabbard. $155 £85

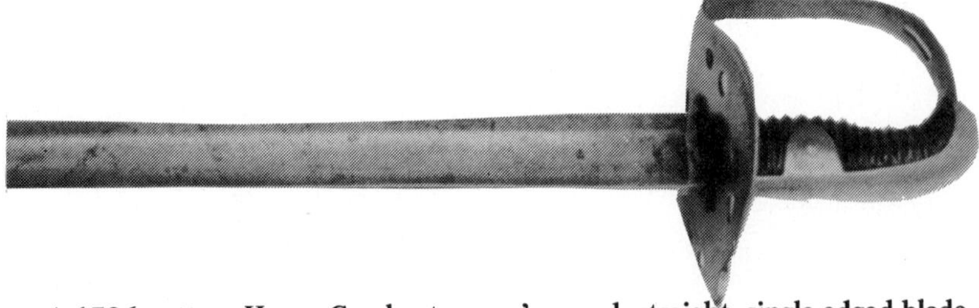

A 1796 pattern Heavy Cavalry trooper's sword, straight, single edged blade, 33in., with spear point, stamped on backstrap 'Osborn & Gunby', ordnance stamp at forte, steel hilt, the knucklebow with 7th Dragoon Guard markings 'G. 42. D.7.G', ribbed leather covered grip. $155 £85

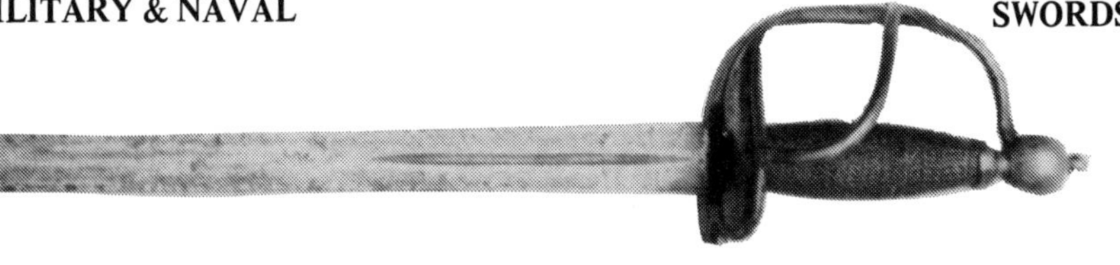

A French Infantry sword, circa 1750, straight tapering blade 30in., with single short fuller at forte and with 'fleur-de-lys' mark on both sides, brass heart-shaped guard, knucklebow, single side loop and ovoid pommel, copper wirebound grip. $165 £90

A Naval officer's sword, slightly curved, pipe-backed, clipped back blade 29in., by 'W.K.C.', gilt hilt with large and small folding guards, lion's head pommel, wirebound white ivorine grip, in its leather scabbard with 3 gilt mounts and with silver bullion dress knot. $165 £90

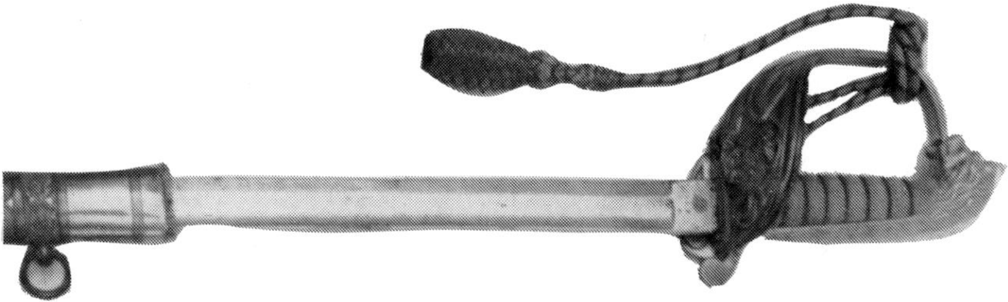

A Victorian Naval Flag officer's sword, blade 30in., by 'Gould & Son, Devonport', etched with crown, fouled anchor, Royal Arms and foliage, copper gilt hilt with folding side guard, wirebound fishskin covered grip, bullion dress knot, in its patent leather covered scabbard with 3 gilt mounts. $170 £90

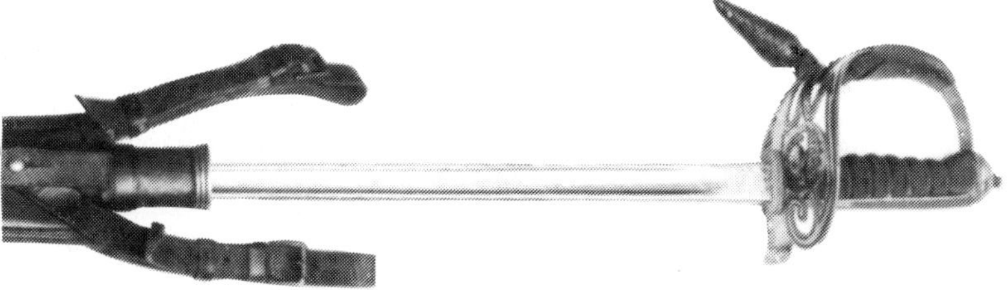

A George V Grenadier Guards officer's sword, plated blade 32in., by Wilkinson Sword, etched with crown, Royal cypher, Regimental badge, Battle Honours to World War I, plated hilt, wirebound fishskin covered grip, leather dress knot, in its leather covered Field Service scabbard with Sam Browne frog. $185 £90

A George V R.A.F. officer's sword, blade 32in., by Gieves, etched with Royal Arms, R.A.F. Eagle, blank scrolls etc., gilt brass guard, Eagle's head pommel, wirebound, white fishskin covered grip, original bullion dress knot, in its black patent leather scabbard with brass mounts. $205 £100

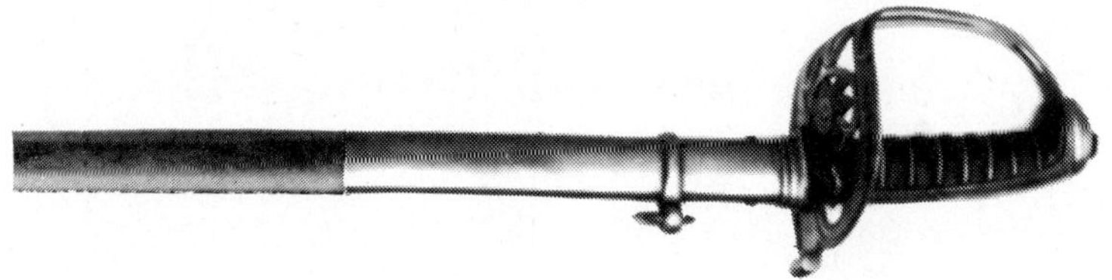

A Victorian Scots Guards Light pattern officer's sword of Lieut. Col. Francis Haygarth, slightly curved blade 32in., by 'Henry Wilkinson, Pall Mall', no. 7844, well etched with crown, interlaced 'V.R.' cypher, Regimental badge, foliage and Battle Honours to the Crimea, steel hilt, silver wirebound, fishskin covered grip, in its steel scabbard. $240 £100

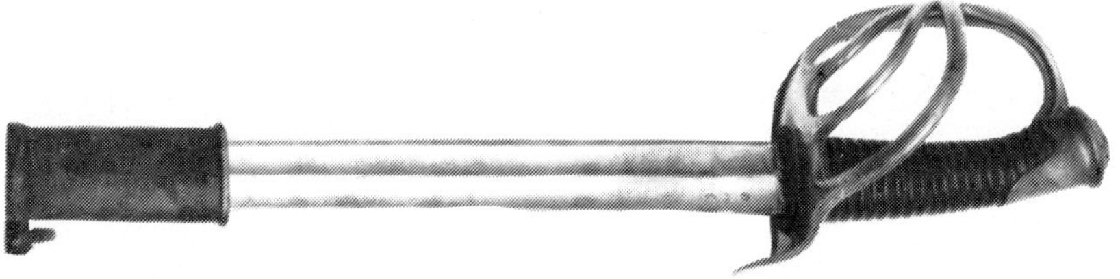

A French AN XI Cuirassier trooper's sword, straight, single edged blade 37½in., with spear point, double fullered, ordanance stamps at forte, engraved on back-strap 'Mfture Impale du Klingenthal Octobre 1813', triple bar brass guard, ribbed, leather covered grip, in its steel scabbard. $290 £120

A Victorian Naval officer's sword, slightly curved blade 32½in., by 'Warren, Cursitor St., London', copper gilt hilt, lion's head pommel, wirebound, white fishskin covered grip, folding side guard, in its leather scabbard. $305 £125

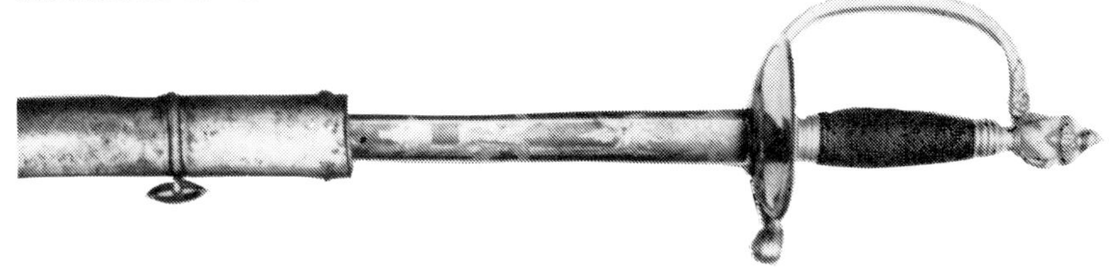

A Georgian 1796 pattern Infantry officer's sword, straight, single edged blade 31½in., marked on backstrap 'J. J. Runkel, Solingen', etched with crown, 'G.R.', foliage, 1801-16 Royal Arms, double shellguard chiselled at base with foliage, urn pommel, silver wirebound grip, in its steel scabbard. $305 £125

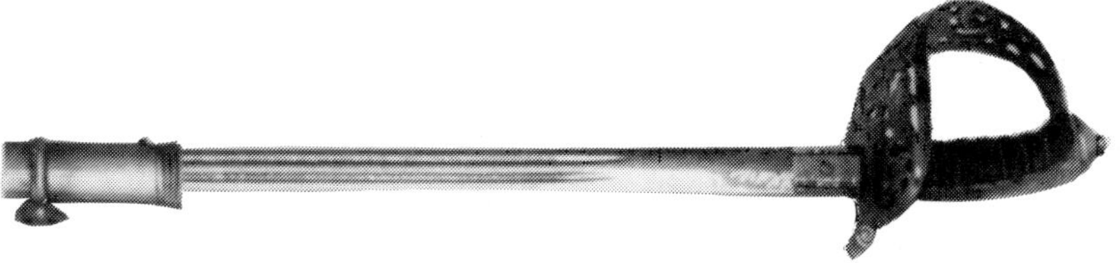

A Victorian Scottish Field officer's sword, double fullered, double edged blade 32½in., by 'E. T. Thurkle Denmark St.', etched with crown, 'V.R.', thistles and foliage also Regt. 'The Royal Scots (Lothian) Regiment', with steel 1857 Engineer pattern hilt, wirebound fishskin covered grip, in its steel scabbard. $245 £130

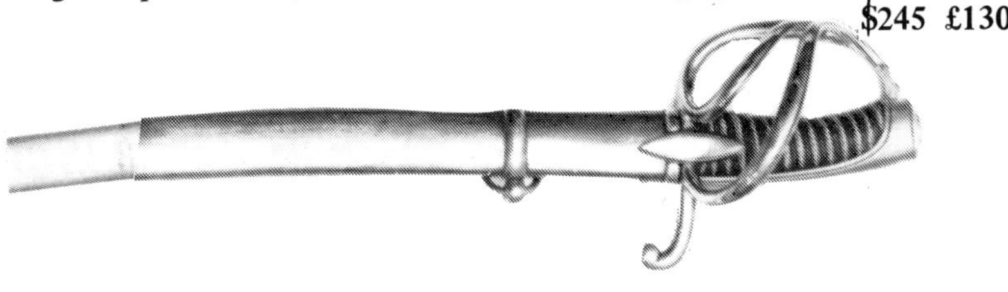

A Georgian officer's sword, circa 1780, straight, single edged blade 32in., with narrow back fuller, steel half basket looped guard with oval cartouche pierced with crown above pierced design of Rose and Thistle with border containing the motto 'Pro Aris Et Focis', half sphere pommel, wirebound fishskin covered grip. $270 £130

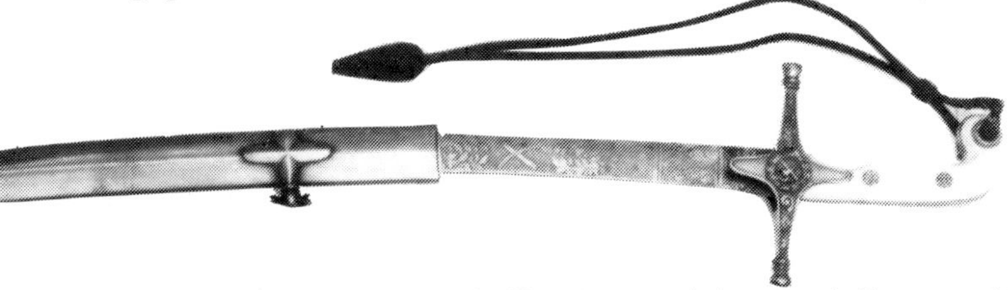

A Victorian 1831 pattern general officer's mameluke sword, flat curved blade 31in. by Hawkes, Moseley & Co., etched with 'V.R.' cypher, crossed baton and sword within foliate panels, ivory grip with gilt strap, rosettes and cross-piece in its brass scabbard. $320 £135

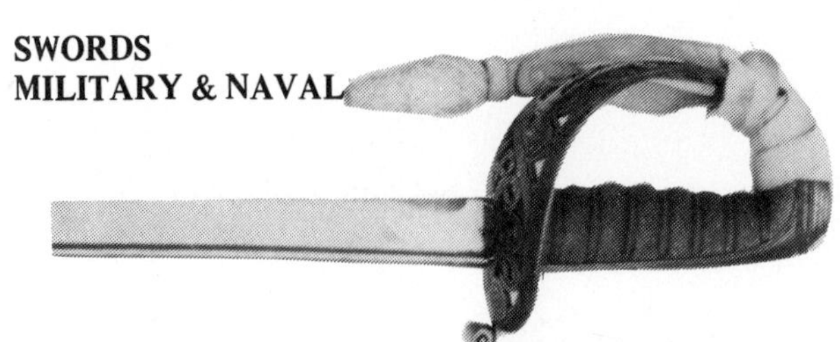

An early Victorian 1821 pattern Heavy Cavalry officer's un-dress sword, slightly curved narrow pipe-back, clipped backed blade 32in., width 1in., by 'Hamburger Rogers & Co., 30 King St., Covt. Garden, London', steel pierced hilt, wirebound fishskin covered grip, in its steel scabbard. $255 £140

A Victorian 1821 Light Cavalry officer's sword of The 12th Lancers, slightly curved blade 35in., by 'Hawkes, London', well etched with crown, 'V.R.', foliage, Regt. badge 'XIIth The Prince of Wales Royal Lancers', also Battle Honours, steel hilt, copper wirebound, fishskin covered grip, in its steel scabbard. $255 £140

An 1889 pattern Prussian Infantry officer's sword, straight, plated, multi-fullered blade 29in., by W.K.C., brass hilt with extra engraved decoration of Prussian Eagle chiselled on both sides of folding shell guard, knucklebow decorated inside and out with laurel sprays, the pommel with crowned Eagle and military trophies, wirebound ribbed grip, with crowned 'W.R.II' cypher, in its black painted metal scabbard. $330 £140

An 1822 pattern Infantry officer's sword, 1855, of the Scots Fusilier's Guards, slightly curved fullered blade 32½in., by Henry Wilkinson (No. 6445) etched with Battle Honours: Lincelles to Sevastopol and badge of Dalrymple family, wirebound fishskin covered grip, in its steel scabbard. $340 £145

A George V Scottish Field officer's sword, blade 32½in., by 'Henry Wilkinson Pall Mall', etched with crown, Royal cypher, Regiment 'Argyll and Sutherland Highlanders', thistles etc., plated 1857 hilt, copper wirebound, fishskin covered grip, in its leather covered Field Service scabbard with plated mounts. $325 £150

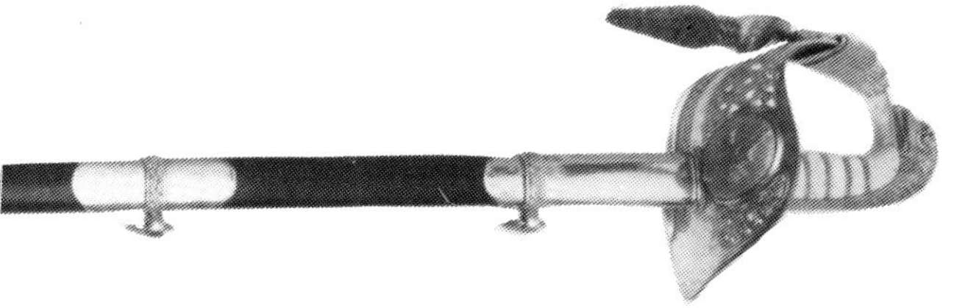

A George VI R.A.F. officer's sword, blade 32in., etched with Royal Arms, R.A.F. Eagle, blank scrolls and laurel sprays, gilt hilt, eagle's head pommel, gilt wirebound, white fishskin covered grip, original bullion dress knot, in its leather scabbard with gilt metal mounts. $395 £165

An ER II 1831 pattern General officer's mameluke sword, curved, clipped back blade 32in., by 'Wilkinson Sword', and etched with crown, Royal cypher, General's insignia and foliage, gilt crosspiece and mounts, white grips, in its plated scabbard with bullion dress knot. $330 £175

A French Revolutionary period AN IV Cuirassier trooper's sword, long, plain single edged blade 38½in., with hatchet point, brass semi-basket hilt, one bar of guard in the form of a Cap-of-Liberty upon Fasces, brass wirebound, leather covered grip. $540 £230

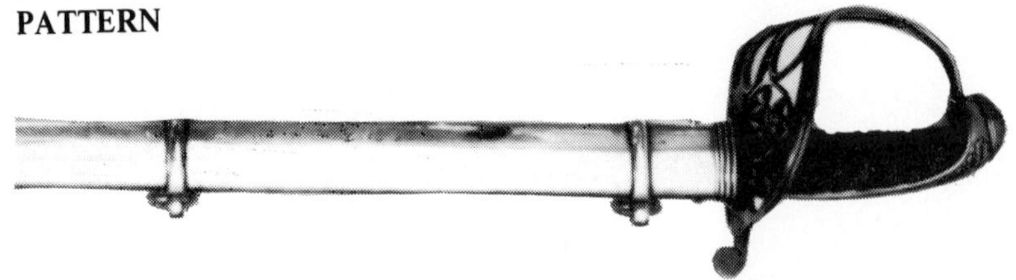

A Victorian 1822 pattern Infantry officer's sword, slightly curved blade 32in., etched with lion, foliage, Royal Arms, 'Singapore Police', and presentation inscription, plated hilt with folding side guard, wirebound fishskin covered grip, in its plated scabbard. $155 £70

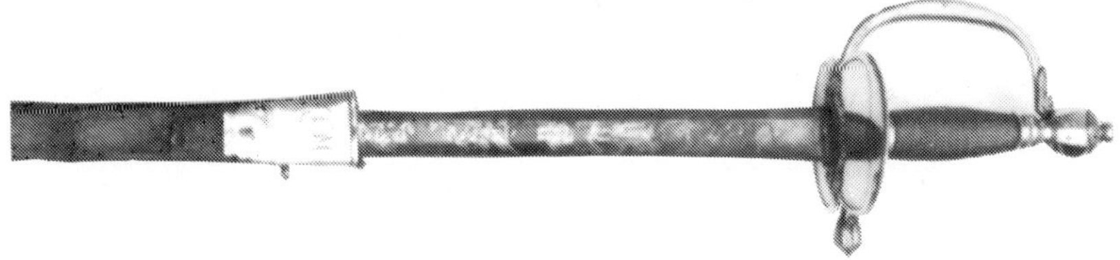

A Georgian 1796 pattern Infantry officer's sword, straight, single edged blade 32in., engraved on the backstrap 'J. J. Runkel, Solingen' and etched with pre-1801 Royal Arms, crown, 'G.R.' and foliage, copper gilt hilt with double shell guard, urn pommel, silver wirebound grip, in its leather scabbard. $185 £85

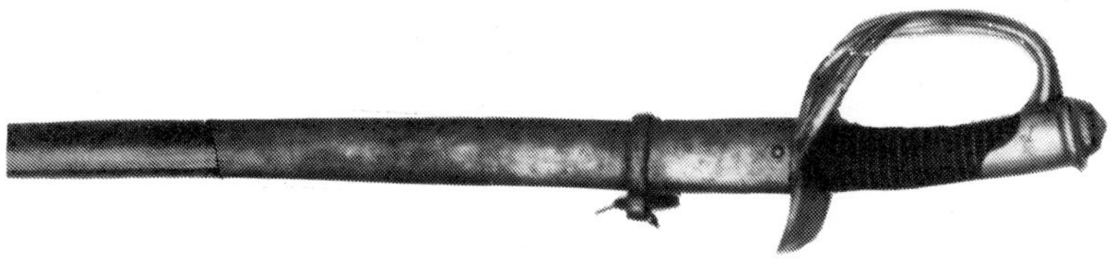

A French 1854 pattern Cuirassier's sword, straight, single edged, tapering blade 37in., with raised central rib, traces of engraving on backstrap 'Mfr Impale De Chatt Mars 1858', triple bar brass guard, brass mounts, brass wirebound, leather covered grip, in its steel scabbard. $230 £100

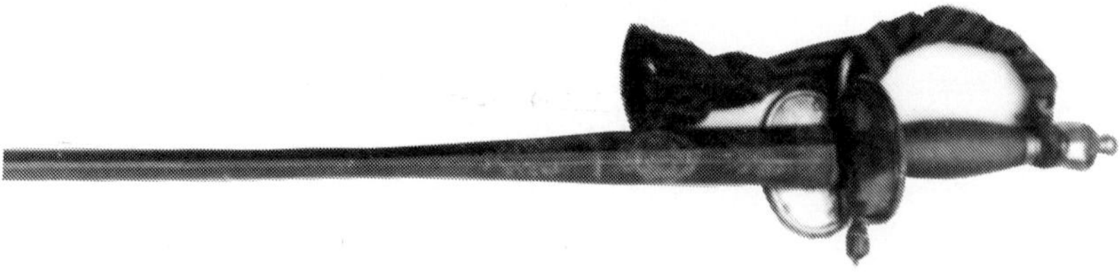

A Georgian Infantry officer's 1796 pattern sword fitted with Spanish blade, double edged, straight, shallow diamond sectioned blade 34in. of Colichemarde form, copper gilt regulation hilt, folding shell guard, silver wirebound grip, red and yellow bullion dress knot. $225 £105

A Hungarian silver gilt mounted dress shamshir pattern sword, plain single edged, curved blade 28in., the crosspiece of Eastern silver gilt mounted with coloured stones and decorated with scrolls, horn hilt with silver pommel cap, in its green velvet covered wooden scabbard with 4 mounts of Eastern silver gilt. $400 £165

A Victorian General officer's and Staff officer's 1822 pattern sword, straight blade 33in., by 'Henry Wilkinson, Pall Mall', No. 14842, steel hilt, copper wirebound fishskin covered grip, in its brass scabbard. $410 £200

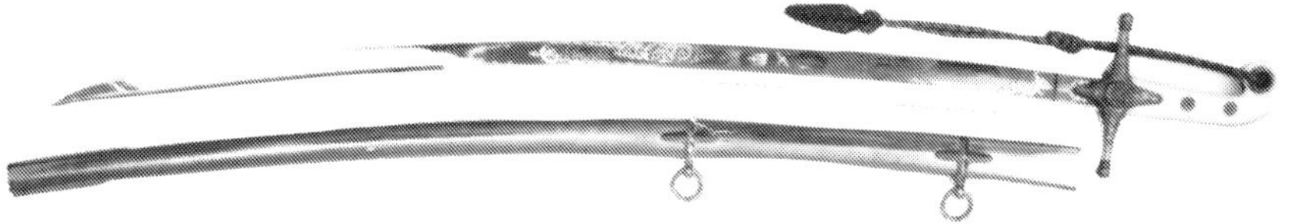

A George V 1831 pattern General officer's mameluke sword, curved, clipped back blade 32½in., and etched with crown, Royal cypher, General's insignia and foliage. Gilt crosspiece and mounts, ivory grips secured with two gilt rosettes, original bullion dress knot, in its plated scabbard. $455 £210

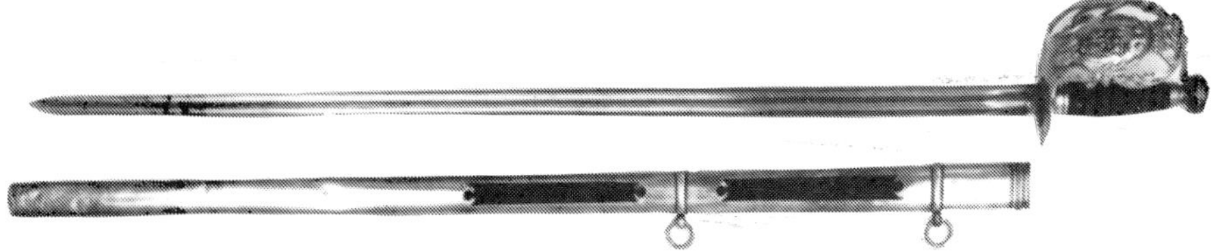

An 1814 pattern Household Cavalry officer's dress sword, straight, single edged, plain fullered blade 34½in., copper gilt semi-basket guard, scrolled panel affixed with lion above crown, copper gilt mounts, circular pommel, copper wirebound fishskin covered grip, in its brass scabbard. $1,230 £570

A Russian 1881 pattern Cossack trooper's sword shasqua, single edged curved fullered blade 34½in., dated '1909' stamped 'A.A.48', regulation brass hilt dated 1909 in its brass mounted leather scabbard. $250 £105

A Caucasian shasqua, curved blade 30½in., with double back fuller, etched 'K.K.B.', within foliate panel at forte, plain eared horn grips, in its leather covered wooden scabbard with four white metal mounts decorated with foliate niello patterns. $250 £125

A scarce Soviet 1881 pattern military shasqua, single edged, slightly curved blade 31½in., retaining virtually all original polish, stamped with cyrillic lettering at forte, spiral wood grip, brass mounts, the pommel with Soviet emblem and 'C.C.C.P.', in its leather covered wooden scabbard. $350 £145

A Caucasian horsemans silver mounted sword shasqua, curved single edged double fullered blade 31in., silver nielloed hilt embossed with foliage flowers and scrolls with large eared, pommel decorated with star and crescent, in its silver nielloed mounted leather covered wooden sheath. $530 £230

A European smallsword circa 1710, flat, tapering double edged blade 30in., struck with 'Man-in-the-Moon' crescent mark, also 'A.F.A.R.A.R.A.' brass hilt with double shell guard cast and decorated with seated goddess, cherub, etc., copper wirebound grip with 'Turks Head'. $115 £60

A mid 18th century smallsword, straight blade 29½in., of flattened diamond section struck with pellet marks at forte, and etched with Talisman lettering for two thirds of length with traces of gilding, iron hilt, with double shell guard with incised edge. $145 £60

An 18th century smallsword, tapering triangular hollow ground blade 30in. etched with foliate scrolls at forte, plain steel hilt, small double shell guard, slim knucklebow, ovoid pommel, wirebound grip. $175 £80

An early 18th century transitional smallsword, plain double edged blade 27½in. brass hilt with double shell guard pierced with foliage and decorated with figures, rounded pommel with allegorical figures, brass roped wirebound grip. $230 £120

A French late 18th century silver hilted smallsword, slim plain tapering triangular blade 33½in., bowl guard with simple decoration with small hallmarks, the quillon block and rounded grip with hallmarks, and flattened knuckle- bow, ovoid pommel with simple decoration. $290 £140

A French russet-gilt hilted smallsword circa 1770, hollow ground blade 32¾in. etched with small trophies, hilt chiselled with trophies within laurel wreaths, floral swags and scrolls against a gilt punctate ground, silver wire and tape bound grip with woven Turks heads. $390 £190

SOCIETY

A U.S. Society sword, plain plated blade 28in., gilt 'Gothic' hilt, with pierced shell guard with crossed swords, crown, etc, single knucklebow and side-loop with cast foliate pattern, crowned 'Globe-of-the-World' pommel ivorine grip decorated with Masonic emblems, in its plated sheath. $95 £40

A U.S. Society sword, blade 29in. by Petibone, etched with Medieval Tournament, foliage, owner's name 'Purity Commandery K. of M. No. 280', gilt 'Gothic hilt, pierced crosspiece, central Masonic device, plumed helmet pommel,wood grip inset with enamelled cross. $110 £45

A U.S. Society sword, blade 27½in. by Godfrey Jepson, retaining most original polish, and etched with pickaxe, shovel, etc., foliage and 'Shekinah Chapter R.A.M.' gilt 'Gothic hilt, with elaborate crosspiece, 'Turk's bonnet' pommel chain knucklebow, ivorine grip, in its gilt scabbard. $120 £50

A U.S. Society sword, blade 29½in. by 'Russell, New York', etched with Medieval Tournament, owner's name, foliage, etc., plated 'Gothic hilt, elaborately pierced crosspiece shell guard with enamelled Masonic emblem, plumed helmet pommel, ivory grip with Masonic emblems, in its plated scabbard. $120 £50

A U.S. Society sword, blade 28in., retaining some original polish, etched with foliage, owner's name and 'Ivanhoe Commandery' gilt 'Gothic' hilt, shell guard with pierced decoration, skull and crossbones to crosspiece, plumed helmet pommel, ivory grip, in its gilt scabbard. $120 £50

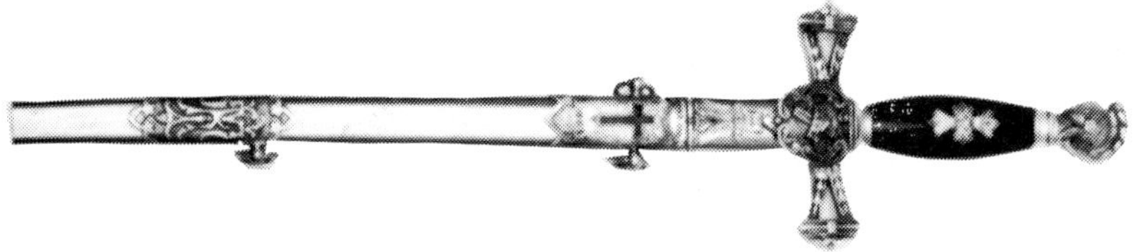

A U.S. Society sword, blade 29½in. by 'Horstmann P.A.', etched with Medieval Tournament, owner's name, foliage, traces of gold wash background, plated 'Gothic' hilt with pierced crosspiece, masonic emblem to shell guard plumed helmet pommel, in its metal plated scabbard. $170 £70

An interesting decorative walking stick, made of 17 horn segments intersected with bone discs, handle in form of Chinese dragon. $15 £7

A Georgian swordstick, straight, slim, tapering single edged blade 26in., with narrow back fuller, and retaining much blued and gilt etched decoration of floral and foliate scrolls, bulbous gnarled wood hilt, silver thong mounts, in its wooden scabbard. $165 £75

A Late 19th century swordstick, straight double edged slim tapering blade 29in., etched at forte with Spanish arms 'F.D. Toledo Ano de 1870', and with foliate scrolls with gold wash background, malacca hilt with silver pommel cap decorated with foliate scrolls, (hallmarked London 1893) $310 £127

A Victorian swordstick, slim blade 27½in., of diamond section, etched 'Toledo' with foliate scrolls, spring catch, gnarled horn hilt with gilt, hatched band mount, in its malacca scabbard. $260 £130

An unusual 18th century Indian sword Tulwar, curved wavy edged blade 31in. with clipped wavy back edge and struck on both sides with armourers marks (flower head), iron hilt with flower bud langet terminals, swollen quillons and wheel pommel. $95 £50

A Tulwar hilted kora, single edged blade 24in., with small short fullers, iron hilt with wheel pommel and knucklebow, decorated overall with silver and gilt damascene foliate patterns, in its leather covered wooden scabbard. $230 £95

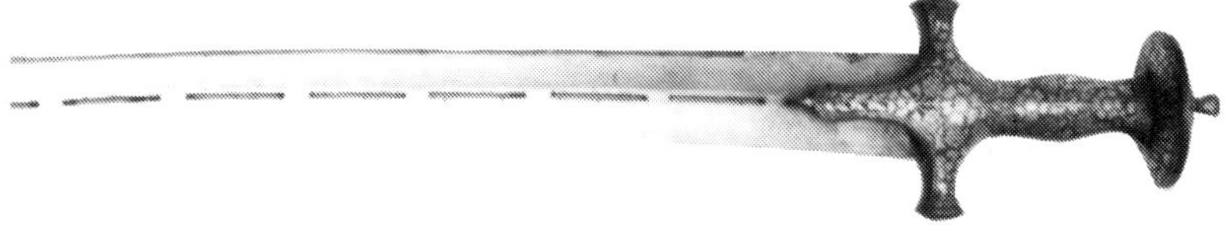

A good Indian Tulwar, curved single edged blade 31in., the centre pierced with slits containing 'tear drop' inserts, iron hilt with gold damascene decoration overall of foliate and floral patterns. $230 £95

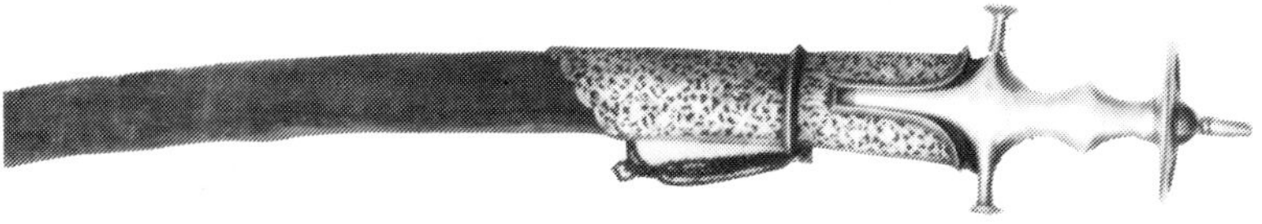

A good Indian silver mounted Tulwar, single edged, slightly curved blade 33in., double fullered, and with imitation European signature in the fullers at forte, the plain hilt of solid Eastern silver, with wheel pommel, in its cloth covered wooden scabbard. $345 £150

An attractive shortsword wakizashi, blade 47cm., signed Musashi No Daijo Fujiwara Tadahiro, 2 mekugi ana, broad gunome hamon with broad nie line, ayasugi hada, pierced iron tsuba signed Mune Hisa, tape bound same tsuka with gilt shakudo fuchi kashira depicting sage on horseback and another riding a dragon. $485 £220

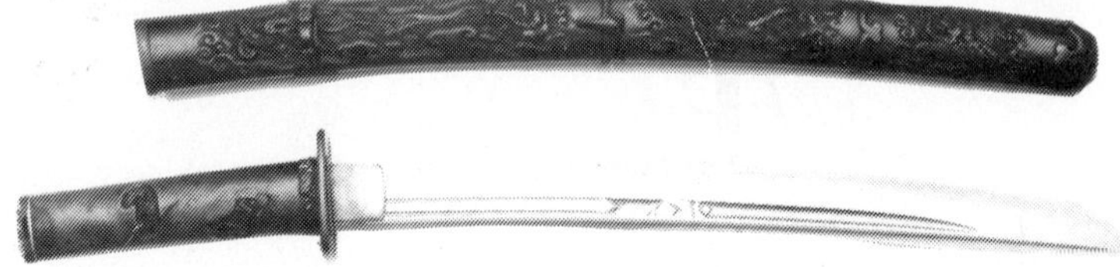

An attractive Japanese shortsword wakizashi, blade 39½cm. mumei, hira zukuri, 3 mekugi ana, bo-hi and gomobashi with horimono of ken, sacred jewel and 2 bonji characters, itame hada, ich-mai, chu-suguha hamon, broad nie line, wooden saya signed with ancient seals. $670 £290

An attractively mounted Japanese sword wakizashi, blade 51.5cms., mumei,2 mekugi ana, suguha hotsure hamon with gunome-ashi-iri, chu-nioi line, muji hada, tape bound tsuka, in its black lacquered saya. $1,140 £475

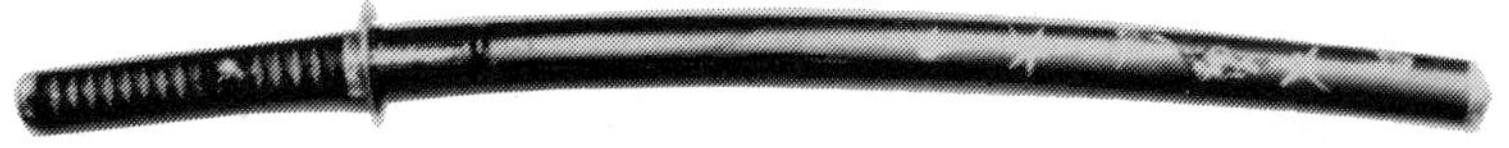

An attractively mounted Japanese sword wakizashi, blade 60.5cms., signed 'Seki Zen . . . ' (tang shortened), 2 mekugi ana, koshi-hi, gomobashi, ito-suguha hamon, tight itame hada, black hair bound tsuka with silver mounts, in its black lacquered mokume saya with gilt lacquered insects. $1,740 £725

An attractively mounted Japanese sword wakizashi, blade 50.6cms., signed Hizen no Kuni Kawachi no Daijo fujiwara no Masahiro, dated Shoho (1646 A.D.), 2 mekugi ana, mimi-gata hamon, thin nioi line, itmae hada, in its black lacquered saya with circular gilt lacquered dragons. $1,860 £775

FLINTLOCK & MATCHLOCK WEAPONS

A Turkish flintlock 'knee-blunderbuss', 17¼in., flared steel barrel 8¼in., chiselled trophy at breech, traces of silver damascened decoration, fullstocked, engraved lock, cast brass mounts. $350 £190

A steel barrelled flintlock blunderbuss by Conway of Manchester, fitted with spring bayonet, circa 1810, 30¼in., half octagonal flared barrel 13¾in., Birmingham proved, roller bearing frizzen spring. $770 £320

An unusual massive Dutch-Irish brass barrelled flintlock blunderbuss, overall length 34½in., bottle-neck barrel 18½in., maker's initials 'I.E.' and 8 London proof marks, engraved brass furniture. $760 £330

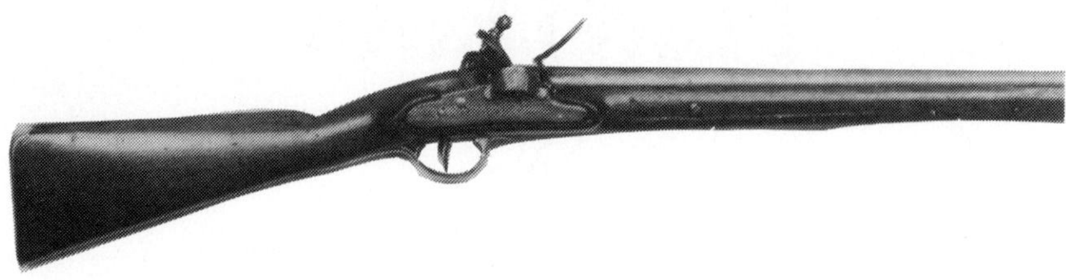

A rare 10-bore 1796 pattern flintlock Dragoon carbine with Nock screwless lock, 41in., barrel 25¾in., Tower proved, fullstocked, lock struck with government inspector's stamp, engraved H. Nock, flashguard to pan, engraved with crowned GR, regulation brass mounts, buttcap spur engraved B-47. $825 £450

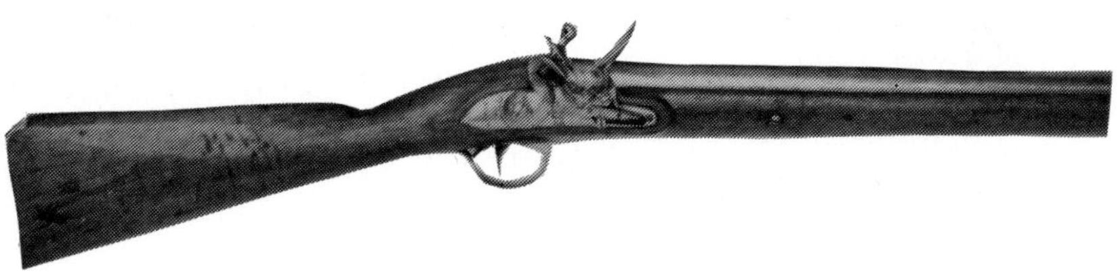

A 1796 pattern .76in. heavy Dragoon flintlock carbine of The 4th (Royal Irish) Dragoon Guards, 41½in., barrel 26in., Tower proved, fullstocked, border engraved lock with crowned 'G.R.' cypher and 'Tower' on tail, regulation brass mounts, buttcap tang engraved '4 DG.E.14'. $1,080 £450

An 18-bore German rifled flintlock carbine, circa 1760, 28in., octagonal barrel 13in., chiselled 'Leo: Sp: Nau', brass foresight, two leaf rearsight, fullstocked, flat lockplate, unbridled frizzen, brass furniture, trigger guard with finger rest, sliding patch box, two steel sling swivels, steel fore-cap band. $1,340 £550

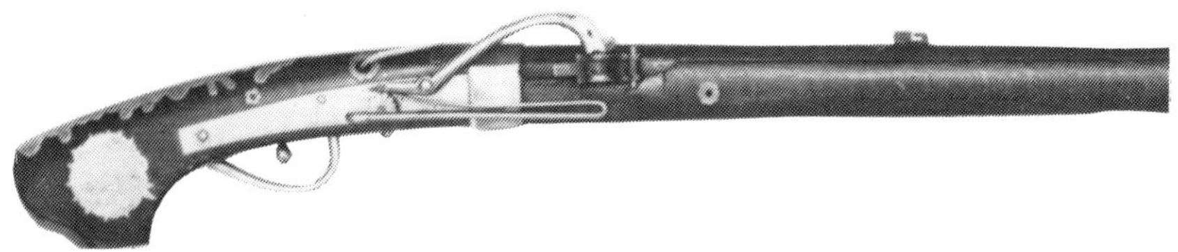

A 22-bore Japanese matchlock musket, 54in., octagonal barrel 42in., ribbed corners, block sights, fullstocked, back-action brass lock, brass swivel pan cover, stock inlaid with brass plates engraved as flower heads, kabuto, clouds, dragon, birds, brass trigger guard. $880 £360

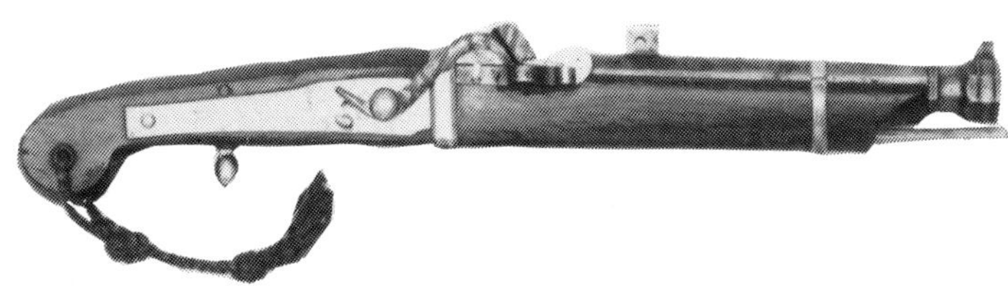

A scarce 22-bore Japanese back-action matchlock pistol, 14½in., octagonal barrel 8¼in., mumei, swollen ribbed muzzle, block sights, fullstocked in magnolia wood, brass lockplate, linear engraved steel serpent, 2 brass barrel bands, brass button trigger, butt pierced for green silk cord. $890 £370

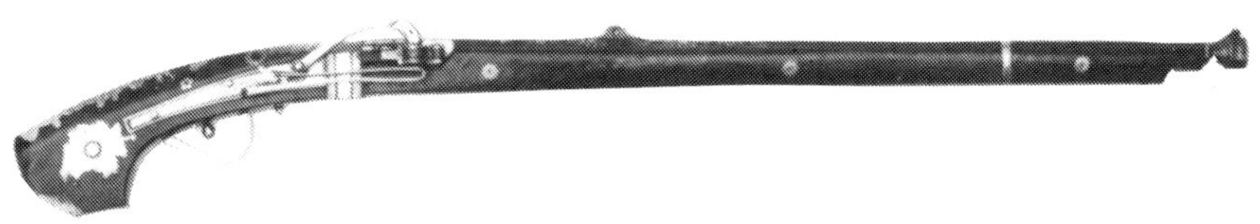

A good 32-bore Japanese matchlock gun, 41in., barrel 29½in. of octagonal section with concave facets, signed Tanaka Yasubei of Settsu province, 'twisted forging', tapered barrel with swollen muzzle, block rearsight, inlaid in silver for half its length with horse tethered to flowering cherry tree. $1,296 £600

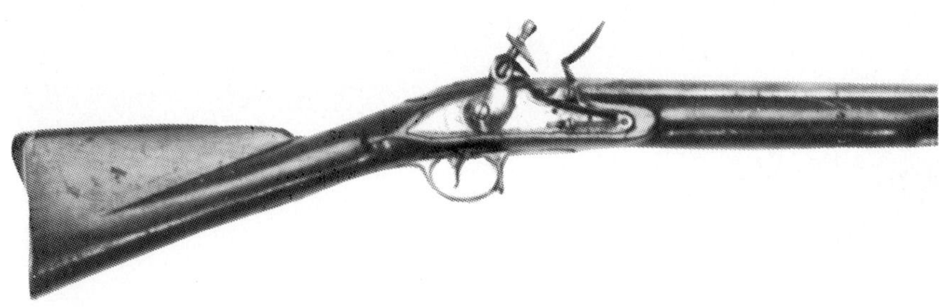

A 10-bore India pattern Brown Bess flintlock musket, 55½in., barrel 29½in., Tower proved stamped with Irish census number M-N 1724, fullstocked, regulation lock with throathole cock, engraved border, Tower and crowned GR, regulation brass mounts, buttcap engraved 'Is. BL Y. 254', stamped M-N 1724. $415 £190

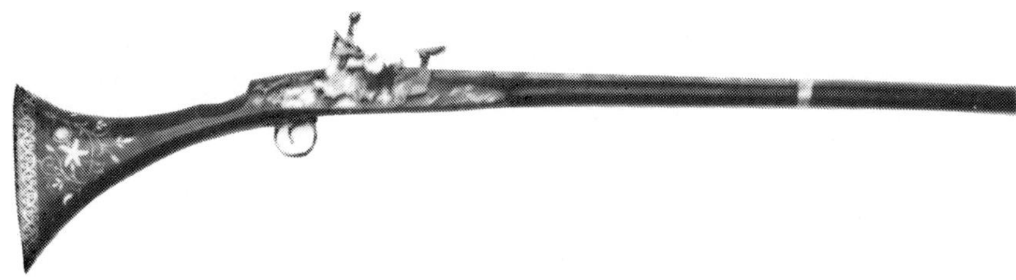

An unusually good 25-bore snaphaunce musket kabyle, 63in., half octagonal barrel 49in., inlaid with foliate engraved silver and brass plaques for half its length, and at swollen muzzle, fullstocked, well made lock with automatic sliding pan cover inlaid en suite with barrel. $475 £220

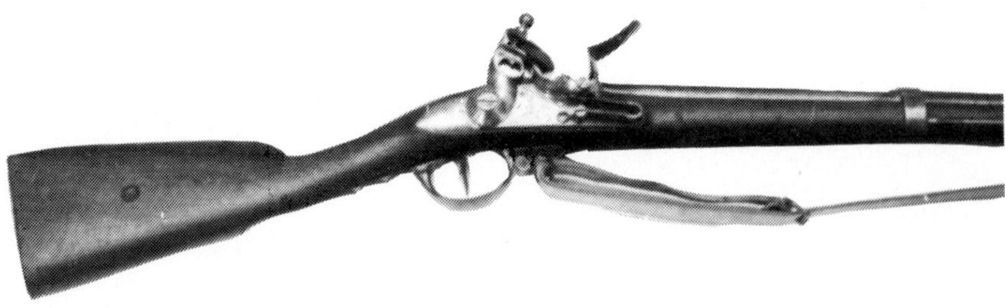

A good 13-bore French military flintlock musket, 56in., barrel 40in., stamped 'C.1819 MR' with arsenal marks at breech, fullstocked, lock engraved 'Manuf. Roy de Maubeuge', brass pan regulation steel mounts struck with arsenal marks, steel ramrod, white buckskin sling, carved cheekpiece. $660 £280

A decoratively stocked 10-bore Balkan miquelet flintlock musket, 56½in., barrel 41¼in., etched for full length with silver damascened arabesques and Arabic inscription, fullstocked, gold damascened Kurdish lock with removable striated frizzen, stock entirely overlaid with diamond-shaped bone and wooden sections. $960 £400

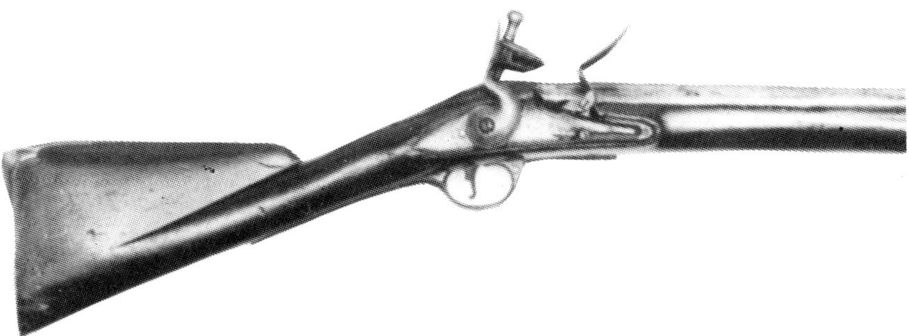

A scarce 10-bore long land pattern 46in. Brown Bess flintlock musket, 62in. overall, barrel 46in., Tower proved struck with small '21' star and 'O', full-stocked, slightly rounded lock, border engraved with crowned 'GR' and 'Grice 1760', regulation brass furniture including flush escutcheon. $2,300 £950

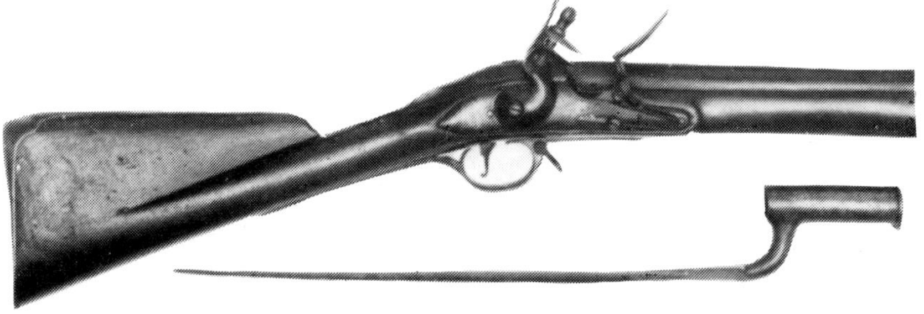

A scarce 10-bore short land pattern 42in. Brown Bess flintlock musket of American Revolutionary vintage, 58in. overall, barrel 42in., Tower proved, stamped I.B., engraved '29 Regt' (The 29th Worcestershire Regiment served in Canada from 1776 to 1787). $2,650 £1,100

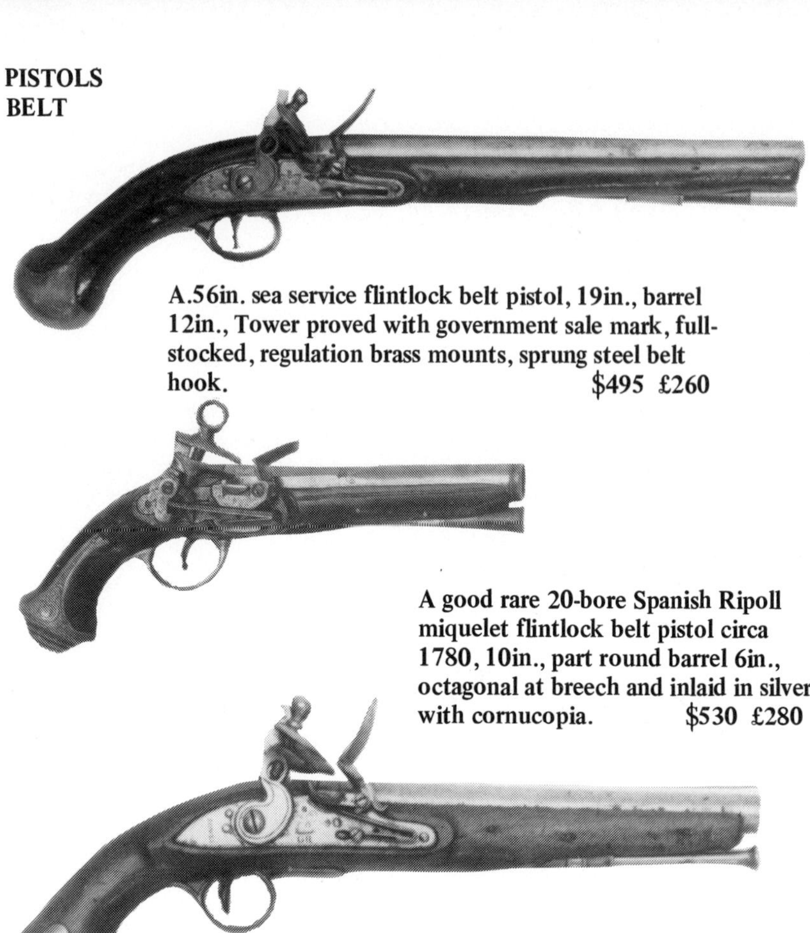

A.56in. sea service flintlock belt pistol, 19in., barrel 12in., Tower proved with government sale mark, full-stocked, regulation brass mounts, sprung steel belt hook. $495 £260

A good rare 20-bore Spanish Ripoll miquelet flintlock belt pistol circa 1780, 10in., part round barrel 6in., octagonal at breech and inlaid in silver with cornucopia. $530 £280

A .56in. short sea service flintlock belt pistol, 15in., barrel 9in., Tower proved, fullstocked, regulation lock engraved with 'Tower' and crowned 'GR' with inspector's stamp, regulation brass mounts, trigger guard ramrod and sprung steel belt hook. $570 £300

A 26-bore Scottish all-steel flintlock belt pistol, 13½in., barrel 8in. with turnings and raised breech, fullstocked, unbridled frizzen, sear pierces through lockplate, steel ramrod, button trigger, pricker and ram's horn butt. $840 £350

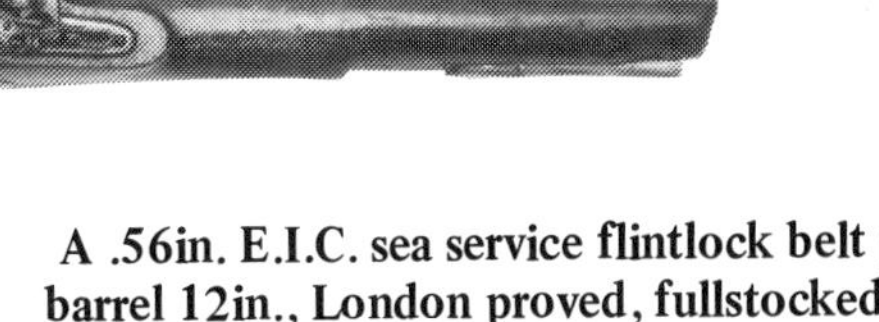

A .56in. E.I.C. sea service flintlock belt pistol, 19in., barrel 12in., London proved, fullstocked, lock engraved with E.I.C. lion rampant, regulation brass mounts, stock with inspector's marks. $865 £360

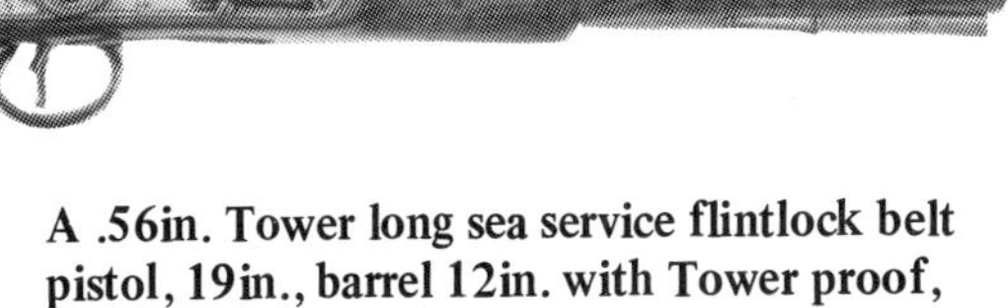

A .56in. Tower long sea service flintlock belt pistol, 19in., barrel 12in. with Tower proof, brass mounted walnut fullstock, sprung belt hook. $880 £360

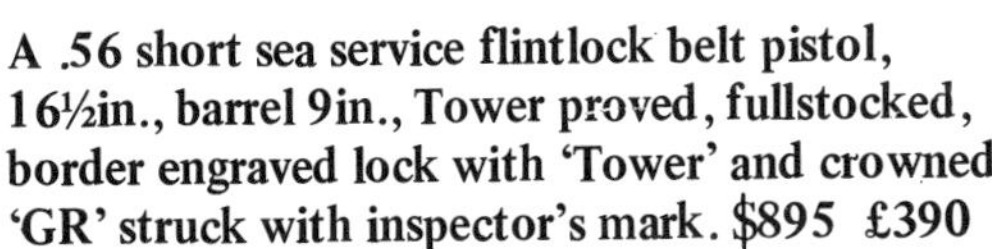

A .56 short sea service flintlock belt pistol, 16½in., barrel 9in., Tower proved, fullstocked, border engraved lock with 'Tower' and crowned 'GR' struck with inspector's mark. $895 £390

A .56in. sea service flintlock belt pistol, 19in., barrel 12in., Tower proved, fullstocked, regulation lock with crowned 'GR' cypher, 'Tower' and struck with inspector's mark. $800 £420

A good .56in. sea service flintlock belt pistol, overall length 19in., barrel 12in., Tower proved, fullstocked, regulation lock border engraved with crowned 'G.R.' and 'Tower', regulation brass mounts, stock struck with inspector's marks and storekeeper's mark dated 1805. $1,080 £450

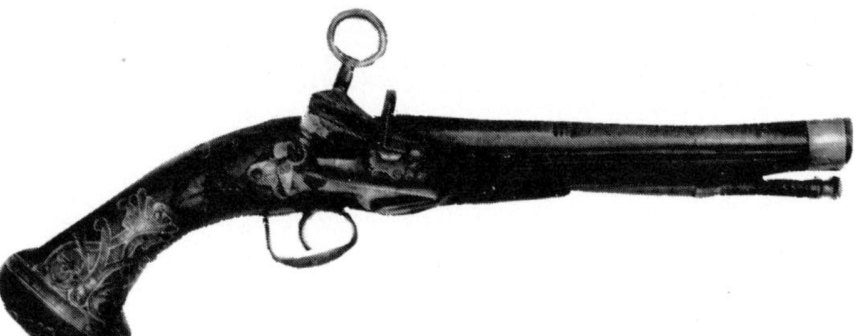

A 15-bore Spanish Ripoll miquelet flintlock belt pistol, circa 1720, 15in., half octagonal barrel 8¾in., full-stocked, lock with external mainspring and frizzen spring, striated frizzen stamped with maker's mark of 'Vasy' within heart shape, rare ovoid butt barrel tang, steel trigger guard. $1,600 £650

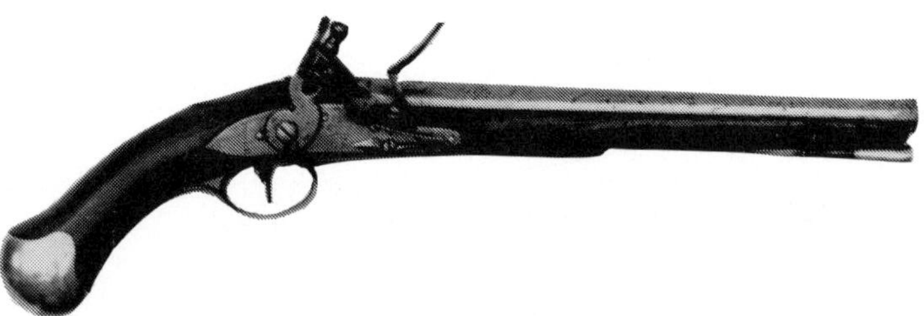

A .56in. sea service flintlock belt pistol, circa 1760, overall length 19in., barrel 12in., Tower proved, full-stocked, flat lockplate engraved Tower with crowned 'G.R.', flat cock, squared unbridled frizzen, faceted pan, regulation brass mounts sprung steel belt hook. $1,560 £650

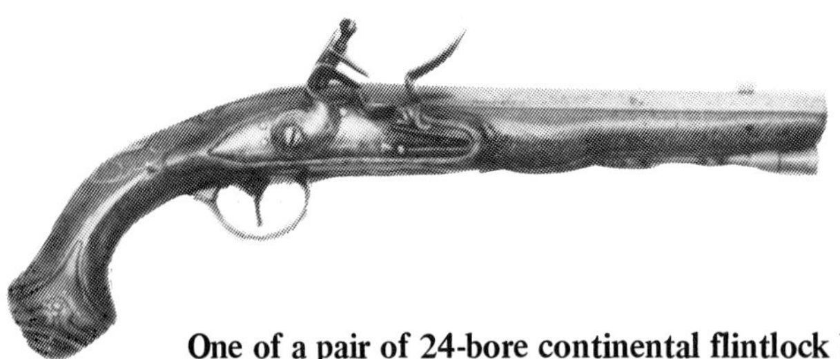

One of a pair of 24-bore continental flintlock belt pistols, circa 1775, 14½in., barrels 8½in., with top sighting flats. Fullstocked twin line border engraved locks with unbridled frizzens, brass furniture chiselled with flower, foliate finialled trigger guards. $1,700 £700

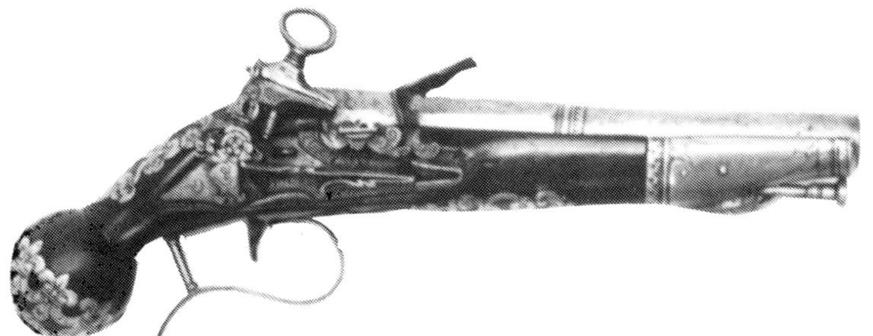

A fine 11-bore Neapolitan miquelet flintlock belt pistol, by Luigi Sarli of Briola, dated 1805, 12¾in., half octagonal barrel 8¼in., foliate chiselled at step, fullstocked foliate engraved lock with 'lvigisarl' beneath pan, 'A Briola' beneath sear and '1805' on shoulder of frizzen. $2,200 £900

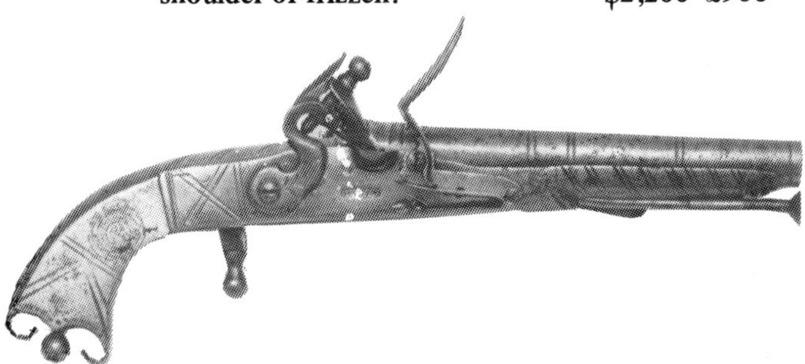

A rare 24-bore Scottish all steel military flintlock belt pistol by Iohn McVey for the 2nd Battalion Breadalbane Fencibles (1793-1799), 11¾in., barrel 6½in. with raised breech, ribbed with chevron decoration, all steel fullstock incised with chevron decoration overall. $2,375 £1,100

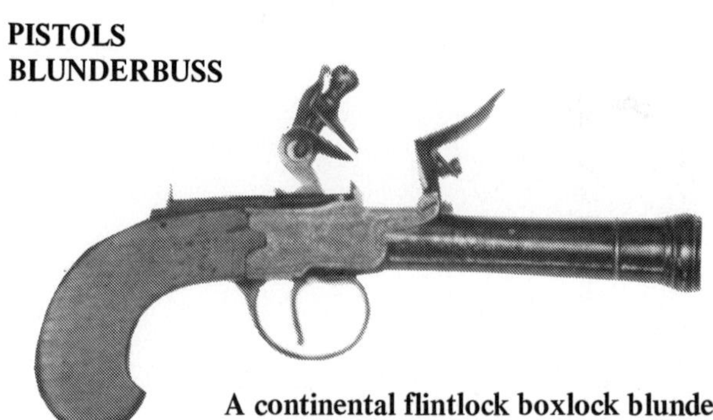

A continental flintlock boxlock blunderbuss pocket pistol, 7¾in., turned barrel with flared muzzle 3in., plain walnut slab butt, line and star engraved iron trigger guard, top plate thumb sliding safety locking cock and frizzen through fence. $350 £160

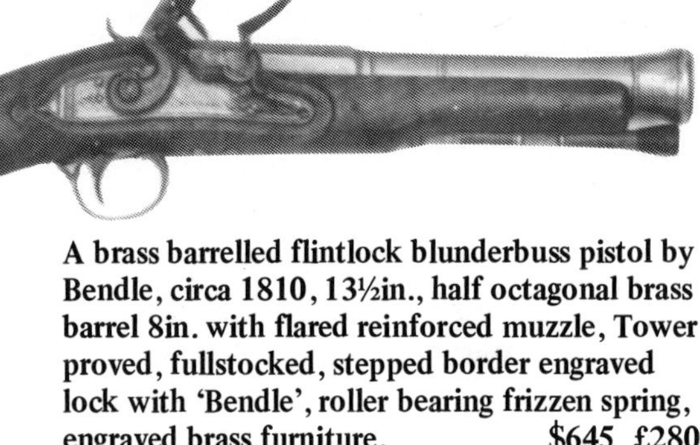

A brass barrelled flintlock blunderbuss pistol by Bendle, circa 1810, 13½in., half octagonal brass barrel 8in. with flared reinforced muzzle, Tower proved, fullstocked, stepped border engraved lock with 'Bendle', roller bearing frizzen spring, engraved brass furniture. $645 £280

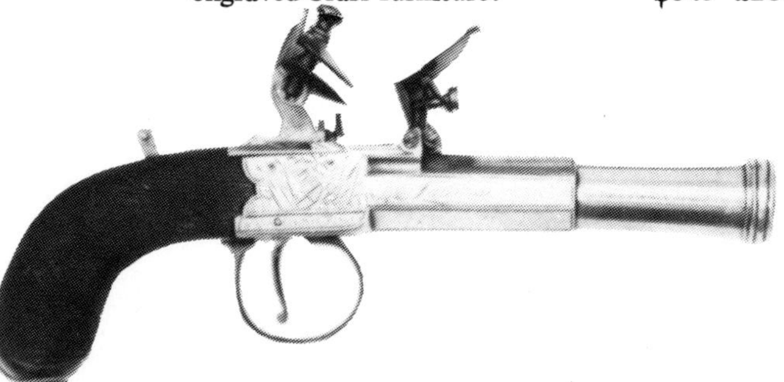

A brass framed brass barrelled flintlock boxlock blunderbuss pistol of the type favoured by Naval officers, 9½in., flared half octagonal barrel 5in., Birmingham proved with reinforced muzzle, breech side engraved 'Mortimer London' in script. $735 £340

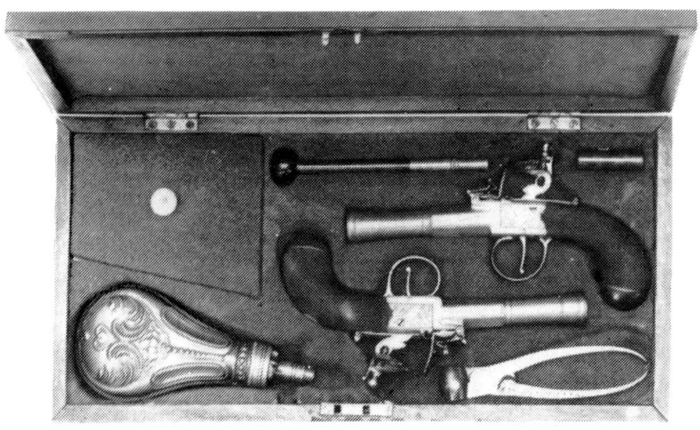

A pair of brass barrelled brass framed boxlock flintlock blunderbuss pistols by H. Nock, circa 1815, of the type favoured by Naval officers, 9in., half octagonal flared barrels 4in., with turned reinforces, Birmingham proved, border engraved frames with 'H. Nock, London' within ovals upon military trophies of arms. $2,450 £1,000

DUELLING

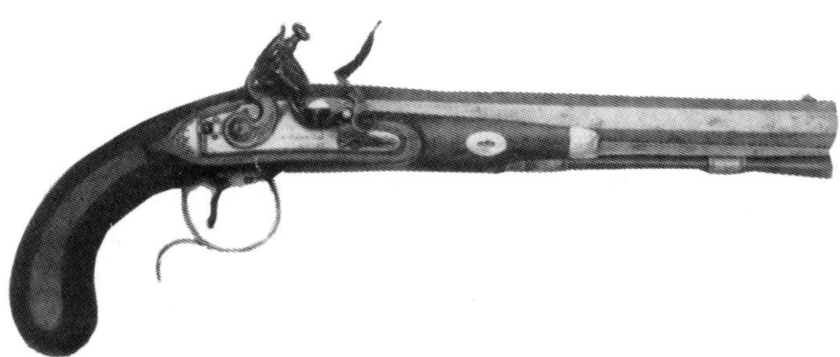

A 16-bore officer's flintlock duelling pistol by W. Parker, circa 1800, 15½in., slightly swamped octagonal twist barrel 10in., engraved 'W. Parker-Holborn-London' on top flat, gold inlaid breech line and vent, halfstocked in finely figured French walnut, stepped bolted detented lock with capstan screw adjustable set trigger. $1,375 £725

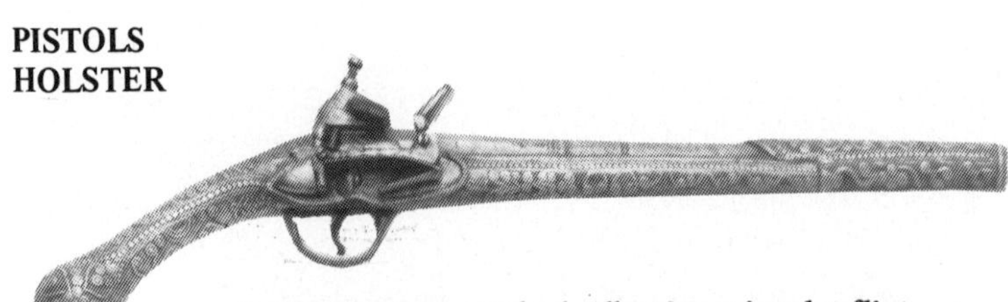

A 20-bore brass stocked Albanian miquelet flint-lock 'rat-tailed' holster pistol, 19in., barrel 12¼in. octagonal at breech, lock with external mainspring and striated frizzen. $110 £55

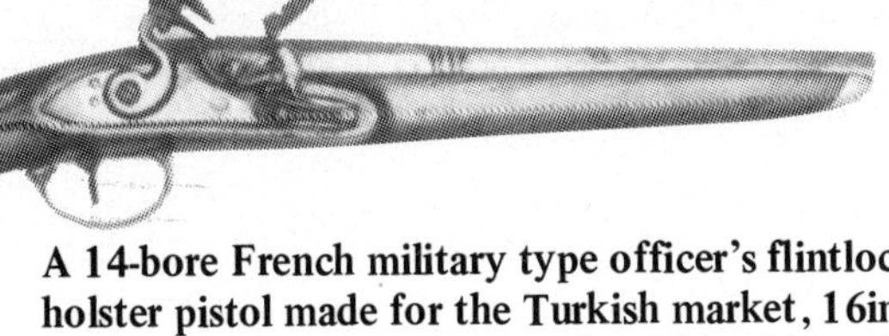

A 14-bore French military type officer's flintlock holster pistol made for the Turkish market, 16in., half octagonal barrel 10in. with gold inlaid toughra at breech, fullstocked, lockplate struck with Turkish mark, bridled frizzen. $140 £65

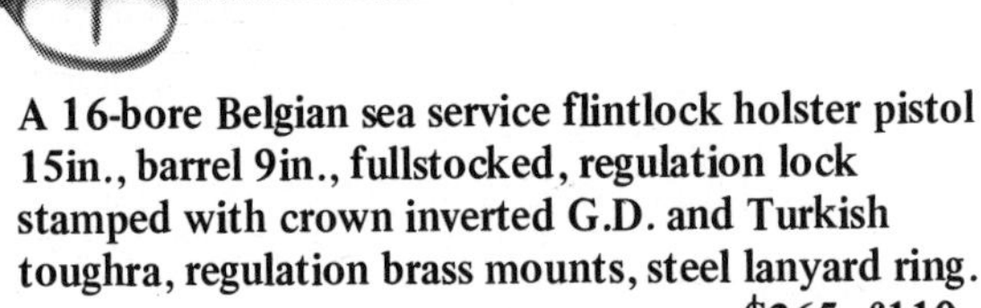

A 16-bore Belgian sea service flintlock holster pistol 15in., barrel 9in., fullstocked, regulation lock stamped with crown inverted G.D. and Turkish toughra, regulation brass mounts, steel lanyard ring. $265 £110

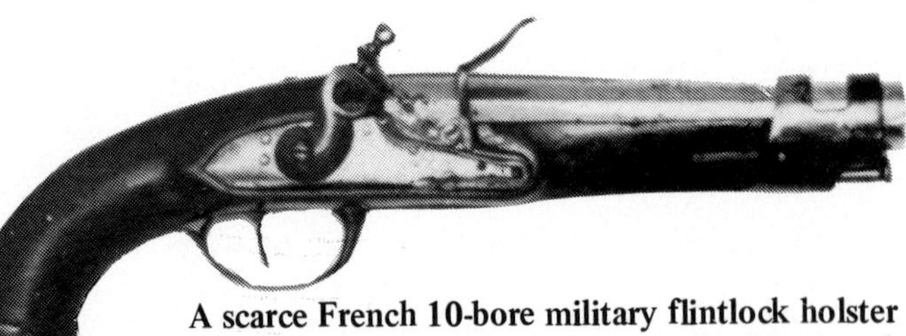

A scarce French 10-bore military flintlock holster pistol, 11¾in., barrel 6½in., stamped with arsenal mark at breech, fullstocked, regulation lock with brass pan, regulation steel mounts sprung steel muzzle sheath, bird's head beak buttcap. $295 £120

An attractive 18-bore silver mounted Turkish flintlock holster pistol circa 1800, 16½in., half octagonal swamped barrel 10in. inlaid with copper breech line and maker's marks, engraved borders and foliate motifs, fullstocked, foliate engraved lock. $300 £140

A scarce 16-bore French military flintlock holster pistol of unidentified pattern, 13½in., barrel 8in., octagonal at breech, brass foresight, fullstocked, flat lockplate with rounded tail, brass pan, brass mounts, stepped flat oval brass buttplate. $320 £140

An interesting 14-bore fullstocked flintlock holster pistol, 15in., round barrel 9in., London proved, walnut stock with brass trigger guard, ramrod throat pipe and 's' shaped sideplate, border engraved lockplate engraved 'Reynolds' with throathole cock and sprung frizzen. $370 £160

One of a pair of 20-bore Balkan ball butted inlaid and chiselled flintlock holster pistols, 16½in., barrels 10¾in., foliate chiselled in low relief at breeches and central sections, border engraved facets, fullstocked, lockplates, cocks, frizzens and jaw screws well foliate chiselled in low relief against a punctate ground. $390 £170

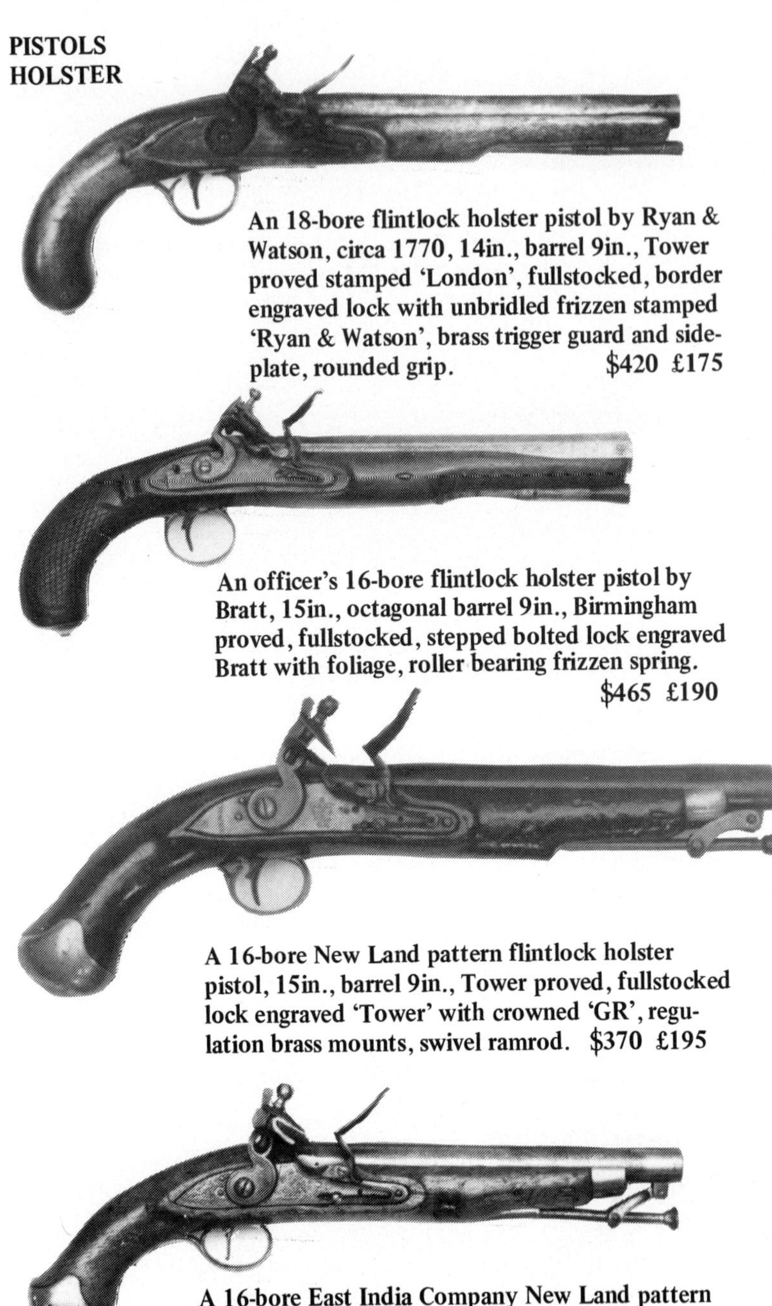

An 18-bore flintlock holster pistol by Ryan & Watson, circa 1770, 14in., barrel 9in., Tower proved stamped 'London', fullstocked, border engraved lock with unbridled frizzen stamped 'Ryan & Watson', brass trigger guard and side-plate, rounded grip. $420 £175

An officer's 16-bore flintlock holster pistol by Bratt, 15in., octagonal barrel 9in., Birmingham proved, fullstocked, stepped bolted lock engraved Bratt with foliage, roller bearing frizzen spring. $465 £190

A 16-bore New Land pattern flintlock holster pistol, 15in., barrel 9in., Tower proved, fullstocked lock engraved 'Tower' with crowned 'GR', regulation brass mounts, swivel ramrod. $370 £195

A 16-bore East India Company New Land pattern flintlock, holster pistol, 5in., barrel 9in., London proved with inspector's mark, fullstocked, lock engraved 1813 with East India Company lion rampant and inspector's mark. $400 £200

A .65 Tower New Land pattern Yeomanry flintlock holster pistol, 15½in., barrel 9in., the carbine lock stamped with crown 'GR' and 'Tower' the safety bolt officialy removed and filled, walnut fullstock with regulation brass mounts including additional ramrod throatpipe. $480 £200

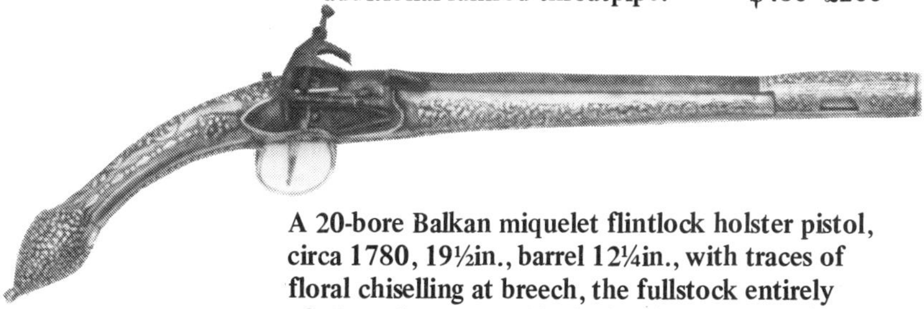

A 20-bore Balkan miquelet flintlock holster pistol, circa 1780, 19½in., barrel 12¼in., with traces of floral chiselling at breech, the fullstock entirely of silvered copper, ribbed plated trigger guard lock with heavy external main spring. $490 £200

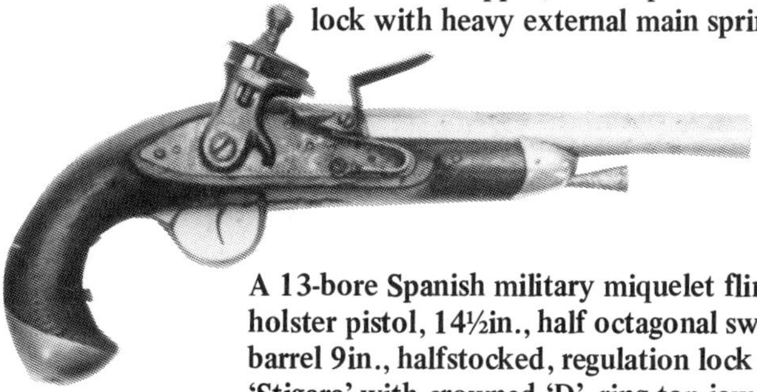

A 13-bore Spanish military miquelet flintlock holster pistol, 14½in., half octagonal swamped barrel 9in., halfstocked, regulation lock stamped 'Stigara' with crowned 'D', ring top jaw screw, brass pan. $490 £200

A Belgian brass framed brass barrelled boxlock flintlock holster pistol fitted with spring bayonet, 9in., octagonal barrel 4½in., Leige proved, maker's mark 'I.M.', sliding top thumb safety locks cock and frizzen to fence. $490 £210

A 16-bore flintlock East India Company style military holster pistol, 15½in., round barrel 9in., struck with London proof, brass mounted military style walnut fullstock, lanyard ring to buttcap.
$505 £210

A heavy 16-bore Volunteer flintlock holster pistol, 14½in. overall, browned twist barrel 9in., with top flat impressed 'W. & J. Rigby, Dublin', and with single proof mark of crowned 'P' in oval, plain flat lock impressed 'W. & J. Rigby', rainproof pan.
$585 £240

A 26-bore French fullstocked flintlock holster pistol, 10in., elegantly swamped octagonal barrel 5½in., walnut chequered fullstock with iron mounts including buttcap, trigger guard with urn finial, sideplates and ramrod throat-pipe. $475 £250

A 16-bore William IV New Land pattern flintlock holster pistol, 15in., barrel 9in., military proof mark, fullstocked, stepped bolted lock with twin line borders, 'Tower' on tail and crowned 'WR', regulation brass mounts, swivel ramrod. $475 £250

A scarce 14-bore Light Dragoon pattern military flintlock holster pistol of The 16th Queen's Light Dragoons, 15in., barrel 9in., Tower proved swamped, engraved 'QLD', fullstocked, rounded border engraved lockplate with inspector's stamp, engraved Tower with crowned 'GR'. $540 £250

A 16-bore New Land pattern flintlock holster pistol, 15in., barrel 9in., Tower proved, fullstocked, bolted regulation lock engraved Tower with crowned G.R., regulation brass mounts and swivel ramrod. $575 £250

A 34-bore brass framed brass barrelled Queen Anne style boxlock flintlock holster pistol by Ls Alley of Dublin, circa 1775, 12¼in., turn-off barrel 5¼in., London proved, sliding trigger guard safety, frizzen spring sunk in breech top. $575 £250

A 20-bore Turkish flintlock holster pistol, 17½in., half octagonal barrel 10½in., with false proof marks and maker's mark. Fullstocked, foliate engraved lock, striated frizzen. Engraved silver muzzle sheath. $605 £280

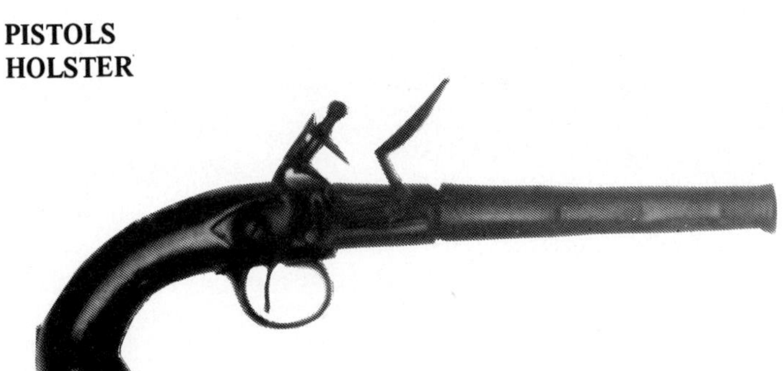

A silver mounted Queen Anne flintlock boxlock side-cock cannon barrelled holster pistol by Wilson, circa 1770, 11½in., turn off cannon barrel 5¼in., London proved, maker's mark RW beneath star, sliding trigger guard safety, rounded walnut butt with silver mounts. $605 £280

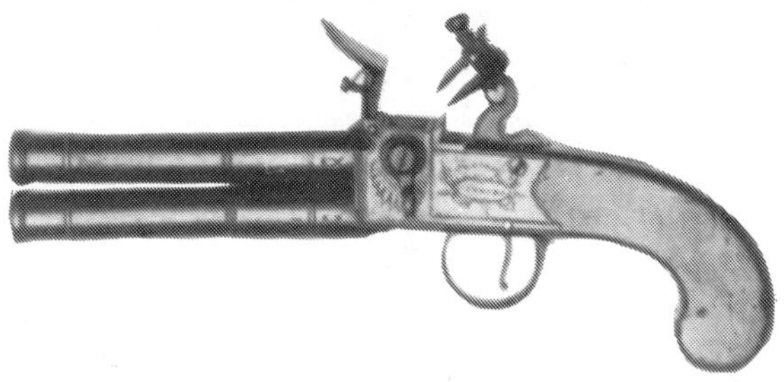

An unusual 40-bore DB O&U flintlock tap-action cannon barrelled holster pistol by Sanders circa 1775, 9¾in., turn off barrels 4in., Tower proved, thunderburst engraved tap, throathole cock, engraved top plate and trigger guard. $605 £280

A fine 16-bore silver mounted Turkish flintlock holster pistol, 18½in. half octagonal damascus barrel 11½in. thickly silver inlaid with scroll work, full stocked, rounded lock, striated frizzen, roller bearing frizzen spring, silver furniture, silver buttcap. $530 £280

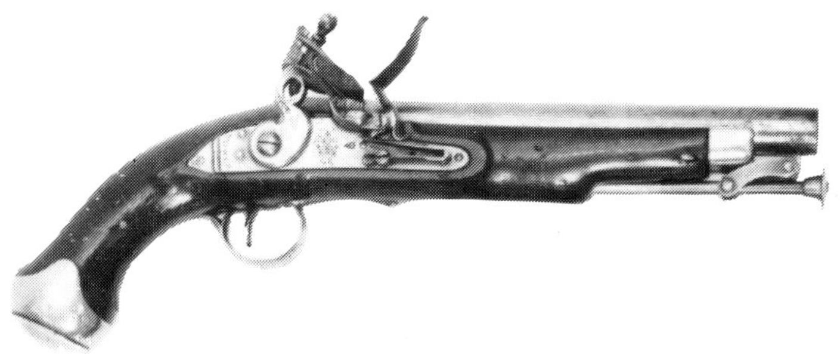

A 16-bore New Land pattern Yeomanry flintlock holster pistol, 15in., barrel 9in., Tower proved, fullstocked, stepped lock with engraved 'O.Y. E37' (Oxfordshire Yeomanry), swivel ramrod, stock struck with crowned GR storekeeper's mark. $660 £280

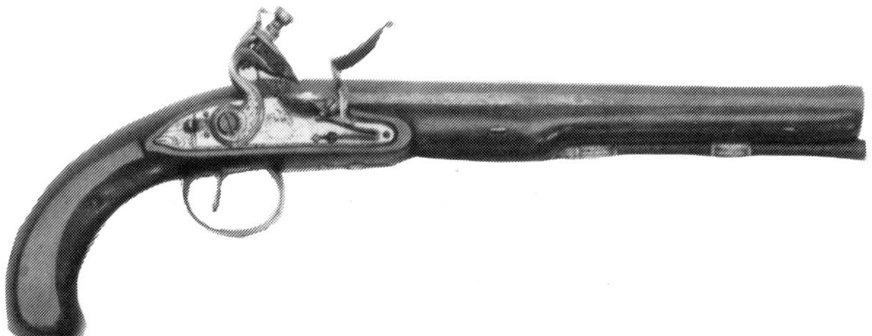

A scarce 28-bore flintlock holster pistol with fitting for detachable shoulder stock, by Wogdon, 15½in., slightly swamped octagonal barrel 10½in., gold inlaid 'Wogdon London', fullstocked, stepped bolted detented lock engraved 'Wogdon' on gold oval, engraved steel furniture, set trigger, acorn finialled trigger guard. $570 £300

An 18-bore cannon barrelled sidelock flintlock Queen Anne style holster pistol by J. Hall, circa 1765, 13in., turn off barrel 6in., London proved with maker's mark I.H. breech foliate engraved with 'London', halfstocked, border engraved lock with 'J. Hall' beneath L-shaped frizzen spring under pan, brass furniture. $720 £300

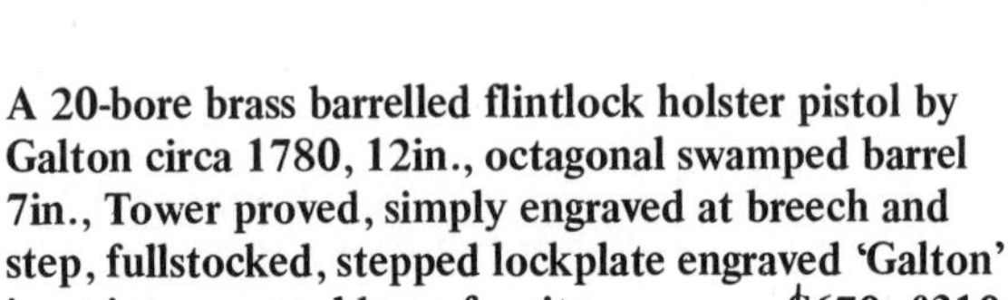

A 20-bore brass barrelled flintlock holster pistol by Galton circa 1780, 12in., octagonal swamped barrel 7in., Tower proved, simply engraved at breech and step, fullstocked, stepped lockplate engraved 'Galton' in script, engraved brass furniture. $670 £310

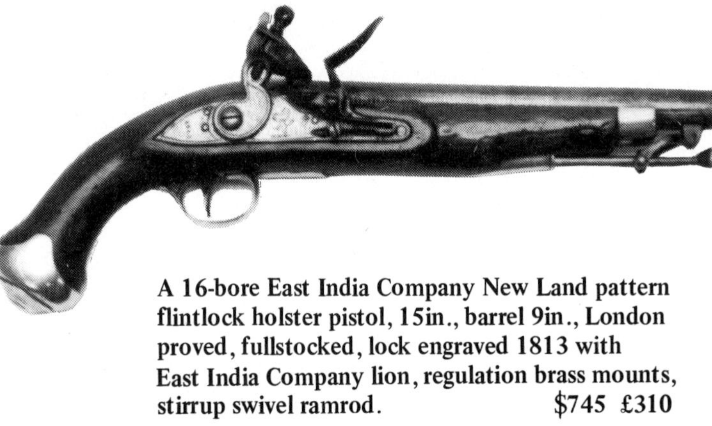

A 16-bore East India Company New Land pattern flintlock holster pistol, 15in., barrel 9in., London proved, fullstocked, lock engraved 1813 with East India Company lion, regulation brass mounts, stirrup swivel ramrod. $745 £310

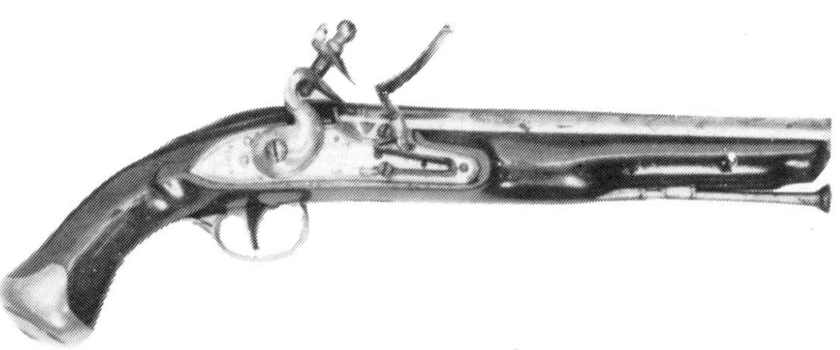

A 16-bore Volunteer Light Dragoon flintlock holster pistol, 15in., barrel 9in., Birmingham proved, fullstocked, slightly rounded lock engraved with 'Tower' and crowned 'G.R.', regulation brass mounts. $755 £320

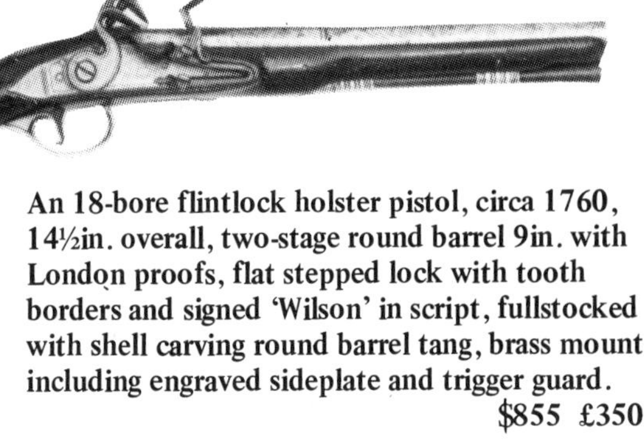

An 18-bore flintlock holster pistol, circa 1760, 14½in. overall, two-stage round barrel 9in. with London proofs, flat stepped lock with tooth borders and signed 'Wilson' in script, fullstocked with shell carving round barrel tang, brass mounts including engraved sideplate and trigger guard.
$855 £350

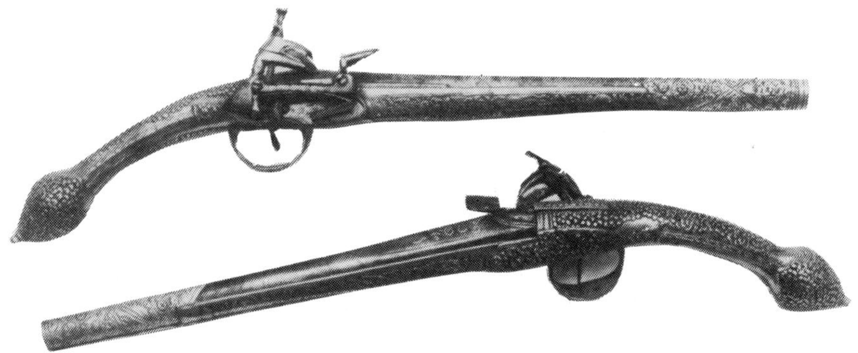

A good pair of 18th century 22-bore Balkan 'rat-tailed' flintlock holster pistols, 20in., barrels 12½in., inlaid with silver geometric designs at breech together with a chiselled apron, fullstocked exterior mainsprings, striated frizzens. $640 £350

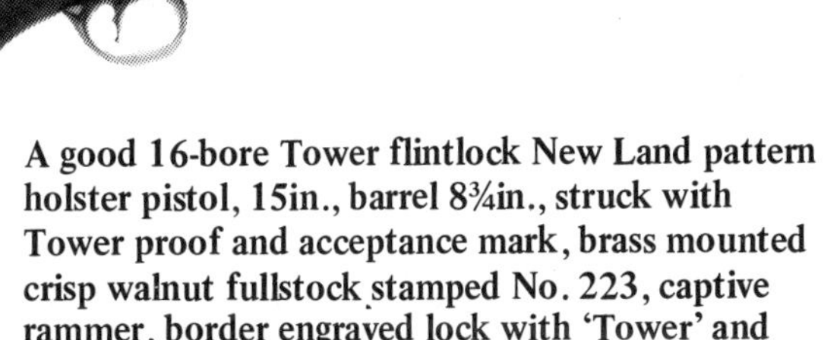

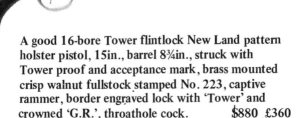

A good 16-bore Tower flintlock New Land pattern holster pistol, 15in., barrel 8¾in., struck with Tower proof and acceptance mark, brass mounted crisp walnut fullstock stamped No. 223, captive rammer, border engraved lock with 'Tower' and crowned 'G.R.', throathole cock. $880 £360

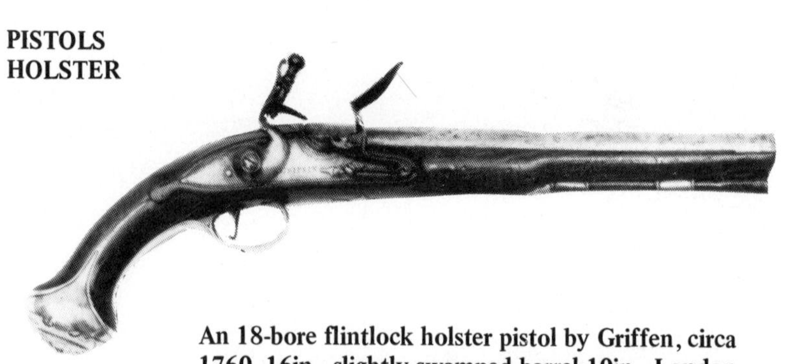

An 18-bore flintlock holster pistol by Griffen, circa 1760, 16in., slightly swamped barrel 10in., London proved with maker's mark, engraved 'Griffen, London' within teardrop, fullstocked, slightly rounded lock-plate with dog tooth border and 'Griffen', cock and frizzen engraved en suite. $930 £430

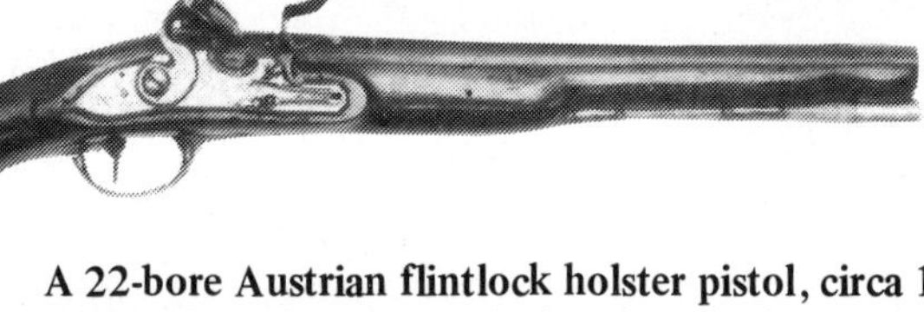

A 22-bore Austrian flintlock holster pistol, circa 1765, 18¾in., barrel 12½in., inlaid with maker's initials M.E.B. engraved with trophy of arms, unbridled frizzen, engraved brass furniture with traces of original gilding. $1,200 £500

A pair of 22-bore cannon barrelled flintlock holster pistols by Gandon, circa 1750, 11¾in., turn-off cannon barrels 5in., foliate engraved breeches, London proved, maker's mark 'P.G.', engraved 'Gandon', halfstocked, border engraved partially rounded lock with 'Gandon', 'L' shaped frizzen springs, unbridled frizzens. $1,225 £510

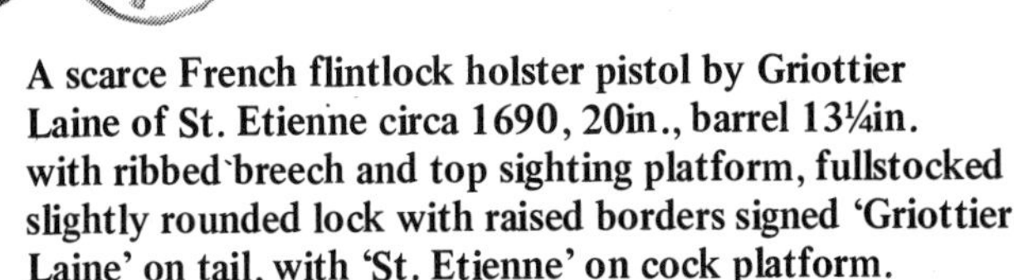

A scarce French flintlock holster pistol by Griottier Laine of St. Etienne circa 1690, 20in., barrel 13¼in. with ribbed breech and top sighting platform, fullstocked slightly rounded lock with raised borders signed 'Griottier Laine' on tail, with 'St. Etienne' on cock platform.
$1,145 £625

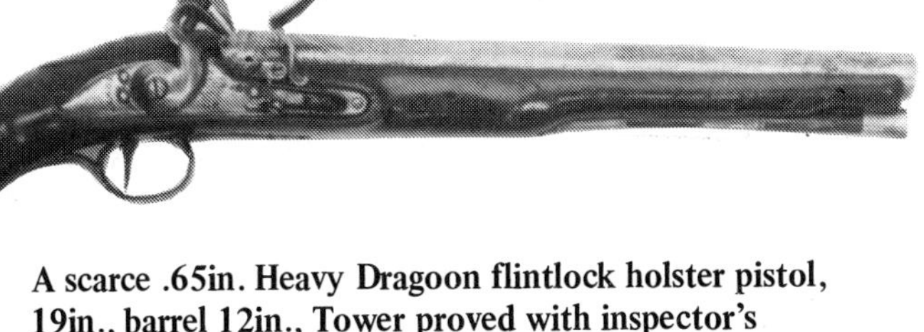

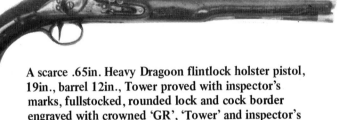

A scarce .65in. Heavy Dragoon flintlock holster pistol, 19in., barrel 12in., Tower proved with inspector's marks, fullstocked, rounded lock and cock border engraved with crowned 'GR', 'Tower' and inspector's stamp, regulation brass mounts. $1,185 £625

A pair of 16-bore flintlock holster pistols by Hartshorn, circa 1800, 13½in., octagonal twist barrels 8in. with some browned finish, fullstocked, stepped bolted detented locks, roller bearing frizzen springs, gold vents.
$1,950 £800

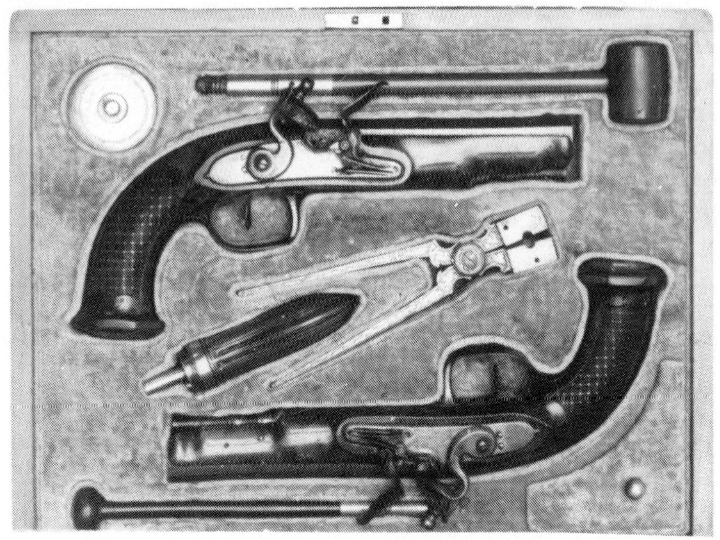

A pair of 20-bore French rifled flintlock holster pistols circa 1800, 11in., brown octagonal twist hairgroove rifled slightly flared barrels 6in., fullstocked roller bearing frizzen springs with curled finials and frizzen tips, engraved polished steel furniture, foliate finialled trigger guards with dogs on bows, 2 piece foliate sideplates. $1,770 £820

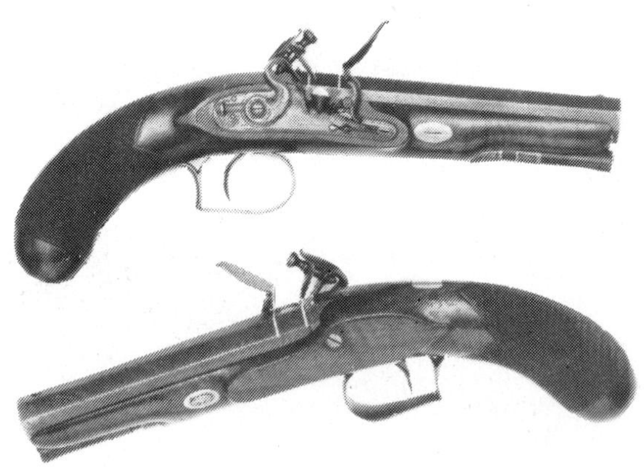

A fine quality and desirable pair of 20-bore flintlock holster pistols by Staudenmeyer of London, No. 1377, circa 1810, 11½in., octagonal barrels 6in. with twin silver breech lines and oval silver maker's poincons stamped 'Staudenmeyer London' with foliate device. $1,805 £950

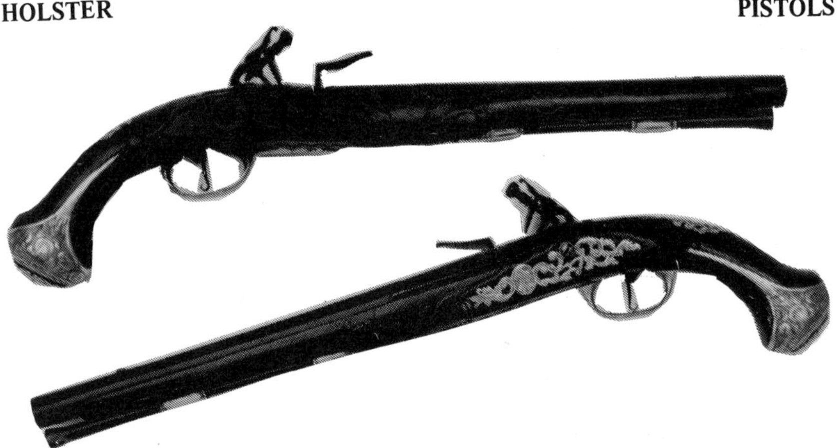

A fine extremely long pair of 20-bore Flemish flintlock holster pistols, circa 1720, overall length 21½in., barrels 14½in. with chevron moulded breeches and top sighting flats, retaining traces of etched and gilt decoration including military trophies, fullstocked, foliate engraved frizzens and frizzen spring, foliate finialled and chiselled brass furniture with traces of gilding.

$4,320 £1,800

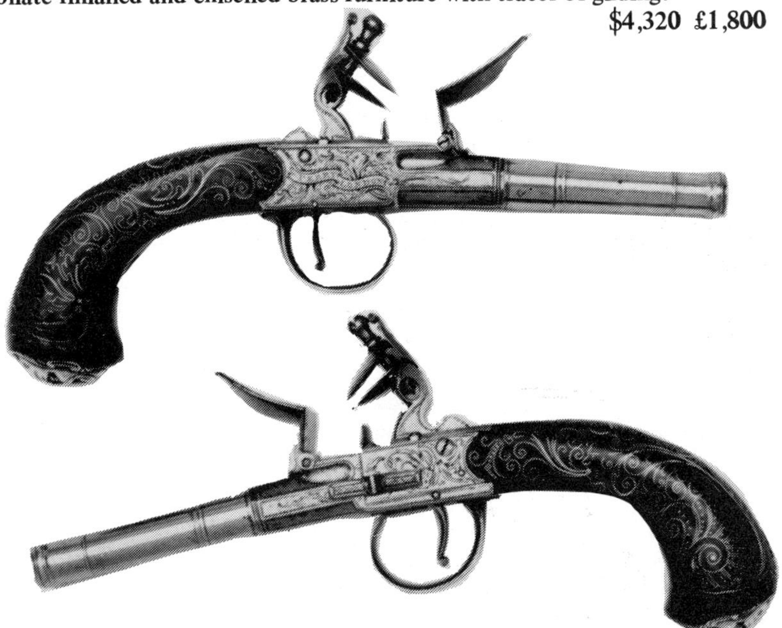

An exceptional pair of 50-bore Queen Anne style double cannon barrelled silver mounted boxlock flintlock holster pistols by Perry of London, circa 1780, with selective sliding pan covers, overall length 10½in., turn-off cannon barrels 3¼in., muzzles slotted for key, numbered 1-4 with Tower proved breeches. $5,520 £2,300

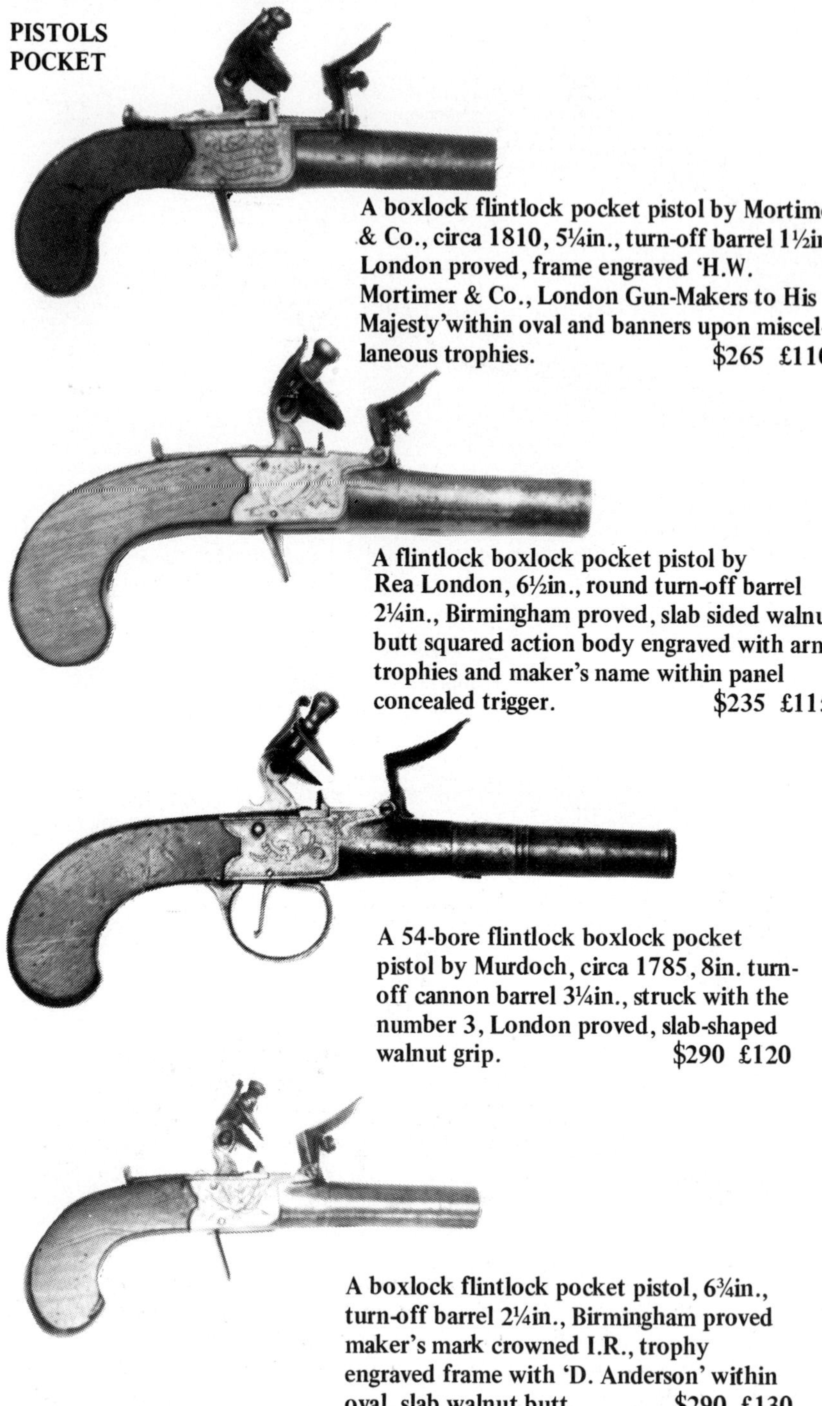

A boxlock flintlock pocket pistol by Mortimer & Co., circa 1810, 5¼in., turn-off barrel 1½in., London proved, frame engraved 'H.W. Mortimer & Co., London Gun-Makers to His Majesty'within oval and banners upon miscellaneous trophies. $265 £110

A flintlock boxlock pocket pistol by Rea London, 6½in., round turn-off barrel 2¼in., Birmingham proved, slab sided walnut butt squared action body engraved with arms trophies and maker's name within panel concealed trigger. $235 £115

A 54-bore flintlock boxlock pocket pistol by Murdoch, circa 1785, 8in. turn-off cannon barrel 3¼in., struck with the number 3, London proved, slab-shaped walnut grip. $290 £120

A boxlock flintlock pocket pistol, 6¾in., turn-off barrel 2¼in., Birmingham proved maker's mark crowned I.R., trophy engraved frame with 'D. Anderson' within oval, slab walnut butt. $290 £130

An interesting late 18th century 70-bore French side-lock flintlock pocket pistol, 8in., barrel 3¾in., turn-off muzzle 2¼in., panel chequered walnut halfstock with iron domed buttcap. $300 £135

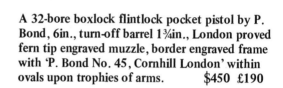

A 32-bore boxlock flintlock pocket pistol by P. Bond, 6in., turn-off barrel 1¾in., London proved fern tip engraved muzzle, border engraved frame with 'P. Bond No. 45, Cornhill London' within ovals upon trophies of arms. $450 £190

A charming 50-bore halfstocked flintlock side-lock pocket pistol by 'T. Hudson', circa 1735, 7in., turn-off cannon barrel 2 1/8in., struck with London proofs, bulbous walnut stock with brass trigger guard with husk finial. $460 £200

A double barrelled .36in. continental all-steel boxlock side-by-side flintlock pocket pistol, 6in., turn-off cannon barrels 1 3/8in., broad bulbous engraved butt, double triggers. $710 £290

An interesting 54-bore double barrelled flintlock boxlock tap action pocket pistol by A. Weston of Lewes, 8½in., turn-off barrels numbered 4 and 5 2 7/8in., London proved plain walnut slab shaped grip, top plate thumb safety, throathole cock, spring teardrop frizzen, the left side of frame fitted with lever to turn flashpan tap to select over or under barrel, (restored).

$550 £250

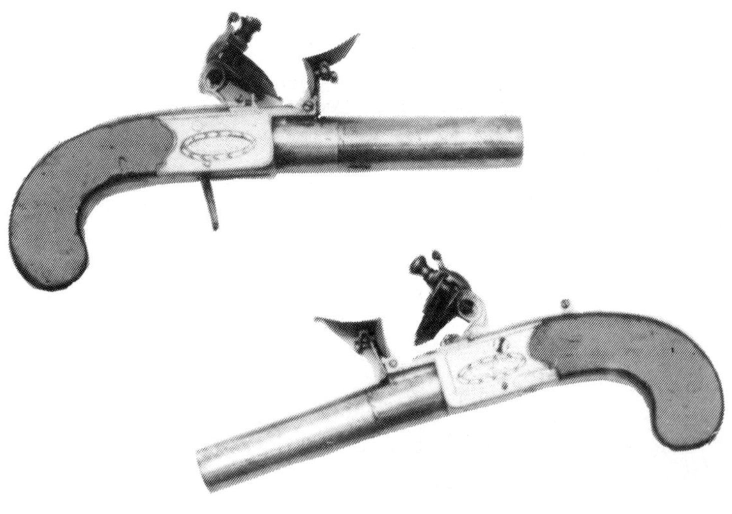

A pair of 48-bore boxlock flintlock pocket pistols by Mortimer circa 1800, 7in., turn-off barrels 2½in., London proved, border engraved frame with H.W. Mortimer, London, Gun-Maker to His Majesty within ovals, sliding top thumb safety catches locking frizzens to fences, raised pans, concealed triggers.

$960 £400

A good pair of boxlock flintlock pocket pistols, 5¾in., turn-off blued barrels 1½in., Birmingham proved, border engraved frames with Britannia shield centred military trophies and 'Wm. Bond London' within panels, sliding top thumb safety catches lock frizzens to fences. $855 £450

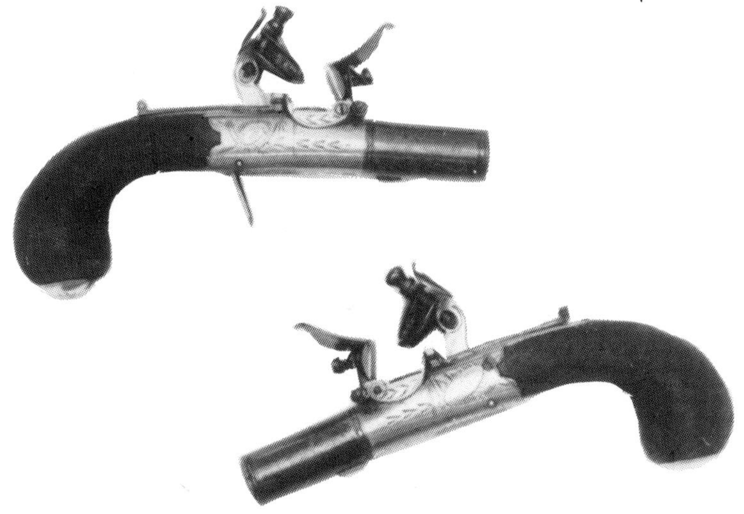

A good pair of 32-bore rifled boxlock flintlock pocket pistols by Lord of Scarboro', 6½in., turn-off blued rifled barrels 1¾in., Birmingham proved, round brass frames with foliate sprigs and 'Lord Scarboro' within oval upon trophy arms, sliding top thumb safeties through throathole cocks locking twin roller bearing frizzens to fences. $1,250 £520

A 60-bore French provincial flintlock travelling pistol, circa 1785, 6½in., slightly swamped steel barrel 3¼in., fullstocked, slightly rounded lock with bridled pan, border engraved steel furniture, foliate finialled trigger guard with circular shape to front of bow.
$325 £125

A 55-bore cannon barrelled flintlock boxlock travelling pistol by Wise of Bristol, circa 1780, 8¼in., turn-off cannon barrel 2¾in., Tower proved, border engraved frame with 'Wise', 'Bristol' within ovals up military trophies, sliding trigger guard safety, frizzen spring sunk in breech top. $430 £180

A fine quality boxlock flintlock travelling pistol fitted with spring bayonet, by D. Egg, London, circa 1790, 7¼in., integral steel barrel 3in., London proved engraved 'D. Egg London' at breech sides.
$680 £310

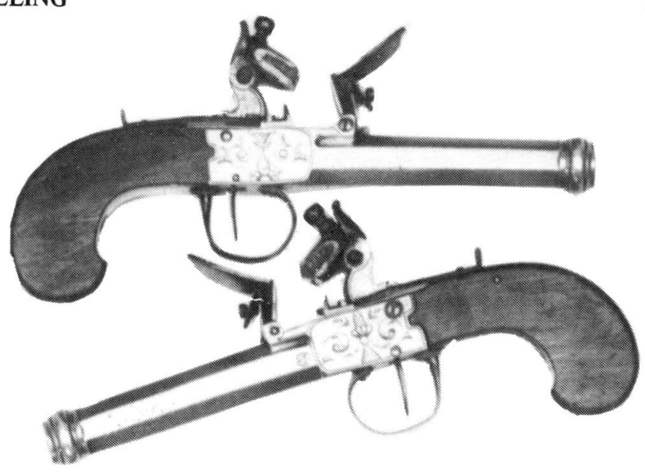

A pair of 32-bore brass framed brass barrelled Belgian flintlock boxlock travelling pistols, 8½in., octagonal barrels 4in., Liege proved, maker's mark I.M., turned reinforced muzzles, sliding top thumb safety catches through throathole cocks locking frizzens to fences, foliate engraved frames, slab walnut grips. $880 £400

A pair of 30-bore flintlock travelling pistols by I. Blanch, circa 1800, 7in., browned twist barrels 3in., gold line breeches, silver vents and bead fore-sights, integral top ribs engraved 'London', fullstocked, stepped bolted locks engraved 'I. Blanch' with foliage and traces of colour hardened finish, roller bearing frizzen springs. $915 £500

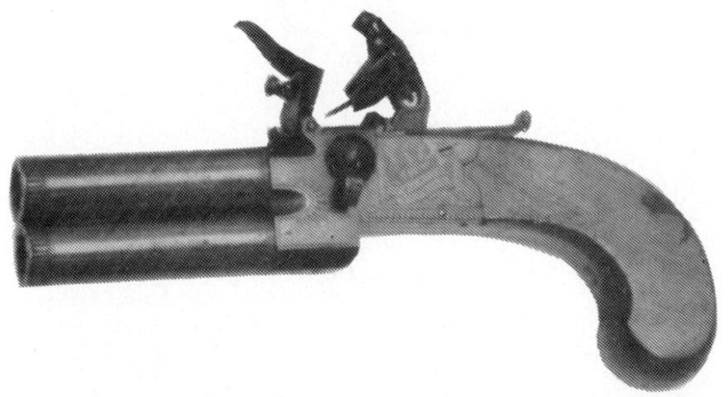

A good quality 46-bore double barrelled over and under flintlock boxlock tap action travelling pistol by W. Parker circa 1800, 8½in., turn-off barrels 3in., foliate tip engraved muzzles slotted for key, London proved, trophy of arms engraved frame with 'W. Parker, Holborn, London', sliding top thumb safety locking twin roller bearing frizzen to fence, concealed trigger. $1,200 £500

A very good pair of 58-bore double barrelled over and under tap action boxlock flintlock travelling pistols by Galton, circa 1786, 8½in. overall, turn-off barrels 3in. numbered to Tower proved breeches, border engraved frames with military trophies of arms and 'Galton.' within ovals, sliding top thumb safeties locking frizzens to fences. $2,880 £1,200

A 13-bore French Military flintlock rifle, 56in., barrel 40½in., Liege proved. Fullstocked, regulation lock with brass pan, plate engraved 'Mfre Rle de Tulle'. Regulation iron mounts, three spring retained barrel bands, two sling swivels, steel ramrod. Stock carved with cheekpiece. $500 £250

An attractive 40-bore Turkish miquelet flintlock rifle, circa 1780, 52in., watered steel barrel 38in., chiselled at breech and muzzle with foliage, inlaid with gold maker's poincon, raised top sighting rib, fullstocked, lock inlaid with gold, sher bacha rearsight, green stained ivory forecap. $1,000 £500

A scarce 16-bore Baker regulation military pattern flintlock rifle, 45½in., barrel 30in., Tower proved with inspector's mark, fullstocked, slightly rounded twin line border engraved lock with crowned 'GR', 'Tower' and inspector's mark, regulation brass mounts. $2,530 £1,100

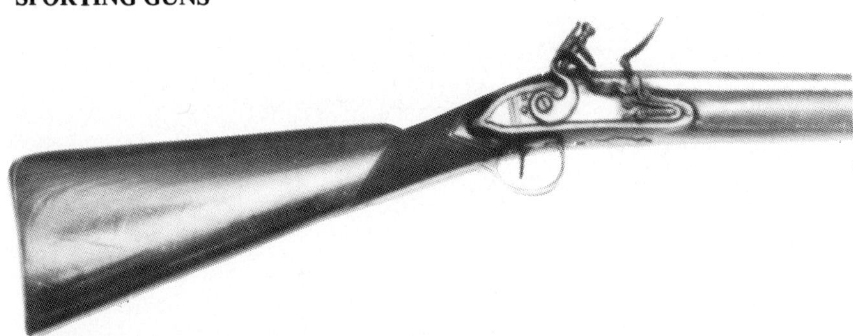

A single barrelled 18-bore flintlock sporting gun by F. Aston, 50¼in., part octagonal part round barrel 34½in., traces of Tower proof, chequered walnut halfstock with brass furniture trigger guard with pineapple finial, ribbed barrel with two ramrod pipes, silver bead foresight. **$370 £180**

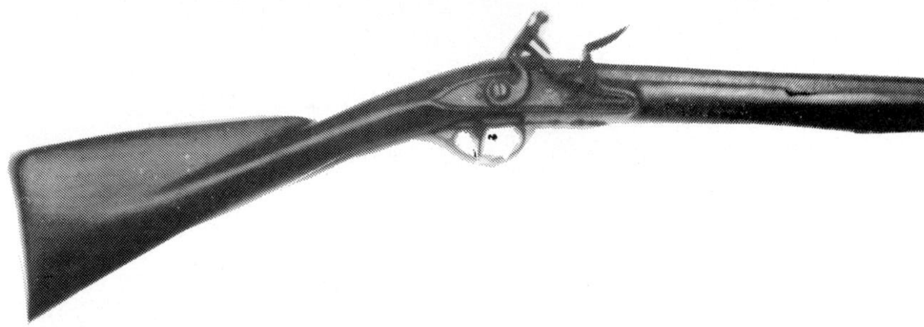

An elegant 10-bore flintlock fowling gun by Ketland & Co., circa 1780, 54in., half octagonal swamped barrel 37½in., engraved 'Ketland & Co.' on top flat, Tower proved, fullstocked, well-made lock border engraved with foliate sprigs, roller bearing frizzen, steel furniture, acorn finialled trigger guard. **$675 £285**

A late 20-bore Belgian double barrelled flintlock sporting gun, 51½in., barrels 35¼in., engraved and stamped with geometric devices at breech, half stocked, foliate engraved locks and cocks, foliate engraved steel furniture, white metal barrel wedge plates and escutcheon, foliate carved fore end. **$910 £480**

A very fine and rare French or German 16-bore double barrelled flintlock sporting gun circa 1830, 47in., browned barrels 31in., chiselled at breeches with foliage, scrolls and rocaille ornament in low relief, half-stocked, slightly rounded browned locks, engraved with rocaille and foliate devices overall, roller bearing frizzen springs, browned steel furniture.
$1,955 £850

A very rare 18-bore German breech loading flintlock sporting gun by J.G. Polz of Carlsbad, circa 1790, overall length 54¼in., barrel 39¼in., engraved on top flat 'Joann Georg Polz A Carlsbad', breech engraved with warrior standing on foliate pediment against trophy of arms within cartouche, separate 'cartridge' containing charge within re-loadable steel tube with pan and frizzen attached slides into breech. $2,760 £1,150

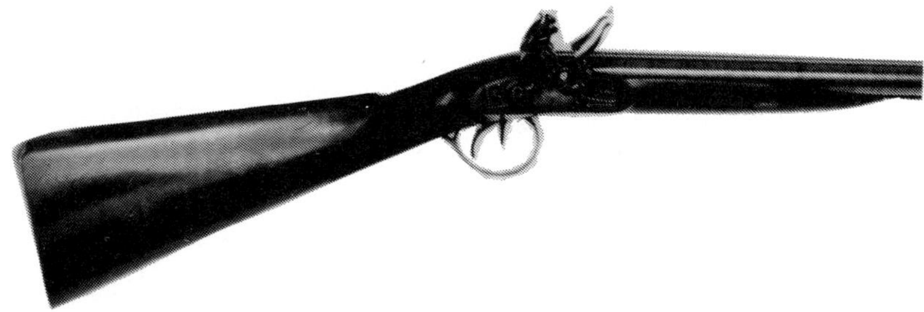

A good scarce 14-bore double barrelled flintlock sporting gun by Keel & Co., circa 1810, overall length 45½in., browned twist ribless barrels 29½in., gold inlaid 'Keel & Co. Patent' with single gold breech lines, halfstocked, border engraved stepped locks with 'Keel & Co', roller bearing frizzen springs, gold lined vents, scrolled cock spurs, engraved steel furniture. $3,600 £1,500

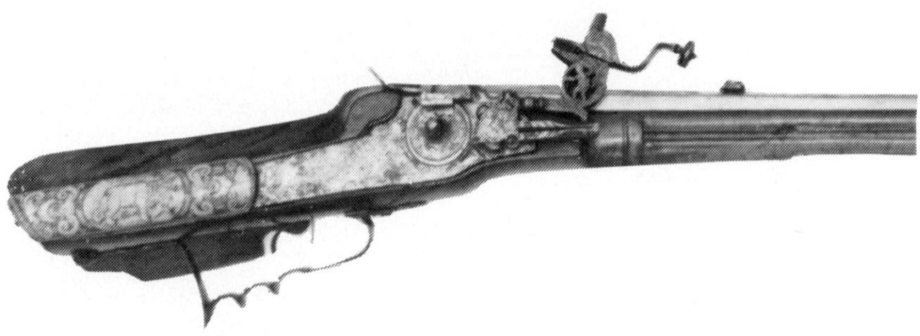

A scarce 16-bore German wheellock rifle, circa 1600, 44in. overall length, octagonal barrel 33¼in., with deep 7 groove rifling, pellet engraved breech, two leaf rearsight with long foliate finial. Walnut fullstock, foliate finialled lockplate engraved with hunter seated with fallen stag beneath trees by waterfall. $875 £400

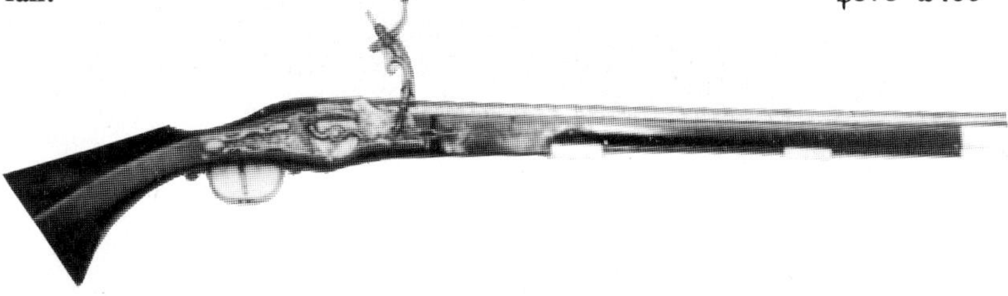

An attractive old 12-bore decorative wheellock carbine, 37½in., barrel 25½in., with traces of engraved decoration, full stocked, lock with external wheel and mainspring, swollen ribbed wheel and cock bridles, pellet and foliate chiselled cock on baluster stem. $1,495 £650

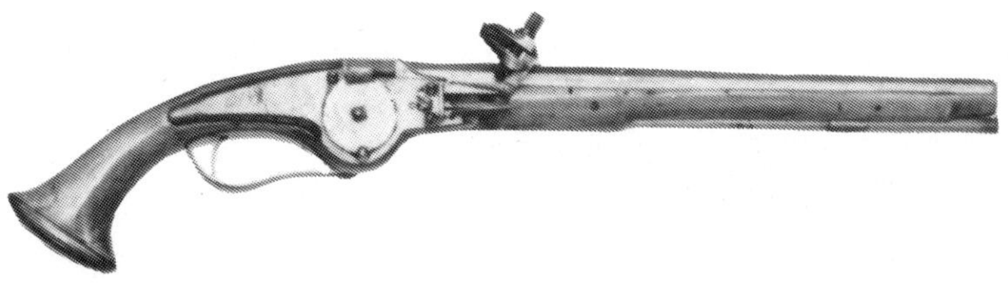

A scarce German 20-bore Military wheellock holster pistol, circa 1620, 23½in., octagonal barrel 15¾in., struck with the Suhl bird mark and 'SVL' (Suhl) beechwood fullstock, lock with bevelled tail, exterior wheel, sliding pan cover, steel trigger guard and buttcap. $2,685 £1,100

MILITARIA

AIR RIFLES

A rare Webley Service mark II barrel cocking air rifle, 41½in., with three barrels in three calibres, .177in., .22in. and .25in., all 25½, no. 7808 receiver stamped 'Webley Service Air Rifle Mark II' with 'Manufactured by Webley & Scott Ltd.' together with winged bullet trade mark and various patent dates.
$1,248 £520

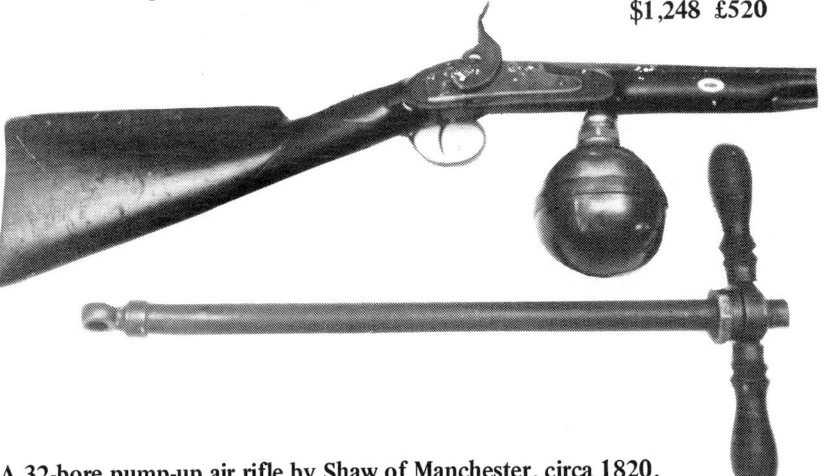

A 32-bore pump-up air rifle by Shaw of Manchester, circa 1820, 47½in., half octagonal rifled barrel 32in., faintly engraved 'Manchester' on top flat, halfstocked, foliate engraved stepped lock with 'Shaw'. steel furniture, silver fore-cap, barrel wedge plates.
$1,275 £540

A well made and detailed miniature suit of 16th century armour, of light metal, fully articulated, with close helmet, mitten gauntlets, large sabatons, etc., some roped decoration to borders, and some studded decoration to edges, holding two handed sword, and mounted on a wooden base, overall height of suit 27in. $935 £425

A fine North Italian (probably Milanese) half-armour of so-called Pisan type circa 1560-70, comprising one-piece cabaset with 'pear-stalk' finial, integral brim with roped border and twin peaks etched with classical figures from mythology within riband cartouches, with bands of 'Pisan' infill, all against stipple etched grounds, breast plate of 'peascod' form en suite with back plate. $5,076 £2,350

An old Congo axe nzappa zap, iron pierced blade 8½in. with openwork twist decoration, central rib chiselled with 4 human masks, cutting edge 9in., on its sheet copper covered haft, 15in.
$140 £65

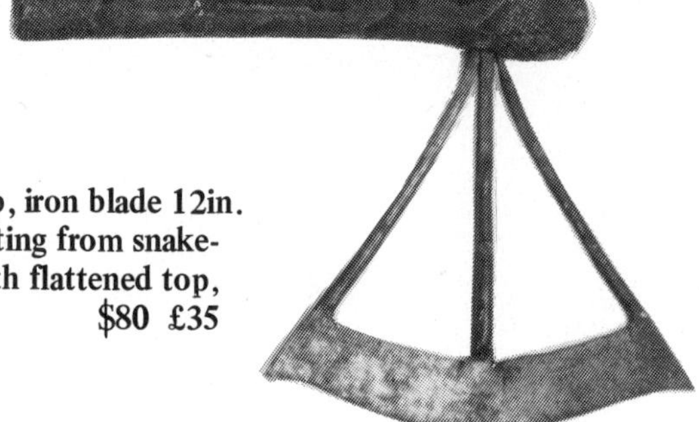

An old Congo axe nzappa zap, iron blade 12in. on 3 iron bar mounts, emanating from snake-skin covered wooden haft with flattened top, 15½in. $80 £35

An old Malabar executioner's axe, curved sickle type blade 18in. with simple incised decoration marked 'Madras', turned wood grip with large iron mounts of rounded cage form, overall length 28in.
$220 £90

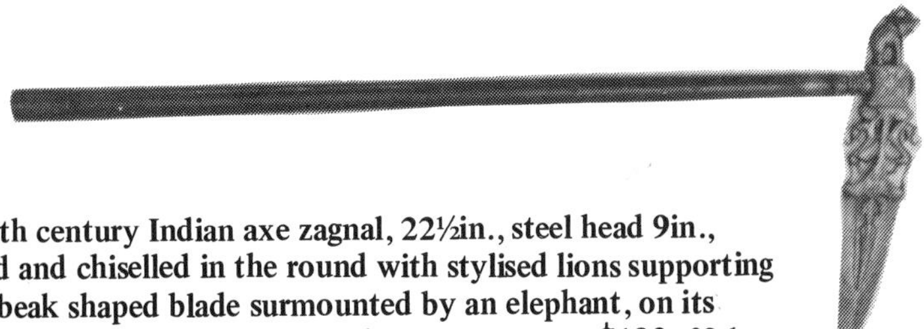

An 18th century Indian axe zagnal, 22½in., steel head 9in., pierced and chiselled in the round with stylised lions supporting head, beak shaped blade surmounted by an elephant, on its steel haft with riveted wooden sides. $180 £96

An Indian fighting axe from the Bikaneer Armoury, 23½in., heavy steel crescent head 4¾in. engraved with the magic square and arsenal mark, steel mounted haft with 2 piece wooden sides retained by ornamental brass headed rivets. $190 £100

A good 16th/17th century German axe head, 13½in., struck with 3 maker's marks, and a series of flower heads and crescent designs, octagonal socket integral with head. $320 £135

An other rank's pre-1881 glengarry of The 38th (1st Staffordshire) Regt. $35 £14

An other rank's pre-1881 glengarry of The 30th (Cambridgeshire) Regt. $35 £14

A pre-1881 other rank's glengarry badge of The 94th Regt. $35 £15

An other rank's pre-1881 glengarry of The 9th (E. Norfolk) Regt. $40 £16

An officer's silver bonnet badge of The Gordon Highlanders, hallmarked Birmingham 1897. $40 £16

An other rank's pre-1881 glengarry of The 70th (The Surrey) Regt. $40 £16

An other rank's pre-1881 glengarry of The 59th (2nd Nottinghamshire) Regt. $40 £16

An other rank's pre-1881 glengarry of The 13th (1st Somerset) Regt. $40 £17

An other rank's pre-1881 glengarry of The 82nd (P.O.W. Volunteers) Regt. (551). $45 £18

A Piper's silvered plaid brooch of The Black Watch. $40 £18

An other rank's pre-1881 glengarry of The 29th (Worcestershire) Regt. $50 £20

A pre-1881 other rank's glengarry badge of The 57th (W. Middlesex) Regt. $50 £20

An other rank's white metal cap of The 2nd V.B. The East Surrey Regt. $55 £22

An officer's silver drill cap badge of The P. O. Wales's Volunteers, plum plume and motto without title. $55 £22

An other rank's pre-1881 glengarry of The 15th (York E. Riding) Regt. $55 £22

A pre-1881 other rank's glengarry badge of The 20th (E. Devon) Regt. $55 £22

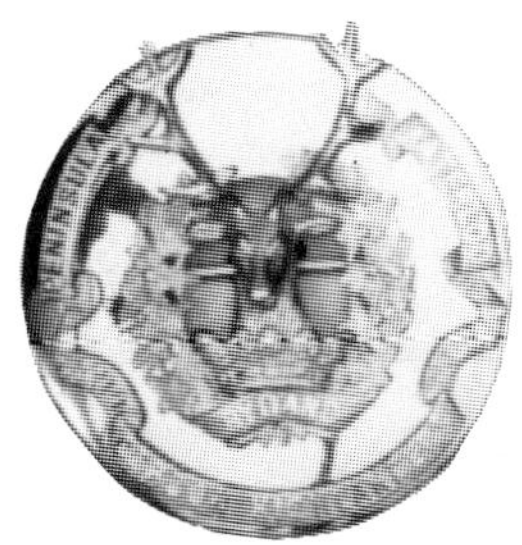

A piper's silvered plaid brooch of The Gordon Highlanders. $50 £22

A pre-1881 other rank's glengarry badge of The 97th (Earl of Ulster's) Regt. $60 £26

An other rank's pre-1881 glengarry of The 40th (2nd Somerset) Regt. $65 £26

A pre-1881 other rank's glengarry badge of The 92nd (Gordon Highlanders) Regt. $65 £26

A Georgian brass badge from a Tarleton helmet, crowned garter with 'GR' in centre. $65 £28

An other rank's white metal cap of The 4th V.B. The East Surrey Regt., King's crown. $70 £28

A Victorian other rank's heavy quality white metal helmet plate of The 48th (Canadian) Highlanders. $70 £28

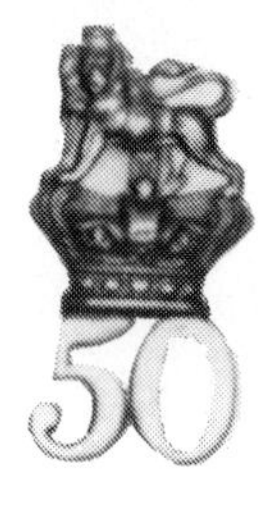

An other rank's pre-1881 glengarry of The 50th (or The Queen's Own) Regt. $70 £28

An officer's silvered and enamel cap of The Guards Machine Gun Battalion. $70 £28

An other rank's pre-1881 glengarry of The 47th (The Lancashire) Regt. $70 £28

An other rank's pre-1881 glengarry of The 4th (The King's Own) Regt. $65 £30

An other rank's white metal cap of The 2nd V.B. The South Lancashire Regt. $80 £34

A post-1902 officer's silver cap of The 'Liverpool Pals', hallmarked London 1914. $85 £34

An other rank's pre-1881 glengarry of The 78th (Highland or Ross-shire Buffs) Regt., $90 £36

A pre-1881 other rank's glengarry badge of The 15th (York, East Riding) Regt. $75 £40

A pre-1881 other rank's glengarry badge of The 70th (Surrey) Regt. $75 £40

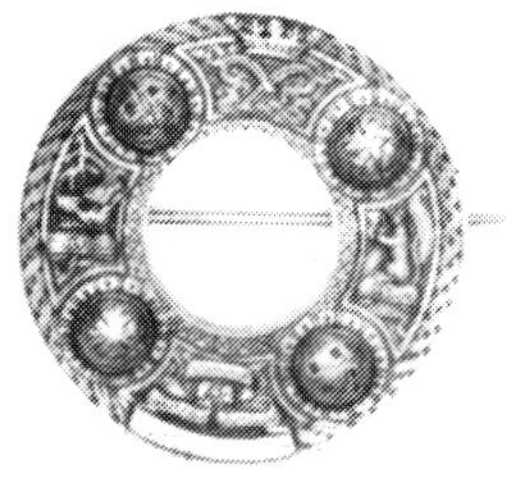

An officer's silvered plaid brooch of The Argyll and Sutherland Highlanders. $90 £40

An officer's cast silver bonnet badge of The Argyll and Sutherland Highlanders, (hallmarked Edinburgh 1898). $100 £45

A Victorian officer's gilt helmet plate of The R. Engineers Militia. $100 £46

A pre-1881 other rank's glengarry badge of The 83rd (County of Dublin) Regt. $95 £50

A pre-1881 other rank's glengarry badge of The 88th (Connaught Rangers) Regt. $95 £50

A pre-1881 other rank's glengarry badge of The 27th (Inniskilling) Regt. $95 £50

A pre-1881 other rank's glengarry badge of The 39th (Dorsetshire) Regt. $95 £50

A Victorian officer's helmet plate of The King's (Liverpool) Regt. $120 £50

A Victorian officer's gilt shako badge of The 3rd City of London Rifle Volunteers. $105 £52

A white metal glengarry badge of The 1st Middlesex Engineer Volunteers. $135 £56

A silvered plaid brooch of The 6th Volunteer Bn. The Gordon Highlanders. $130 £60

A cap badge of The 2nd Birmingham Bn. R. Warwickshire Regt. $140 £60

A Victorian officer's silvered and gilt helmet plate of The 2nd Volunteer Bn. The Middlesex Regt. $145 £60

An officer's helmet plate of The Hertfordshire Rifle Volunteers $145 £70

A bronze and enamel cap badge of The Household Brigade Cadet Bn. $150 £70

A cap badge of The Public Works Pioneer Bn. The Middlesex Regt. $150 £70

An officer's gilt 1878 pattern helmet plate of The 57th (W. Middlesex) Regt. $170 £70

A Victorian officer's gilt and silvered helmet plate of The Welsh Regt. $165 £75

An officer's 1878 pattern helmet plate of The 97th Regt. $180 £75

A Victorian officer's gilt and silvered helmet plate of The Gloucestershire Regt. $175 £80

A silvered plaid brooch of The 1st Royal Lanark Militia. $100 £80

A Victorian officer's gilt and silvered helmet plate of The South Wales Borderers. $175 £80

A Victorian officer's gilt helmet plate of The Royal Canadian Artillery, similar to British but with 'Canada' in place of 'Ubique'. $175 £80

A silver cap badge (not H.M.) of the London Scottish. $192 £80

A bronze cap badge of the Guards Machine Gun Regt. (922). $200 £84

A fine silvered plaid brooch of The 93rd (Sutherland Highlanders), engraved on the back. $195 £90

An officer's gilt and silvered 1869 pattern shako badge of The 9th (E. Norfolk) Regt. $215 £90

A post-1902 officer's silver cap badge of The King's Own Scottish Borderers. $215 £90

A Georgian brass badge from a Tarleton helmet, crowned Garter bearing motto 'Pro Aris et Focis'. $205 £95

An officer's silvered helmet plate of The 1st Glamorgan Rifle Volunteer Corps. $205 £100

A Victorian medical officer's silver helmet plate of the Bearer Company, S. Eastern Volunteer Infantry Brigade. $205 £100

A Victorian officer's silvered helmet plate of The 1st Volunteer Bn. The R: West Kent Regt. $235 £100

A silver bonnet badge of The Argyll & Sutherland Highlanders, H.M. Edinburgh 1844. $240 £100

A Victorian officer's silvered, gilt and enamel helmet plate of The 5th Volunteer Bn. The Royal Scots. $245 £100

An officer's pre-1902 gilt helmet plate of The Suffolk Regiment. $225 £105

An officer's silver and enamel cap badge of The Guards Machine Gun Bn. $240 £110

An officer's 1861 pattern shako badge of The Hampshire Militia. $250 £115

An officer's post-1902 gilt helmet plate of The Worcestershire Regiment. $250 £115

An officer's post-1902 gilt helmet plate of The South Wales Borderers. $260 £120

An officer's post-1902 gilt helmet plate of The West Yorkshire Regiment. $260 £120

An officer's pre-1902 gilt helmet plate of The Northamptonshire Regiment. $260 £120

An officer's post-1902 gilt helmet plate of The Army Service Corps. $270 £125

A Victorian hallmarked silver Coldstream Guards Officers Puggaree Badge, (B'ham 1900). $280 £125

An officer's gilt 1844 (Albert) pattern shako badge of The Royal East Middlesex Militia. $300 £125

An officer's copper gilt helmet plate of The Jaua Mahidpore Horse Artillery, circa 1820. $305 £125

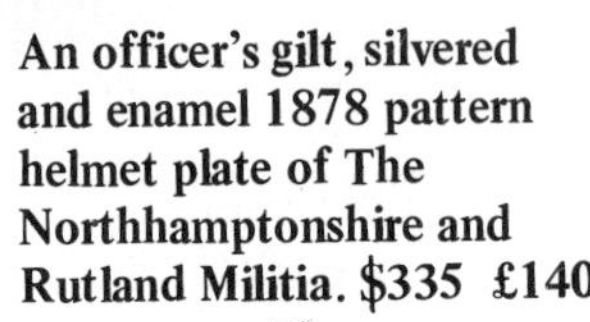

An officer's gilt, silvered and enamel 1878 pattern helmet plate of The Northhamptonshire and Rutland Militia. $335 £140

An officer's post-1902 silvered helmet plate of The 1st. Volunteer Batt. Leicestershire Regiment. $325 £150

A Victorian officer's gilt and silvered helmet plate of The Royal Dock Yard Battalion. $330 £150

A post-1902 impressive gilt silver and enamel large oval badge of The 2nd Batt. South Lancashire Regiment. $380 £175

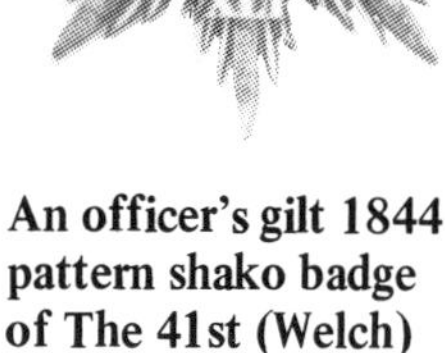

An officer's gilt 1844 pattern shako badge of The 41st (Welch) Regt. $430 £180

An officer's pre-1902 silvered helmet plate of The 1st Cadet Batt. The Norfolk Regiment. $445 £205

A Victorian white metal helmet plate of The 2nd Volunteer Bn. The Scottish Rifles. $450 £205

An officer's 1861 pattern silvered shako badge of The Royal Sark Light Infantry Militia. $455 £210

A Prussian officer's helmet plate of a Reserve Garde Regt $495 £210

A Victorian officer's silver pouch belt badge of the Cape Mounted Rifles, hallmarked London 1863. $495 £220

An officer's helmet plate of a Saxon Garde Reiter Cavalry Regt. $520 £220

A mid Victorian gilt shako badge of The Royal Dock Yard Battalion Band. $605 £280

An officer's gilt 1812 (Waterloo) pattern shako badge of The 29th (Worcestershire) Regt. $805 £350

An officer's gilt, silver and enamel bell-top shako badge of The 1st Somerset Militia, 1829 pattern, large crowned fluted gilt star, bearing smaller size hob-nailed silver star with central device being red enamelled St. George's Cross within garter motto and regimental title in scroll below. $840 £350

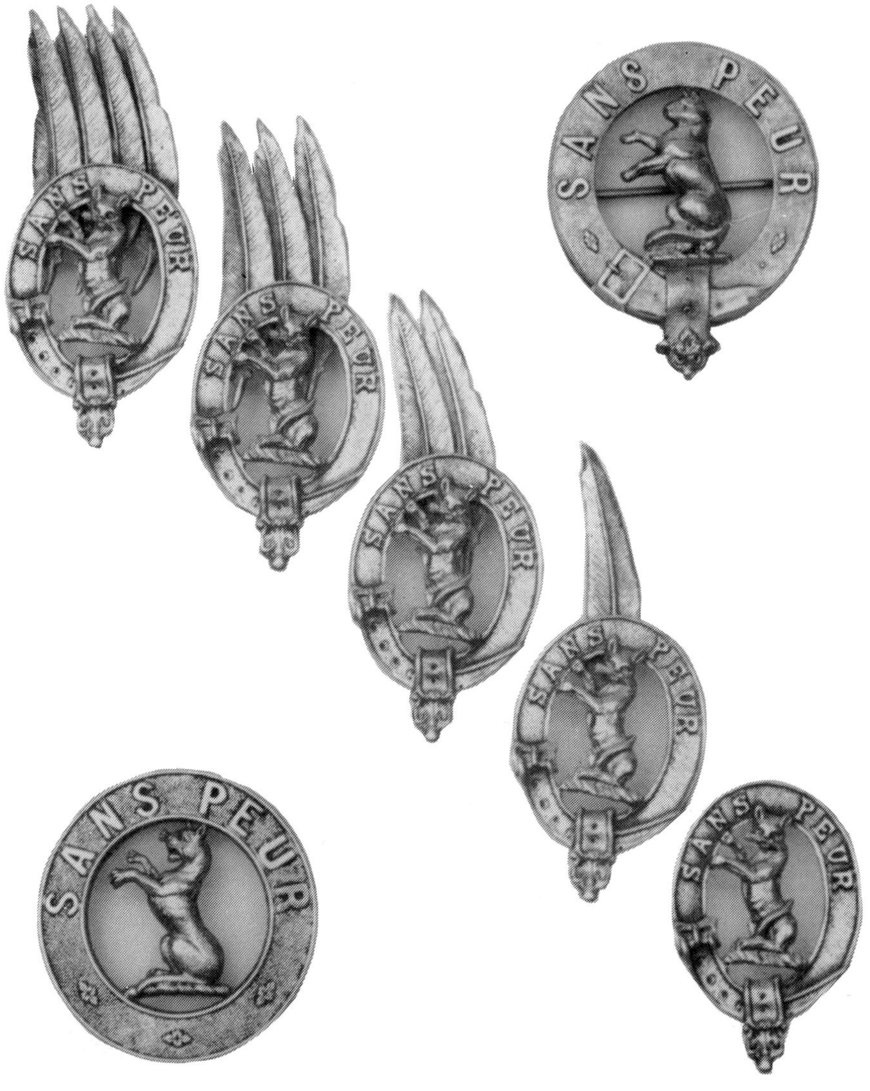

A scarce collection of badges of The 5th Battalion Seaforth Highlanders (Ross-shire Buffs), comprising officer's badges of cast silver to the ranks of Colonel, Field Officer, Captain, Subaltern and Warrant Officer, also other ranks 1st and 2nd pattern in white metal, the design for officer's being a vertical oval strap inscribed 'Sans Peur' and within the strap a cat-a-mountain seated erect on a wreath, feathers are worn behind according to rank.

$1,100 £550

A Cromwellian period siege weight breastplate, ribbed neck section and arm cusps, the medial ridge terminating at flared skirt in small beak.
$290 £120

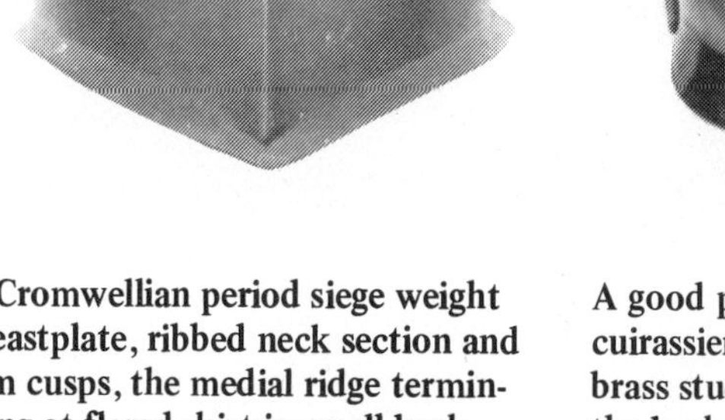

A good pair of 19th century French cuirassier's breast and back plates, brass studs to borders, the inside of the back plate skirt engraved 'Manufre Rle de Klingenthal Juillet 1833' together with number 1525. $410 £190

A pair of late 19th century French cuirassier's breast and back plates, brass studs to borders, the inside of breast plate skirt engraved.
$440 £200

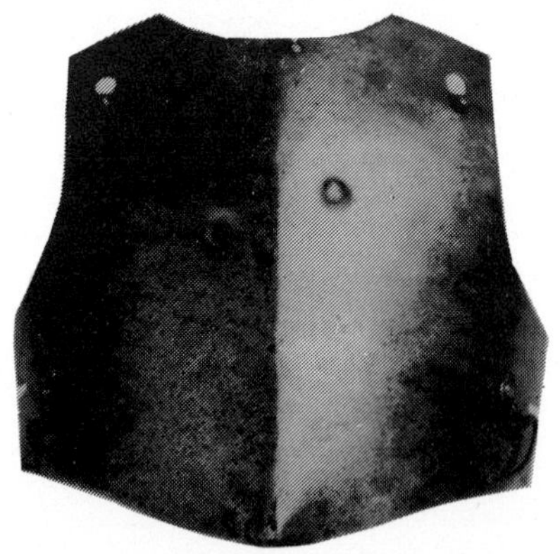

An interesting English Civil War period reinforcing breast plate 'plackart' from the armoury at Apethorpe, Northants.
$450 £220

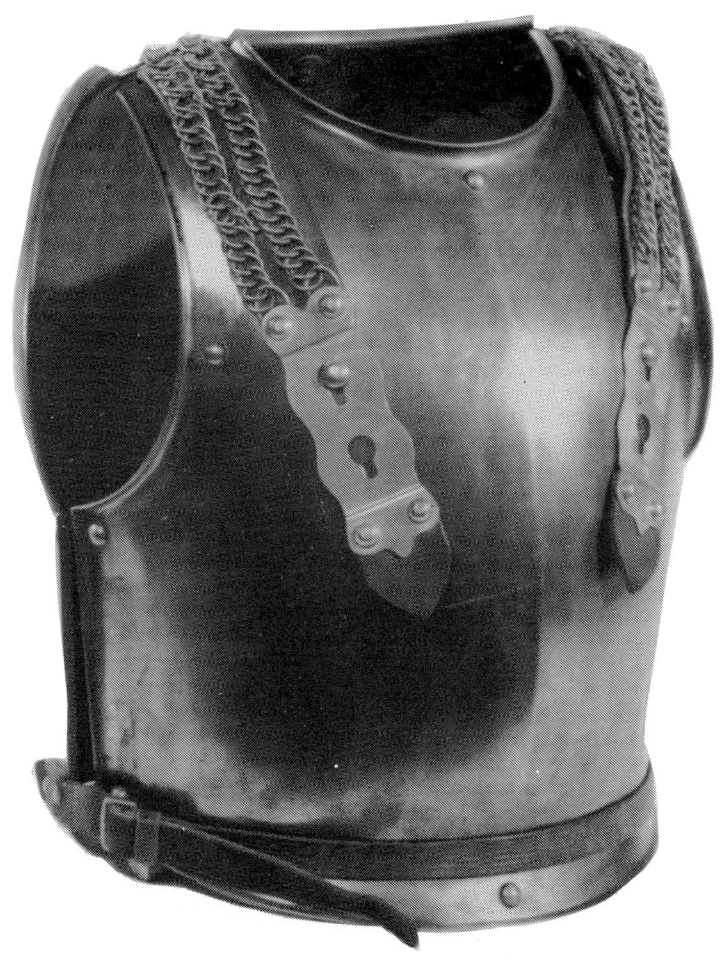

A good French 19th century cuirassier trooper's breast and back plate, the breast plate of heavy form with brass studs, and engraved inside on skirt 'Manufre Nle de Chatellerault Obre 1853, 3T 2L no. 117', the back plate engraved 'Manufre Rle de Chatellerault Fevrier 1846, 3T IL no. 1422', and with original leather backed chain brass mounted shoulder straps and slides. $600 £260

A mid 17th century Cromwellian armour comprising: lobster tail helmet, with triple bar visor to hinged peak, simulated lames to neck guard, raised comb, studded decoration to border; breastplate of siege weight, with musket ball proof mark and with companion backplate with armourer's commonwealth stamp and with a small cannon ball.

$742 £360

A well constructed modern scale model of an English 9pdr. field gun of the Napoleonic war period, circa 1810-25, brass barrel 7in., on its wooden, trailed carriage, with steel rimmed, spoked wooden wheels, and with brake shoe on chain, bucket beneath carriage, elevating screw, steel mounts, overall length 12½in., height 5in., modelled from drawings. $60 £30

A well made model of a French Trafalgar period Naval cannon, turned brass barrel 12in., on stepped wooden carriage mounted on model section of a Man-of-War Hull comprising deck section and open gun-port and ship's side and with soiled ropes, halyards and stays and recoil restraining ropes, overall dimensions of display 10½ x 19 x height 10½in. $310 £130

A Victorian contemporary model of a breech loading siege gun, circa 1870, steel barrel 15in., to cascabel of stepped form, smooth bored of 7/8in. diam. Mounted on a steel truck which incorporates elevating capstan, the truck slides back to absorb recoil on a steel traversing platform with 4 brass wheels.
$310 £150

A factory model 40 pounder muzzle loading siege cannon by Sir W. G. Armstrong & Co. dated 1876. Iron sleeved rifled barrel 12½in., trunnion flat stamped 'Weight 3,800lb. prep 28lb., 40 pr'. Mounted on its mahogany four-wheeled carriage with brass fittings and trunnion caps. Large circular iron wheel controls creeping elevation. $768 £320

A Moghul Indian iron fortress cannon, circa 1620, 45in. overall, chiselled at breech with lion attacking antelope, with iris flowers and foliage, lotus chiselled muzzle. The bore is approximately 1in., trunnion ring, fixed pan of matchlock type, fixed rear sight and integral breech tang pierced twice for fixture to tiller. $360 £190

A 19th century mountain gun, circa 1870, stepped bronze barrel 30in., approx. 1¾in. bore, mounted on old associated wooden tailed carriage with wooden spoked ironshod wheels, overall length 5ft.1in. $864 £360

Zulu War 1879, an African wooden knobkerry stave carved with contemporary inscriptions 'Lt. F. Cookson XCI Highlanders' and with long list of places and Battles in the Zulu War. $90 £41

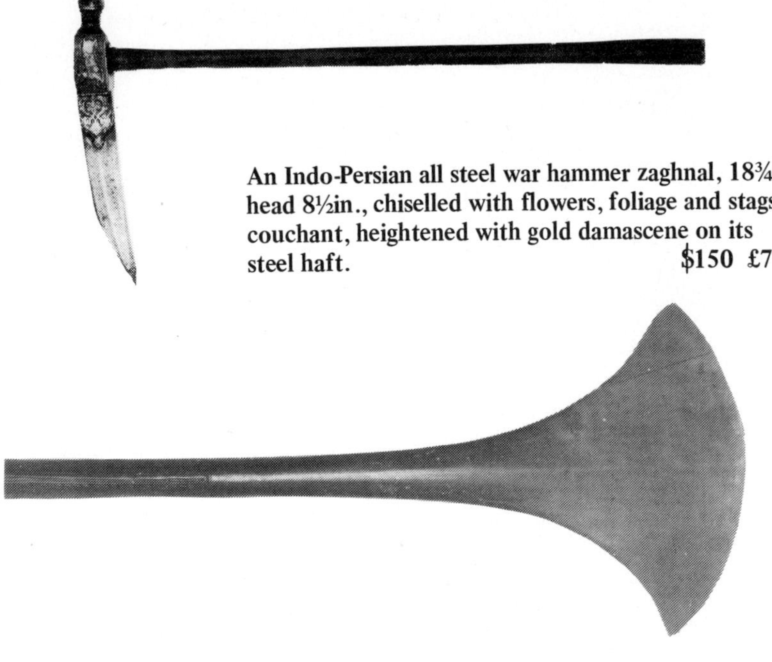

An Indo-Persian all steel war hammer zaghnal, 18¾in., head 8½in., chiselled with flowers, foliage and stags couchant, heightened with gold damascene on its steel haft. $150 £75

A wooden South Seas fighting club, broad blade width 15in., the haft carved at base with zig-zag pattern, overall 36in. $280 £135

A late 16th/early 17th century European War hammer, iron top with 8 flange looped head, long slightly curved diamond section beak on wooden haft with long straps decorated with brass rosettes, overall 32in. $600 £250

An early 19th century Austro-German target crossbow, 33in. overall length, heavy steel bow 25in. span, with contemporary strengthening plate. Walnut stock, micro-adjustable double set triggers, brass furniture with urn-shaped finials. Scrolled trigger guard with adjustable spur on bow of trigger guard. Tall block rearsight of pillar form with micro-adjustable peepholes and foresight. Chequered small of stock, carved cheekpiece inlaid with mother-of-pearl.
$1,440 £600

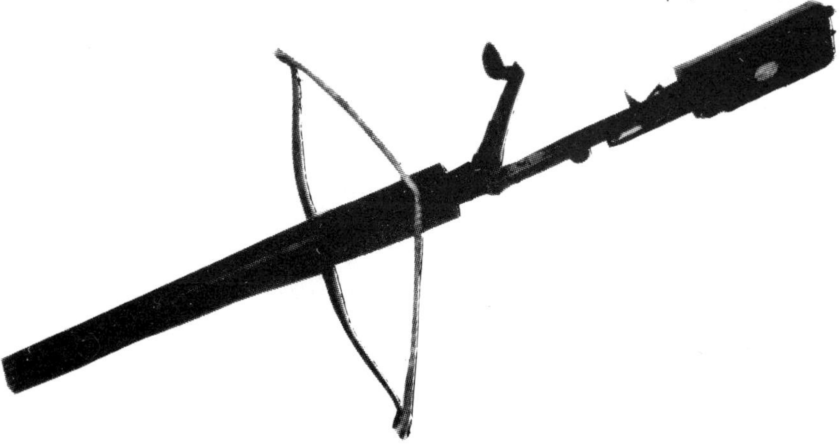

A German self spanning crossbow, circa 1580-60, 35½in. overall length, Steel bow with rounded terminals, 17in. span. Set trigger cocked by pressing button beneath frame. Flip-up rearsight, self setting nut. Sprung retaining catch for loading lever. Baluster trigger guard. Carved fruitwood butt, scroll carved cheekpiece inlaid with oval ivory plaque, iron ball finial. Fruitwood bolt, stock, carved channel with inlaid horn fore-tip. Original fibre wood bow-string.
$2,000 £1,000

A painted brass drum of 517 LAA Regiment R.A. 5th Essex T.A., painted 'E.R.II' Royal Arms, regimental badges and Battle Honours. $225 £105

A painted brass drum of The Royal Artillery, regimental badge, trophies, title and motto scrolls, by Potter, Aldershot. $335 £145

A painted white metal drum of The Rifle Brigade, regimental badge with Battle Honours and title scroll, stamped 'Potter', etc. '1936'. $600 £260

An 18th century Indian elephant goad Ankus, the blade overlaid with chiselled brass decoration, with figures, flowers and geometric patterns, the haft with chevron brass inlaid decoration, brass pommel, unscrews to reveal a square section dagger blade 7in. long, length overall 18in. $130 £55

A huge old Indian elephant goad Ankus, 27½in. overall, iron head with leaf-shaped spike, hook with bird's head scroll, turned wooden haft. $150 £75

An old Indian elephant goad Ankus, heavy blade 6in., reinforced point, curved blade with reinforced point, chiselled with foliage, metal haft with raised bands, copper gilt base mount in the form of an animal, overall 16in. $350 £170

An 18th or 19th century Japanese russet iron face-guard mempo, embossed ears, pointed chin, fluted cheeks, iron projections with ornamental mounts at sides of chin. Hair whiskers, 4 black lacquered laced throat guard plates.
$235 £100

A Japanese iron face-guard mempo, black lacquered exterior, red lacquered interior, with detachable nose, pierced ears, pointed chin, fluted cheeks with 2 hook like projections. Mouth lined by silvered copper teeth, 2 black lacquered laced throat guard plates. $485 £205

An embossed gun sized copper powder flask, 7½in. shell embossed body with 4 suspension rings common brass top stamped 'AM Flask & Cap Co.' $50 £22

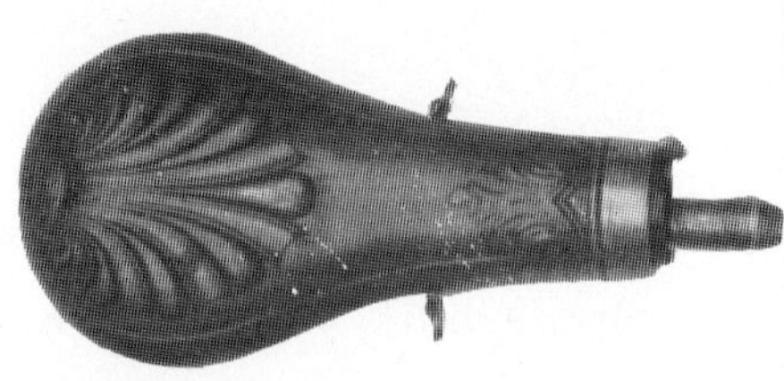

A shell embossed gun sized copper powder flask, 8in. shell and bush embossed with 2 hanging rings, brass top and charger. $70 £30

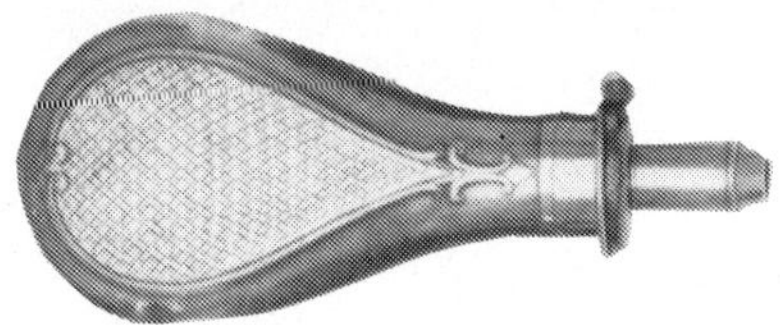

A copper powder flask 'Panel', brass common top charger unit marked 'G. & J. W. Hawksley'. $75 £34

A good copper powder flask 'Shell and Bush', brass charger unit by 'G. & J. W. Hawksley', 4 hanging rings. $80 £40

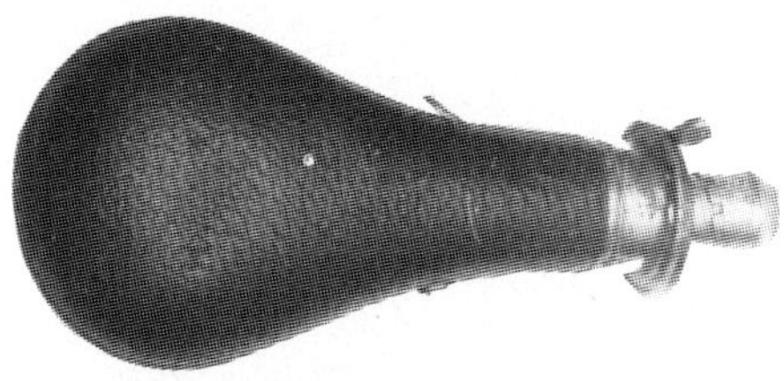

A gun sized leather covered powder flask, 8in. lacquered brass top stamped 'Patent', graduated charger from 3 to 4 drams, mirror blued spring. $85 £40

A copper pocket pistol flask 'Panel' brass charger unit. $90 £40

A cylindrical copper powder flask, 3¾in. overall, common brass top, fixed charger, base unscrews for filling. $95 £40

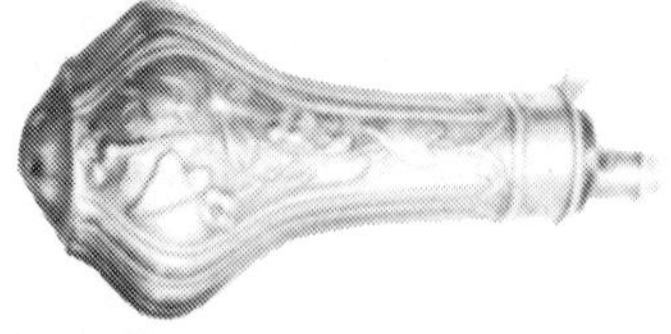

A pistol sized embossed copper powder flask, 5¼in. embossed with trumpet, flowers and devil's tail foliage, common brass top, graduated charger stamped 'Dixon'. $90 £42

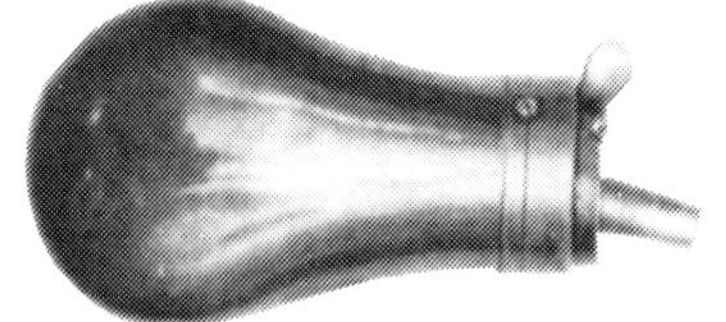

A small copper powder flask with sloping charger, 3½in., swollen body, brass top with sprung lever and sloping charger. $100 £42

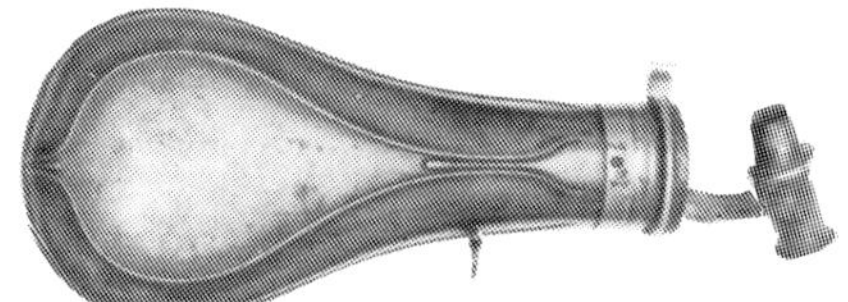

A French copper powder flask, simple panel design, fitted with Boche Patent hinged charger marked 'Boche a Paris'. $110 £45

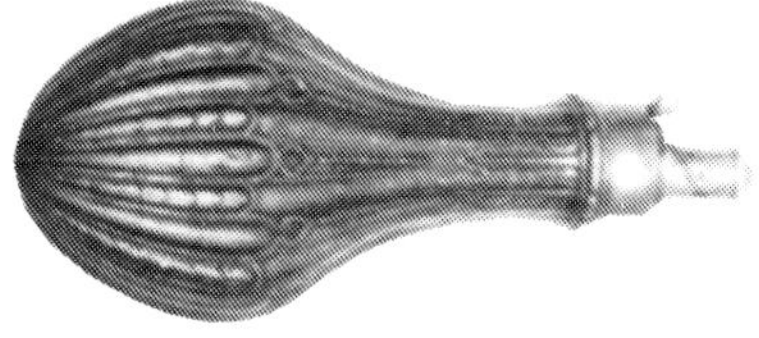

A gun sized fluted copper powder flask, common brass top, graduated charger from 2¼-3 drams, stamped G. & J. W. Hawksley. $110 £45

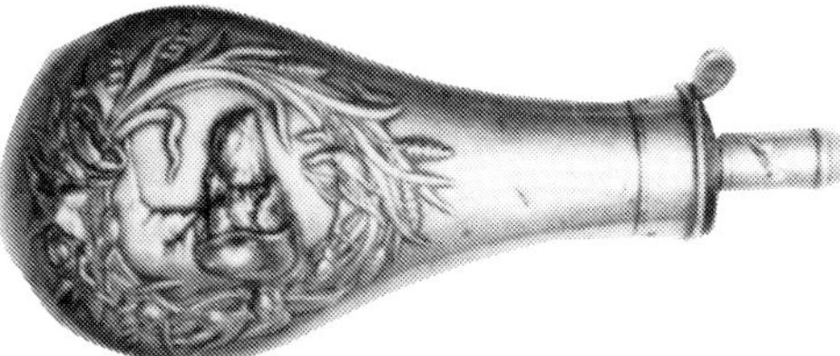

An embossed gun sized copper powder flask, 8in., body boldly embossed with dog's head within garland incorporating foliage, flowers and birds, brass common top stamped 'Dixon'. $110 £50

A copper bodied pistol sized 3-way powder flask, the common top with hinge lidded container for balls and the base with screw capped container for caps. $120 £50

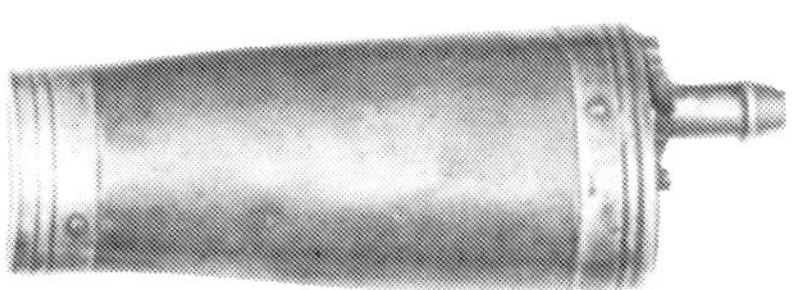

A copper 3-way powder flask, plain brass mounts, screw-on base plate, brass charger unit with hinged swivel lid, overall 5¼in. $120 £50

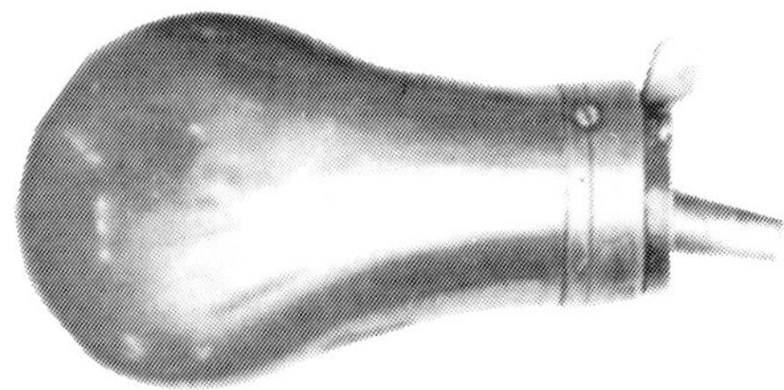

A small copper powder flask with sloping charger, 3½in., swollen body, brass top with sprung lever and sloping charger. $120 £50

A French copper powder flask 'Fluted', by 'B. A. Paris', 2 suspension rings, brass charger unit. $120 £50

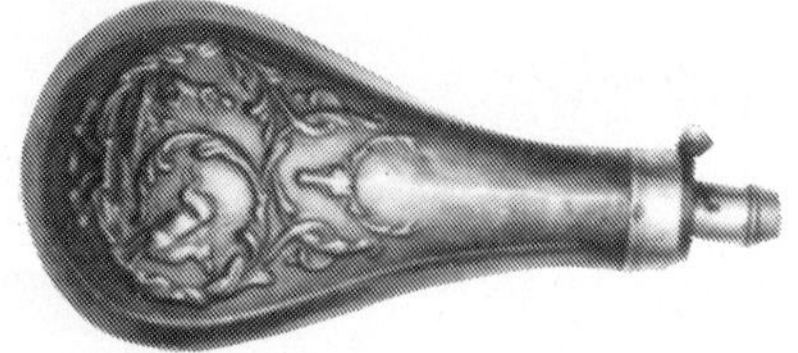

An embossed gun sized copper powder flask, with hunter, stag, stag's head and foliage, common brass top. $130 £55

An embossed gun sized copper powder flask, $7\frac{1}{2}$in., with 2 dogs pointing to a rising bird behind a tree, 2 hanging rings, common brass top. $130 £55

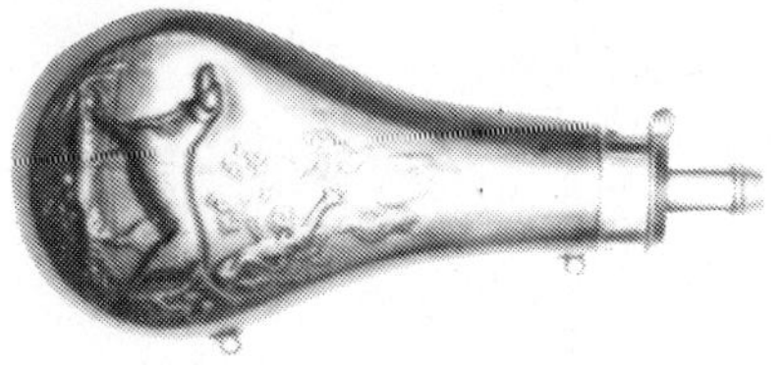

A gun sized copper powder flask, $7\frac{3}{4}$in., body embossed, common brass top with graduated charger, 2 hanging rings to right side only. $130 £55

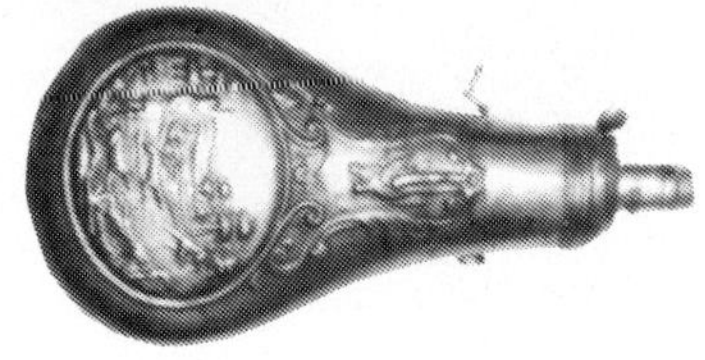

An embossed gun sized copper powder flask, 2 hanging rings, common brass top. $135 £55

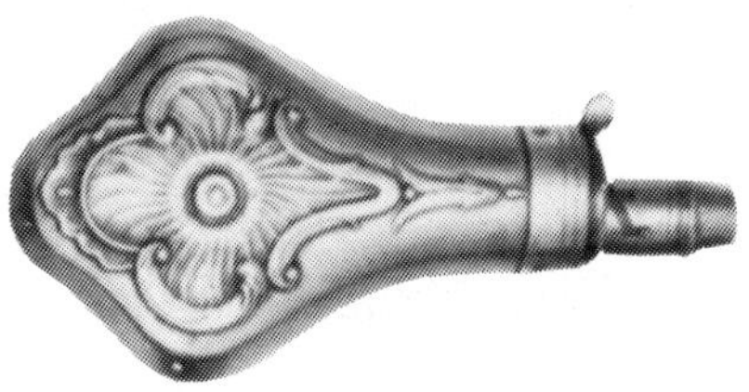

A copper powder flask, 'Panel', brass sprung charger unit, marked 'Dixon & Sons'. $135 £55

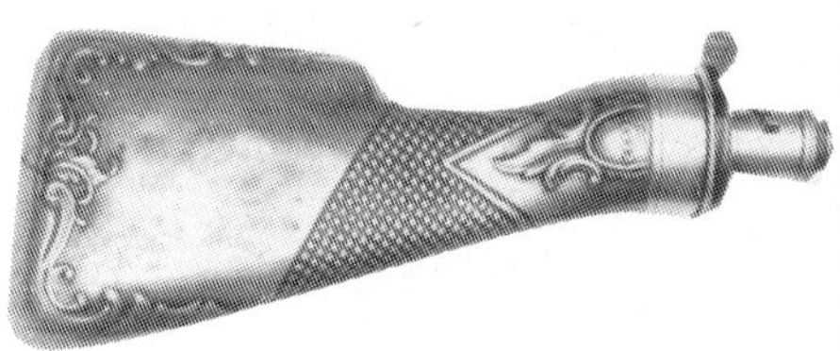

An original Dixon 'Gun-Stock' copper powder flask, $8\frac{1}{2}$in., brass top stamped 'James Dixon & Sons Sheffield', graduated charger $2\frac{1}{4}$ to 3 drams. $135 £60

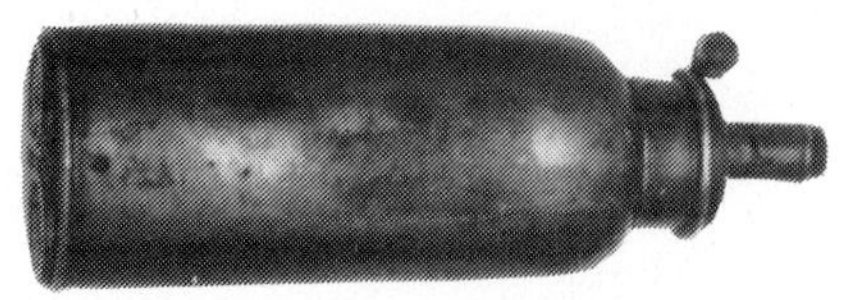

A good copper bodied patent topped 3-way pistol powder flask, graduated brass charger unit to 5/8 drams stamped 'James Dixon & Sons Sheffield'. $130 £60

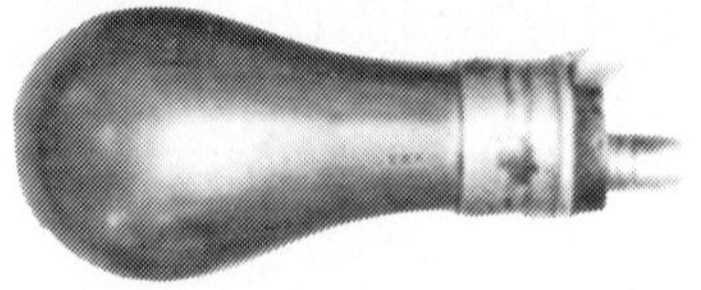

A small copper pocket pistol powder flask, 'Plain Flasks', marked 'Sykes' on body, brass screw top charger unit, overall length $2\frac{3}{4}$in. $140 £60

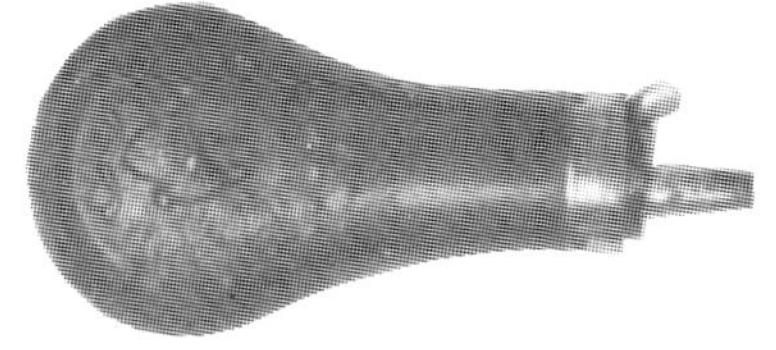

A U.S. copper pistol flask 'Eagle' with motto beneath Eagle 'E. Pluribus Unum', lacquered brass charger unit. $140 £60

A plain copper flattened oval 3-way pistol flask, lacquered brass mounts, and charger unit swivel cover to base compartment and top compartment body marked 'Sykes'. $145 £66

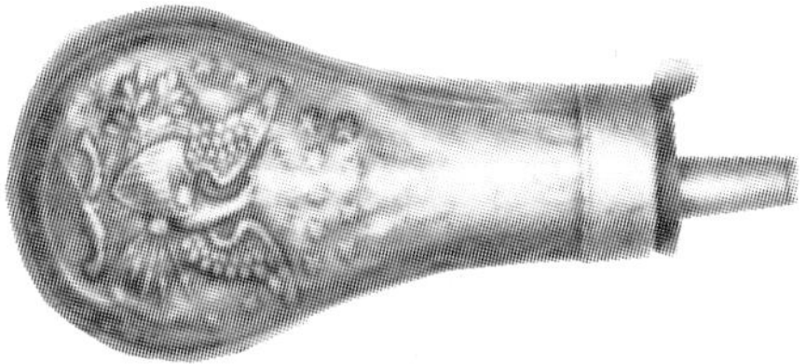

A Colt's Patent copper powder flask, 4¾in., embossed 'Colt's Patent, E. Pluribus Unum', brass sprung charger. $165 £68

A copper bodied French gun sized common topped powder flask, brass graduated charger unit, the body well embossed and with two suspension rings. $185 £75

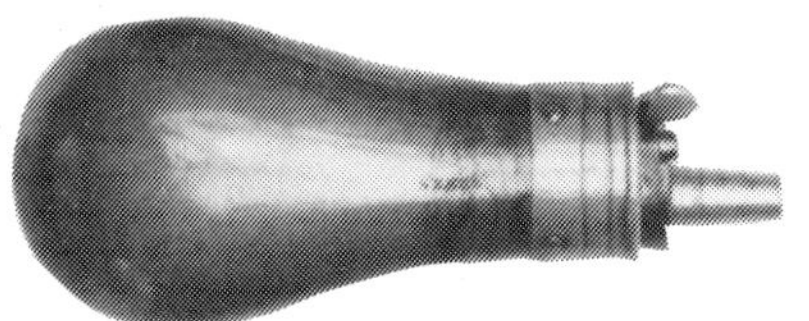

A small copper pocket pistol bag-shaped powder flask, stamped 'Sykes', brass universal pattern charger unit, length overall 3½in. $190 £80

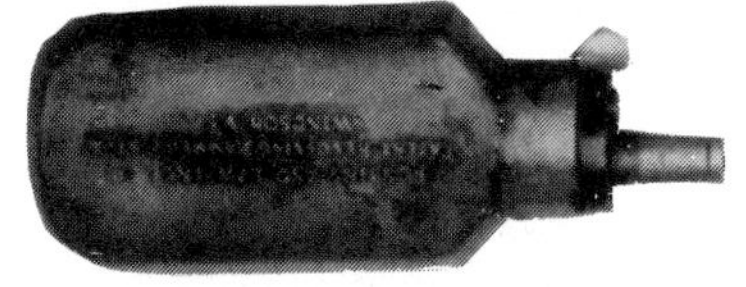

A copper bodied, common topped pistol powder flask for the Robbins & Lawrence pepperbox revolver, brass unadjustable charger unit. $184 £85

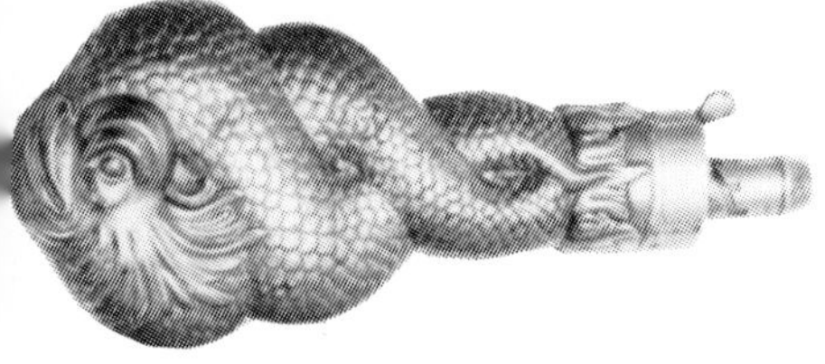

An embossed gun sized copper powder flask, 8in., body embossed as 'entwined dolphin', common brass top. $215 £105

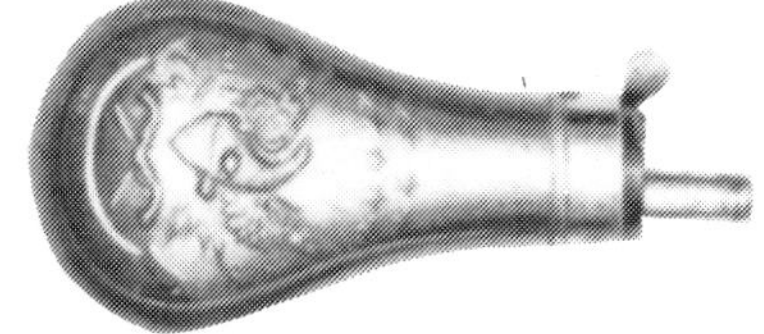

An American copper powder flask for Remingtons, 4in. overall, lacquered body embossed with U.S. eagle etc., common brass top, fixed charger. $250 £105

A very fine large copper gun flask by G. & J. W. Hawksley. Oak-leaf embossed pear-shaped body incorporating stag and fox head above and below. Four steel cord rings with green tassled cord attached. Brass graduated adjustable charger 2¼ to 3 drams external blued spring cut-off. $384 £160

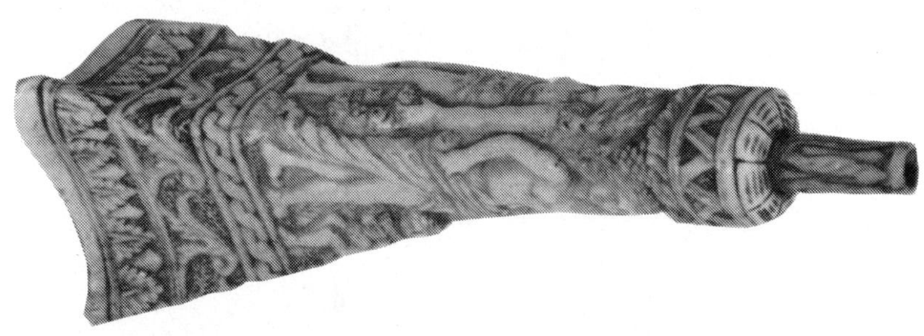

A 17th century German carved bone powder flask, the sides carved with the 'Three Graces' and a seated cherub playing pan pipes, within rustic background, foliate carving to triangular base, overall length 7½in. $635 £260

One of a rare pair of 19th century Indo-Persian chainmail gauntlets, made from butted rings of steel and brass formed to create a python-skin pattern of diamonds with dotted centres. $230 £120

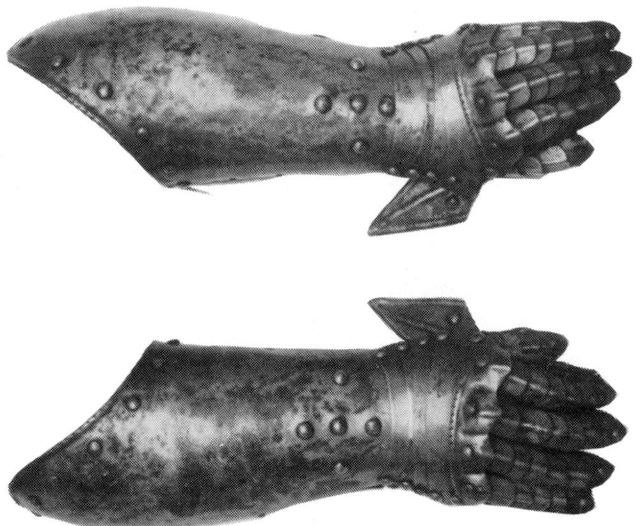

A pair of mid 17th century Cromwellian elbow gauntlets, fully articulated, with finger scales, separate thumbpiece, roped cuffs, and retaining much old wash leather lining. $430 £180

A Georgian officer's universal pattern copper gilt gorget. $130 £55

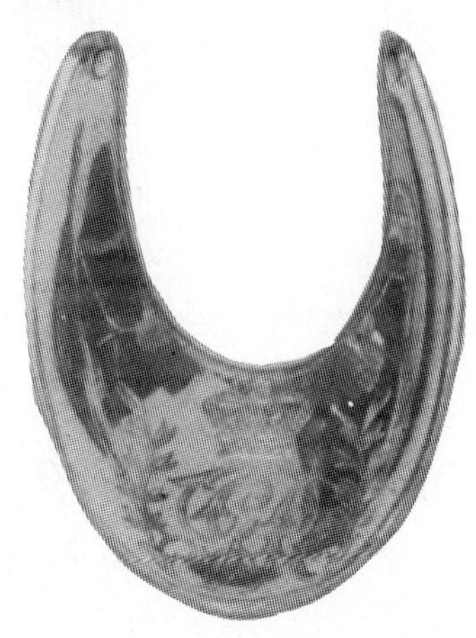

A Georgian officer's copper gilt universal pattern gorget. $110 £60

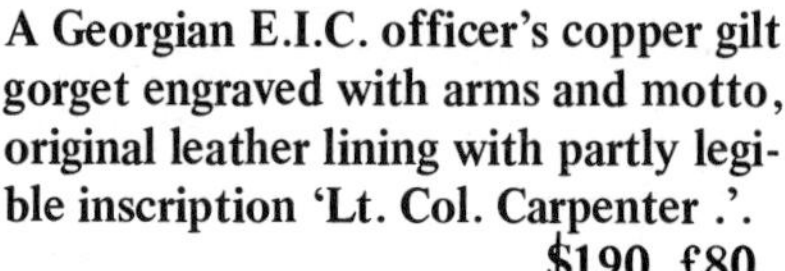

A Georgian E.I.C. officer's copper gilt gorget engraved with arms and motto, original leather lining with partly legible inscription 'Lt. Col. Carpenter .'. $190 £80

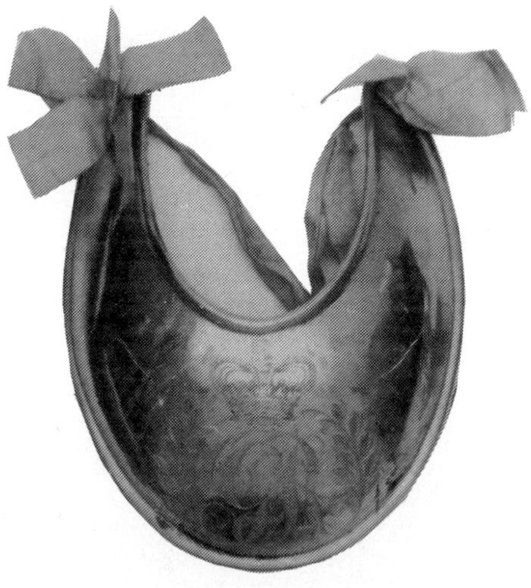

A Georgian officer's universal pattern copper gilt gorget engraved with crown and 'G.R.' within wreath, with its original chamois lining and yellow silk suspension loops. $215 £100

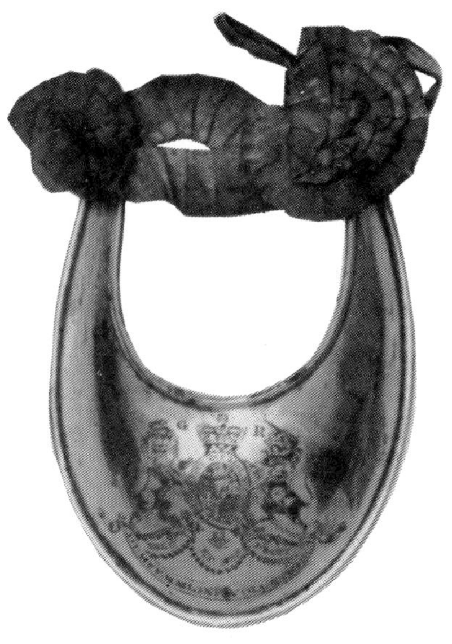

A Georgian officer's copper gilt gorget of The Dunfermline Volunteers, engraved with 1801-16 Royal Arms and title scroll, with original silk suspension and rosettes. $330 £130

An original Nazi S.A. gorget 'Brutschild der Kornett S.A.', of heart form, blue cloth lined with 2 lugs and central disc marked with large 'RZM', S.A. device on brass rayed star to front with hanging chain. $385 £160

A Georgian officer's copper gilt gorget of The Guernsey Royal Artillery. Engraved with the badge of the island and title scroll below. Complete with its original chamois lining and green tapes with one rosette. $700 £325

An officer's silver (not H.M.) gorget of The 10th (Prince of Wales's Own) Light Dragoons, circa 1785. Engraved with the pre-1801 Arms. The shoulders engraved with trophies of ancient arms and 'X P.W.O.' and 'Lt. Dgns'. $905 £420

An officer's gilt and silvered 1844 pattern shako grenade badge of The 7th (or Royal Fusiliers) , design silvered flames and Guelphic crown, gilt ball with wreath, garter and rose. $205 £85

A white metal busby plume-holder grenade badge of The Edinburgh City Artillery, with white horsehair plume. $183 £100

A white metal busby plum-holder grenade badge of The Midlothian Coast Artillery Vols., with white horse-hair plume. $220 £120

An officer's 1844 Albert pattern grenade badge of The Kilkenny Fusiliers, gilt ball and flames, silvered crown and harp within title circle on ball. $300 £145

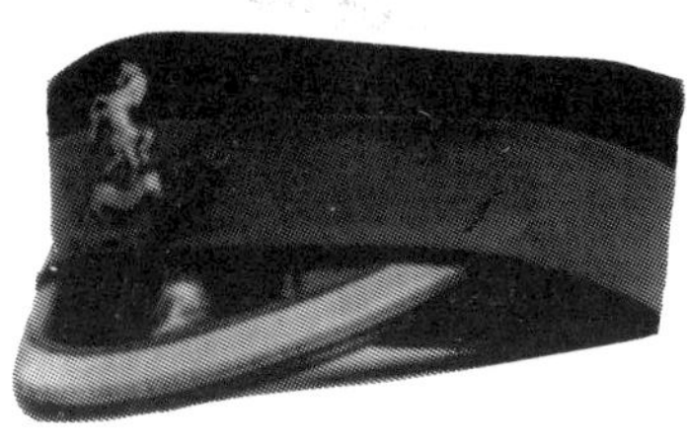

A Victorian officer's peaked forage cap of The Queen's Own Royal West Kent Regt., gilt lace trimmed peak, silvered and embroidered badge.
$115 £50

A Victorian officer's peaked forage cap of The Grenadier Guards, bullion wove gilt grenade badge, silver braided trim to peak, black braided band, patent leather chinstrap, quilted lining with gold maker's printed label of 'Dewsbury & Son, Newgate Street'.
$145 £60

A Bavarian Infantryman's 1915 pattern pickelhaube, grey metal helmet plate and mounts, both cockades, leather lining and chinstrap.
$125 £60

A Baden Artilleryman's 1915 pattern pickelhaube, grey metal helmet plate and mounts, both cockades, leather chinstrap, leather lining, neck guard dated '1916' and with soldier's name.
$135 £65

A Prussian Infantryman's pickelhaube, white metal helmet plate with 'Waterloo' scroll, white metal mounts, leather chinstrap, both cockades, leather lining, neck guard stamped 'R.B.A. 18'. $160 £75

An Imperial Austrian officer's shako, gilt Imperial eagle helmet plate. Patent leather crown, broad bullion cloth band with black cloth covering beneath, braided peak, bullion wire wove cockade with 'F.J.I.' cypher, patent leather chinstrap, original lining. $150 £80

A trooper's busby of the Middlesex Yeomanry, green cloth bag with yellow braid trim, green over crimson horsehair plume in brass holder, leather chinstrap and provision for chinchain. $185 £90

A post-1908 officer's blue cloth ball-topped helmet of the Territorial Artillery, gilt mounts, badge with wreath scroll and velvet backed chin-chain. $185 £90

A cabaset, circa 1600, skull formed in one piece with pear stalk finial, integral brim turned over at border, struck with arsenal mark. $195 £90

A Nazi Panzer NCO's peaked service cap, grey green crown with dark green band, pink piping, metal cap, eagle and cockade, patent leather chinstrap and peak, leather sweat band stamped with maker's stamp, 'Arnstadl' and date '1938'. $200 £90

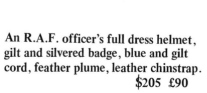

An R.A.F. officer's full dress helmet, gilt and silvered badge, blue and gilt cord, feather plume, leather chinstrap. $205 £90

A post-1902 other rank's shako of The Highland Light Infantry, complete with dark green ball tuft, leather chinstrap, date inside '1912'. $215 £90

A Middle-Eastern Military helmet, circa 1850, steel skull and neck guard, brass bound with adjustable nasal bar in form of arrow with brass flights, steel crescent crest, brass chinchains, star-shaped rosettes, leather lining, brass mail neck guard. $205 £100

A Guard Schutzen NCO's shako, black patent leather, silvered Guard Star helmet plate, one metal cockade, leather chinstrap with plated mounts, silver bullion wire cockade with green cloth centre, original leather and silk lining. $220 £100

A Nazi 1st pattern (Allgemeine) S.S. man's peaked cap, black with white piping to crown, original plate metal cap eagle and death's head badges, leather chinstrap, patent leather peak. $220 £100

A Prussian Infantry officer's pickelhaube, gilt helmet plate, chinscales and mounts, both cockades, leather and silk lining. $215 £100

A Victorian officer's blue cloth spiked helmet of the 2nd Vol. Bn. The North Staffs Regt., silvered mounts, badge and velvet backed chinchain. $245 £100

A cabaset, circa 1600, skull formed in one piece with pear stalk finial, integral brim turned over at border, struck with arsenal mark. $215 £100

A Bavarian Police officer's shako of the period of the Weimar Republic, plated shield helmet plate, bordered with oak-leaf sprays, dark green cloth covered body with patent leather crown and peaks, metal cockade, plated chinscales, green feather side-plume, original silk lining. $230 £100

A post-1902 Royal Artillery Territorial officer's blue cloth ball-topped helmet, gilt badge and mounts, fawn leather backed chinchain, in tin case with painted name 'L.C.L. Moore, RFA'. $250 £105

A scarce kepi type shako of The Inns of Court Rifle Vols., beige cloth buff braid headband and top ornament, bronze badge on scarlet 'ICRV' with wreath over motto scroll, patent leather peak and chinstrap. $250 £105

An R.A.F. officer's full dress parade helmet, leather skull, fur trimmings, white and gilt cord, gilt and silvered badge, lilac feather plume, leather chinstrap, in a tin case. $250 £105

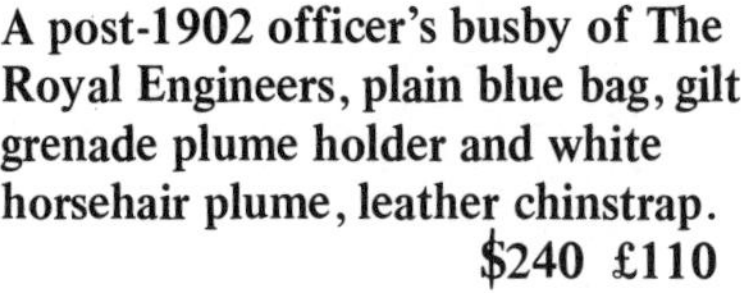

A post-1902 officer's busby of The Royal Engineers, plain blue bag, gilt grenade plume holder and white horsehair plume, leather chinstrap. $240 £110

A Victorian officer's blue cloth spiked helmet of The Army Ordnance Corps, gilt mounts and velvet back chinchain, gilt and silvered badge, in a tin case. $255 £115

A Prussian customs officer's pickelhaube, circa 1900, gilt helmet plate with white metal crowned 'W' cypher, lacquered brass chinscales, fluted spike and mounts, original leather lining, in its black cloth covered conical carrying case. $265 £120

An officer's shako of The South Middlesex Rifle Volunteers, dark grey cloth, scarlet headband with 2 bands silver lace, silver piping to crown, white metal badge, red ball tuft in white metal holder, leather chinstrap. $280 £120

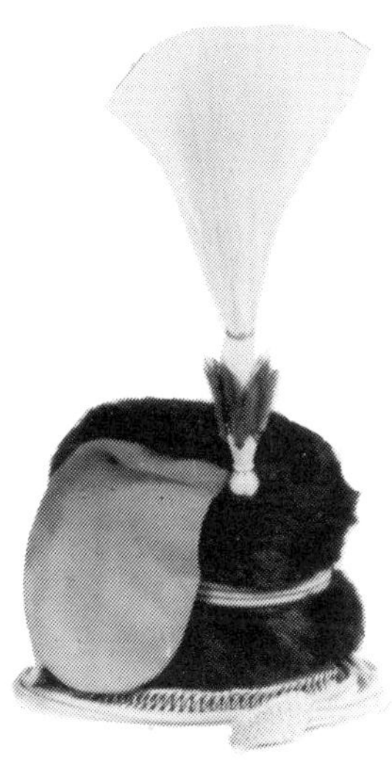

An officer's busby of The Royal Devon Yeomanry, plain scarlet bag, no cockade, silvered cap lines and velvet backed chinchain, white over red plume in holder, in its tin case. $290 £125

A late 19th century French officer's kepi of a 'General De Brigade', red crown with bullion frogging, dark blue band with bullion thread wove foliate pattern, patent leather peak, silk lining with stitched trade label of 'Abrahamiantz Teheran', in its original wooden box. $280 £125

An Indian Army officer's helmet, silvered skull, leaf mount and spike, lion ear bosses, bands with linked circles pattern, and badge of lion's head within wreath, red leather backed chinchain. $270 £130

A Victorian officer's blue cloth helmet of The Royal Military Academy, gilt helmet plate with enamelled centre, gilt spike and mounts, brass velvet backed chinchain. $275 £130

A Prussian Infantry officer's pickel-haube, gilt helmet plate, chinscales and mounts, both cockades, leather and silk lining. $255 £135

A Victorian officer's blue cloth ball-topped helmet of The South Irish Division, Artillery Militia, gilt mounts, badge and velvet backed chinchain. $320 £135

A Victorian Vol. Artillery officer's blue cloth ball-topped helmet, silvered mounts, universal badge and velvet backed chinchain, in its tin case. $320 £140

A post-1902 officer's blue cloth spiked helmet of the 1st Vol. Bn. The Middlesex Regt., silvered badge, mounts and velvet backed chinchain. $335 £140

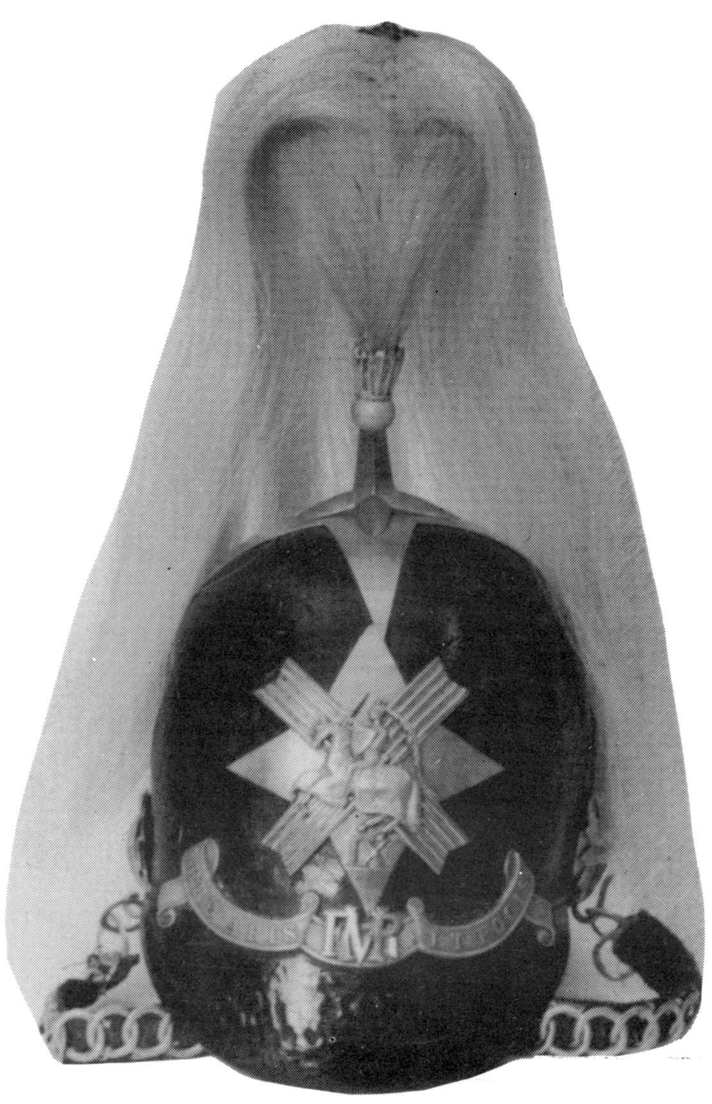

An officer's helmet of the Fife Mounted Rifles, patent leather skull and peak, gilt and silvered badge, motto and title scroll, star mounts and velvet backed chinchain with ear bosses, white horsehair plume in white metal holder, silk lining. $360 £150

A Victorian Lancer officer's foul weather lance-cap, black patent leather skull, top and false rosette, gilt peak binding, beaded-link leather backed chinchain and lion bosses. $365 £155

A Victorian officer's blue cloth spiked helmet of the 1st Vol. Bn. The West Yorks Regt, silvered mounts and badge, white metal leather backed chinchain. $365 £155

An officer's busby of The 8th Kings (Royal Irish) Hussars, scarlet bag, gilt cockade and cap lines, velvet backed beaded link chinchain, 13in. white over red feather plume with holder, in its linen bag and tin case. $370 £160

A post-1902 officer's blue cloth spiked helmet of The South Wales Borderers, gilt mounts and velvet backed chinchain, gilt and silvered badge. $385 £160

A Prussian Infantry officer's pickelhaube, gilt metal helmet plate, chinscales and mounts, both cockades, original leather and silk lining. $390 £160

A cabaset, circa 1600, formed in one piece, pear stalk finial to crown, (rosettes missing). $365 £165

A Victorian Rifle Volunteer officer's dark grey cloth helmet of The South Middlesex Rifle Volunteers, blackened finish to white metal Maltese Cross helmet plate and mounts. $400 £170

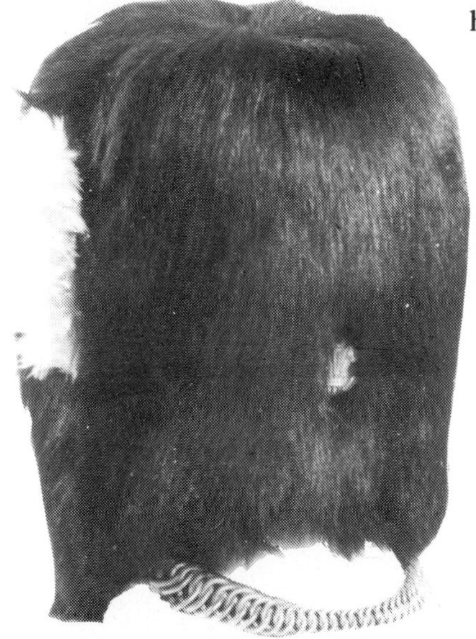

An officer's racoon skin cap of The Royal Welsh Fusiliers, gilt and silvered grenade badge, leather backed graduated link chinchain, white feather side-plume. $400 £175

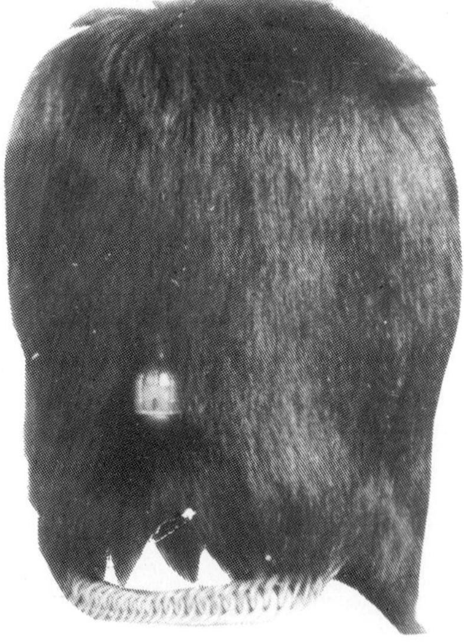

An officer's racoon skin cap of The Inniskilling Fusiliers, gilt and silvered grenade badge, leather backed graduated link chinchain. $400 £170

A Prussian Reservist Infantry officer's pickelhaube, gilt helmet plate with Landwehr Cross, gilt chinscales and mounts, both cockades, original silk and leather lining with blindstamp of Maker. $400 £175

A Bavarian Infantry officer's pickelhaube, gilt helmet plate, brass chinscales, fluted spike and mounts, both cockades, original leather and silk lining, part of paper trade label of 'Awes Marke'. $415 £180

A Prussian Infantry officer's pickelhaube, gilt helmet plate, brass chinscales and mounts, unusually long spike, both cockades, original silk and leather lining. $415 £180

An officer's white cloth spiked tropical helmet of The Royal Welsh Fusiliers, circa 1890, gilt and silvered grenade badge, copper spike, linen backed chinchain. $370 £180

A Victorian officer's grey cloth spiked helmet of The Hants. Rifle Volunteers, white metal badge and mounts including velvet backed chinchain. $430 £180

An Irish Guards officer's bearskin, leather backed, graduated link chinchain, blue feather plume, in its tin case. $400 £180

A Victorian officer's helmet of the 1st Oxfordshire Light Horse Volunteers, black felt with leather front peak, white metal peak binding, simulated chain-link ear to ear band, badge of crown and '1 OLH' cypher and motto 'Fortis est Veritas', white metal comb, velvet backed chinchain and lion bosses, small scarlet 'shaving brush' plume in holder, scarlet falling back plume. $350 £185

A Regency style shako, probably made for a Marshal of the City of London at the Coronation of Edward VII, grey cloth body, leather top and peak, silver lace top band and peak embroidery, gilt cord rosette, gilt chinscales with silvered City Arms ear rosettes, maker's label of the London branch of Ranken & Co. $400 £210

An Indo-Persian turban helmet of plated copper, the surface engraved with foliage, with camail of riveted links. $495 £210

A Bavarian Infantry officer's pickelhaube, silvered helmet plate, chinscales, fluted spike and mounts, both cockades, original leather and silk lining. $585 £240

A Victorian officer's leather helmet of The 9th Fife Mounted Rifles, white metal and gilt mounts, velvet backed chinchain, white horsehair plume. $525 £250

A Prussian Infantry officer's parade helmet, gilt helmet plate, chinscales and mounts, both cockades and with tail spike with drooping black hair parade plume. $600 £260

A scarce Saxony 1867 pattern Heavy Cavalry trooper's Raupen helmet, patent black leather skull with brass framed comb and green wool crest, brass strip mounts to sides. Badge in brass and white metal, plain brass leather lined chin-scales, single cockade, original leather lining, the inside of neck guard stamped 'M.D.' and blindstamped 'K.P. RES R.R. 78'. $600 £260

An Imperial Austrian Dragoon officer's metal helmet, circa 1840, large gilt comb, the side panels embossed with lion attacking snake, laurel sprays to comb, plume slot, maker at base 'Kirzlinger in Wien', gilt helmet plate with 'F.J.' cypher, scallop edging decoration to helmet plate, lion's mask chin-scale brass mounts, original leather lining and chinstrap. $650 £280

An Imperial German officer's busby (Pelzmutze) of the 2nd (Queen Victoria of Prussia) Hussars, plated 'Death's Head' helmet plate, gilt chinscales, silver bullion wire cockade with black centre, white busby bag, silver bullion cap lines taken up at back, leather and white silk lining. $650 £300

An Imperial German other rank's busby (Pelzmutze) of the 17th Hussars, white metal skull and crossbones helmet plate, brass scroll with Battle Honours 'Peninsula, Sicilien, Waterloo, Mars la Tour', brass chinscales, state cockade, scarlet busby bag, blue and yellow cloth cockade, leather lining. $650 £300

A French Chasseurs a Cheval helmet, circa 1900, steel skull, brass mounts, leather backed chinscales and comb with Medusa finial, white metal French bugle badge on ear to ear brass rayed plate, black horsehair neck plume, scarlet side plume. $690 £300

An officer's 1844 Albert pattern shako, stated to be Officer-Surgeon, small crowned star badge bearing cypher within garter, gilt, rope-link, velvet backed chinchain and ear rosettes, white ball tuft in gilt holder. $720 £300

A French Mounted Gendarmerie helmet, circa 1900, brass skull, with white metal mounts, badge and leather backed chinscales, black horsehair 'brush' and neck plume. $715 £310

An officer's 1861 pattern 'quilted' shako of The 41st (Welsh) Regt, single line of gilt lace to top for Major, white over red ball tuft (no holder). $720 £310

An officer's 1847 Albert pattern helmet of The 4th (Royal Irish) Dragoon Guards, copper gilt skull, mounts and velvet backed chinchain, horsehair plume with rosette. $720 £310

A Victorian officer's helmet of The Hertfordshire Yeomanry, silvered skull, gilt mounts, gilt and silvered badge, grey horsehair plume. $720 £310

A white metal helmet with brass mounts, leather backed chinchain, scarlet horsehair plume, from a complete sergeant's full dress uniform of The Duke of Lanc. Own Yeomanry. $735 £320

A Belgian Cuirassier's helmet, white metal skull, comb with white metal grenade finial, shaving brush top plume, horsehair neck plume. $750 £320

A Victorian Albert pattern helmet of The Royal Berkshire Yeomanry Cavalry, Hungerford Troop, black japanned skull, white horsehair plume. $755 £320

A Bavarian Schwere Reiter (Heavy Cavalry) officer's pickelhaube, silvered helmet plate and spike base, with drooping white hair plume. $780 £340

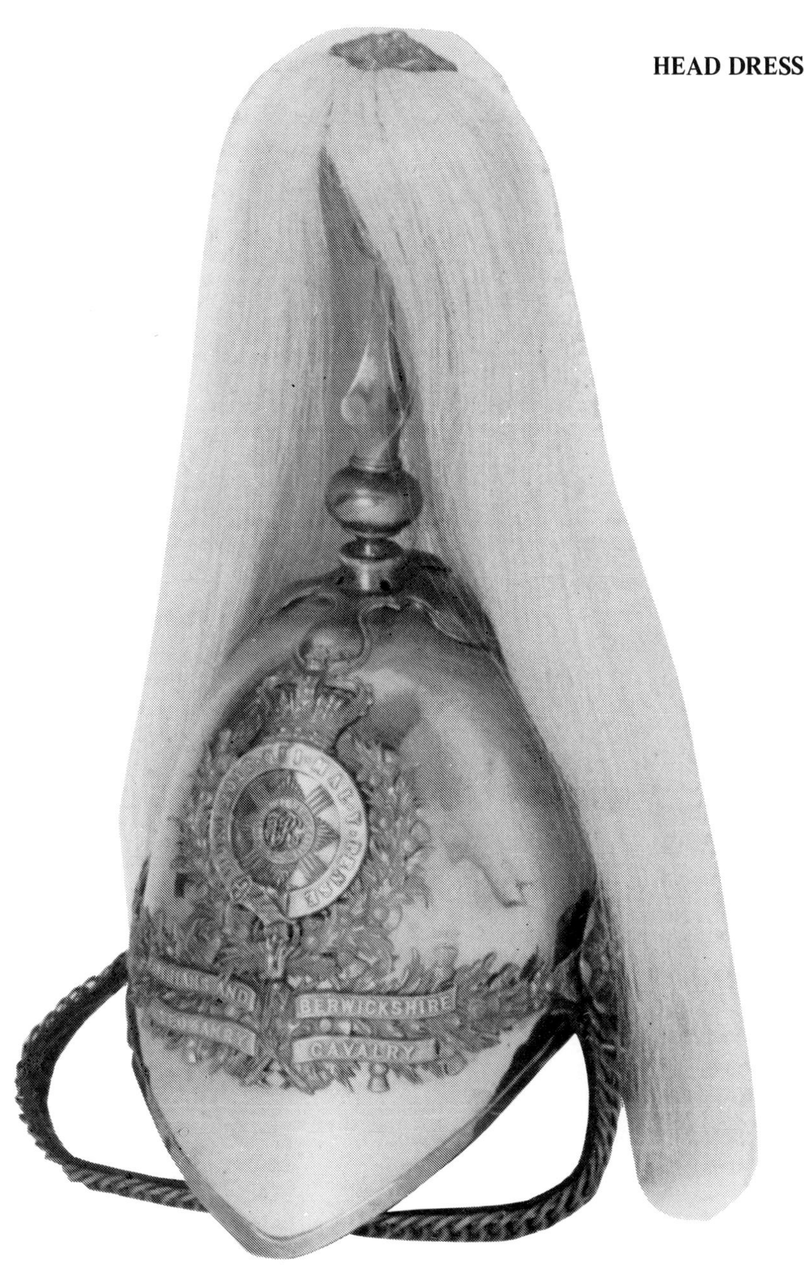

A Victorian officer's helmet of the Lothians and Berwickshire Yeomanry Cavalry, white metal skull with gilt binding and mounts, large gilt and silvered badge, leather backed chinchain, white horsehair plume with gilt rosette. $645 £340

A Bavarian Heavy Cavalry trooper's 'Raupenhelm', circa 1860, leather skull, plated, crowned shield helmet plate, bordered with foliate spray, plated chinscales secured with lion's mask bosses, plate, fluted comb with black hair plume, Bavarian cockade to left of domed skull, original leather lining.
$780 £340

A Belgian Cuirassier's helmet, white metal skull, brass mounts and large lion's head badge, comb with white metal grenade finial, leather backed single piece chinscales with grenade ear bosses, 'shaving brush' top plume, horsehair neck plume. $830 £360

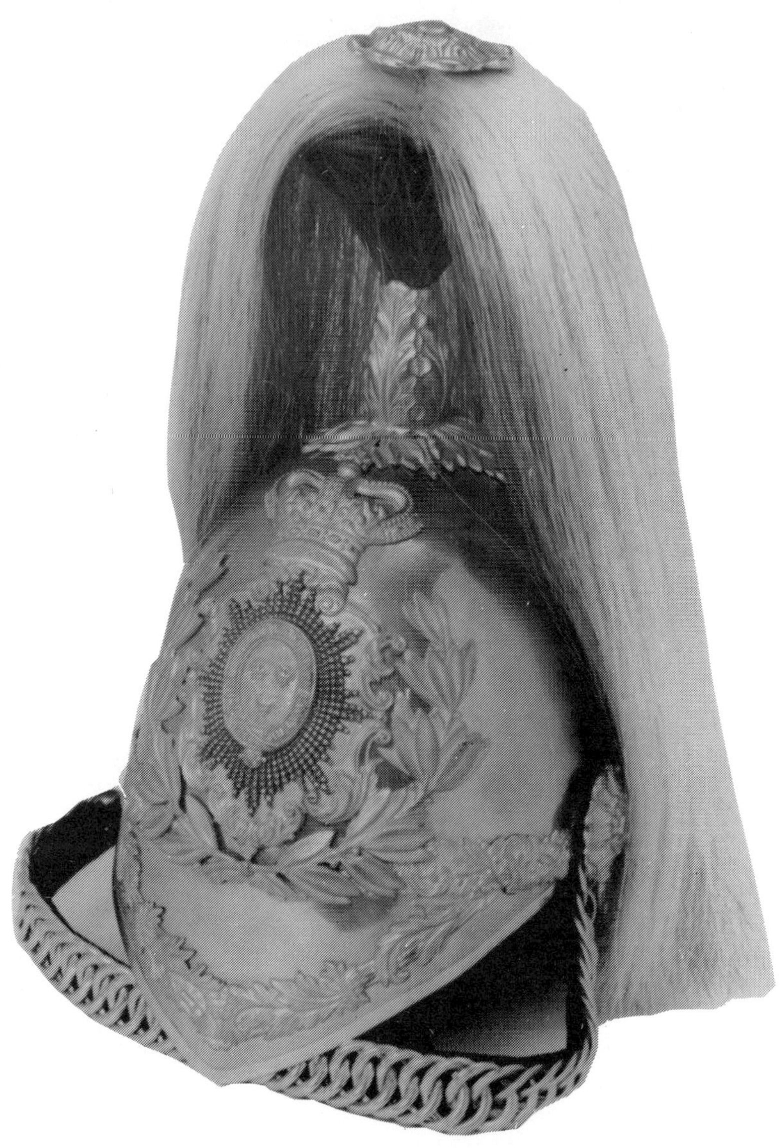

A Victorian officer's white metal helmet of The Shropshire Yeomanry Cavalry, circa 1875, comprising: acanthus plume holder, large crowned laurel wreath with rococo shield in centre bearing a hob-nailed silver star with the regimental device of three leopard heads within garter inscribed with title. Gilt foliage strips to front and back peaks, rose ear bosses and ring scaled chinchain. $780 £360

A Victorian officer's helmet of The Suffolk Yeomanry, circa 1865, leather skull and peaks, gilt peak binding, mounts including embossed plume holder mount, badge of crowned escutcheon bearing 'VR' over 'Suffolk' scroll, velvet backed chinchain with lion ear bosses, red horsehair plume. $750 £365

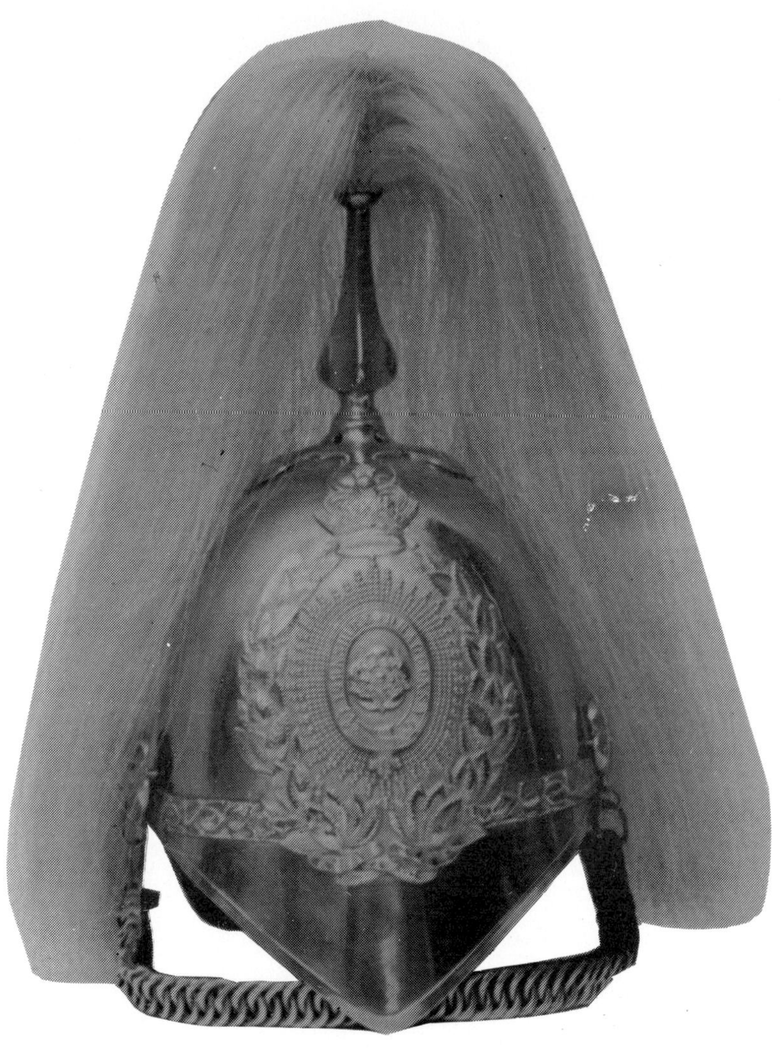

A Victorian officer's 1871 pattern helmet of The Yorkshire Dragoons, white metal skull and mounts including velvet backed chinchain, white horsehair plume and rosette, leather lining. $960 £400

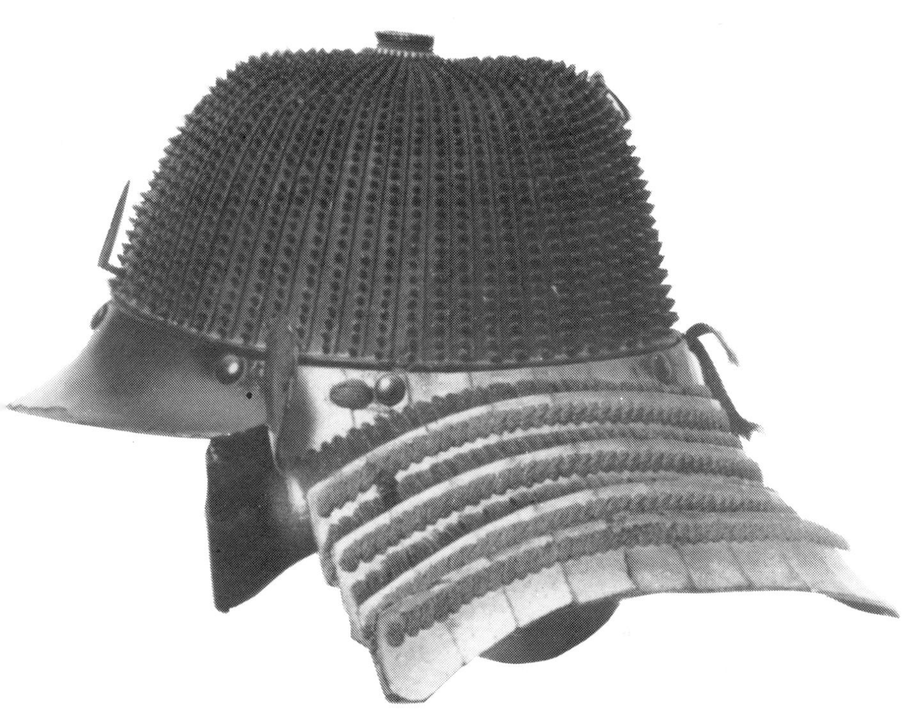

A Japanese helmet kabuto, 64 plate riveted hashi, mumei, gilt tehen and kasa-jiruchi no kuwan. Gilt lacquered blue laced shikoro and fuki gayeshi, black lacquered peak, fabric lining. $885 £410

A Victorian officer's helmet of the Lothians and Berwickshire Yeomanry Cavalry, white metal skull, gilt mounts and badge with silvered garter and title scrolls, chinchain, horsehair plume. $1,100 £450

A Victorian officer's black japanned helmet of The Duke of Lancaster's Own Yeomanry, circa 1865, fine gilt badge of crowned escutcheon bearing three lions, within wreath, gilt mounts including black leather backed chinchain, silk lining, white upright hair plume in gilt foliate mount with falling white hair plume with gilt rose finial. Interior painted green. $1,100 £450

A Cuirassier's helmet, burgonet, circa 1580, probably made for a German City Guard. One-piece skull with four radial bands meeting at raised finial. Peak and pierced ear flaps with turned over roped borders. Original hinged ear flaps with leather securing loops. $995 £460

An officer's shako of The Royal Buckinghamshire Yeomanry, similar style to the 1855 French pattern Infantry shako, beaver body, leather peak with white metal binding, leather top, broad band of silvered lace, white metal Maltese Cross badge with 'VR' in centre, leather backed chinchain, red and white horsehair plume in white metal holder. $1,130 £470

An officer's silvered helmet of The 2nd County of London Imperial Yeomanry, 1902 pattern, brass mounts, large brass star badge with white metal central device with crowned garter and title of regiment below. Gilt numeral '2' in centre and 'I.Y.' at base, leather lining, purple falling plume with rose finial.
$1,130 £475

An officer's 1844 Albert pattern shako of The 94th Regiment, gilt badge, roped, graduated link, velvet backed chinchain and ear rosettes, dark green wool ball tuft. $1,125 £490

A Bavarian Cuirassier trooper's helmet 'Raupenhelm', circa 1865, steel skull, brass comb with narrow front panel embossed with crowned 'L', brass chin-scales and lion's mask bosses, black hair plume, small cockade to left of skull, 'lobster tail' neck guard with brass mounts, skull stamped at right below lion mask '453.2.CR.3E'. $1,150 £500

An 1847 Albert pattern helmet of The 4th (Royal Irish) Dragoon Guards, gilt skull, mounts, badge with silvered cut star, and velvet backed chinchain, white plume with rosette. $1,220 £500

A Victorian officer's rare black leather helmet of The Norfolk Artillery, circa 1870, silvered mounts including large crowned ornamental badge bearing gilt devices of arms of Norfolk within strap containing title and crossed cannon barrels below. Rose ear bosses and black velvet backed chinchain, fluted plume mount, supporting white over red hair plume. $1,200 £500

A Victorian officer's 1871 pattern helmet of The 4th (Royal Irish) Dragoon Guards, copper gilt skull bearing silver hob-nailed star with enamelled regimental device, white horsehair plume. $1,120 £520

A Czapka of Napoleon's Blue Lancer Regiment, mortar board top, ribbed blue cloth to sides, large brass rayed badge plate with crowned 'N' to centre. Brass bound peak, lion head ear bosses. Silver bullion festoon and flounders. Small red, white and blue feather plume. $1,125 £520

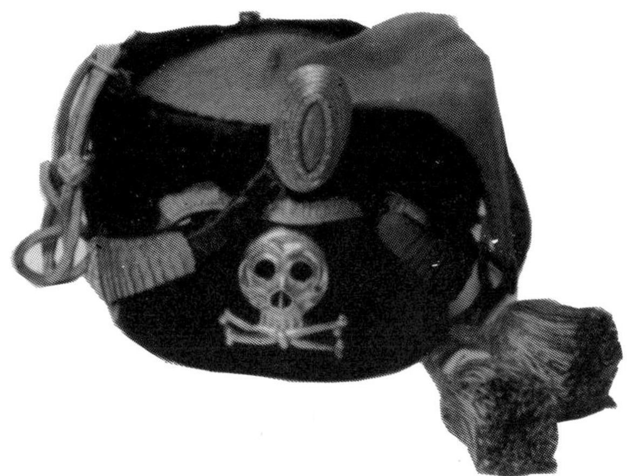

An Imperial German officer's busby (Pelzmutze) of the 17th Brunswick Hussars, plated skull and crossbones helmet plate with gilt metal scroll above with Battle Honours 'Peninsula, Sicilien, Waterloo, Mars la Tour', gilt chin-scales with lion mask bosses, large metal state cockade, gilt bullion wire cockade with blue centre, scarlet busby bag, silver bullion cap lines and tassels. $1,125 £520

An officer's 1844 pattern Albert shako of The 36th (Herefordshire) Regt., gilt badge, velvet backed, beaded, graduated link chinchain, white over red ball tuft (no holder). $1,390 £570

An officer's scarce silvered helmet of The Royal Berkshire Yeomanry Cavalry, circa 1875. Gilt mounts including large hobnailed star bearing silver strap device with regimental title and gilt star and crescent to centre. Rosette ear bosses, velvet lined chinchain. Upright white hair plume, supporting white falling hair plume with gilt finial from gilt acanthus mount, quilted cloth lining.

$1,375 £570

A Victorian officer's helmet of The King's Dragoon Guards, gilt skull and mounts including red leather backed chinchain, gilt, silver (not hallmarked) and enamel badge, with an associated red plume, in its chamois cover and tin case with name plaque. $1,465 £600

A French Napoleonic (1st Empire) period shako of The 23rd Regiment, felt body, leather top, peak, headband and diagonal sidepieces, brass eagle badge with cut-out '23', red, white and blue rosette, brass lion boss cord hooks at top, red horsehair plume. $1,440 £625

A Japanese helmet kabuto, bowl of 62 plates black painted with protruding rivet heads. Black lacquered peak, red lacquered underneath 5 lame laced neck guard, original fabric lining, together with its matching cuirass. $1,500 £625

A French Napoleonic period other rank's shako of The 8th Regt. of Infantry, black felt body, tooled leather peak, leather top, brass diamond shaped badge stamped with crowned eagle over '8', white, red and blue rosette, leather backed, tinned chinscales with stamped grenade ear bosses, scarlet plaited cords and flounders, complete with large red wool ball tuft and short plume.
$1,235 £650

An officer's helmet of The 3rd (Prince of Wales's) Dragoon Guards, gilt skull, gilt, silvered and enamel badge, red leather backed chinchain, ear rosettes, black and red horsehair plume with gilt rosette, silk lining. $1,280 £675

A Victorian officer's 1871 pattern helmet of The King's Dragoon Guards, gilt skull, gilt, silvered and enamel badge, red leather backed chinchain, complete with its red horsehair plume and gilt rosette, name inside 'Williams' (served in the Boer War, Maj. 14.06.06.) $1,620 £675

A George V officer's silvered helmet of The Derbyshire Yeomanry, circa 1911. Gilt mounts including large crowned 'G.V.R.' cypher badge, large rose ear bosses, scarlet leather lined chinchain, acanthus plume mount with upright red plume supporting a falling white over red plume with gilt rose finial. Grey cloth lining. $1,680 £700

A post-1902 officer's lance-cap of The 9th (Queen's Royal) Lancers, gilt mounts including velvet backed, beaded link chinchain, gilt and silvered badge, black over white feather plume in gilt holder, gilt cap lines, in its tin case with painted 'E. R. Pettit, 9th Lancers'. $1,730 £720

An officer's helmet of The 3rd (Prince of Wales's) Dragoon Guards, gilt skull and mounts, gilt silvered and enamel badge, red leather backed chin-chain, black over red horsehair plume and gilt rosette with wooden 'tree' inside to maintain shape. $1,730 £725

A Georgian metal helmet of The Blandford Volunteer Cavalry, circa 1820. Brass fittings comprise high thin crest supporting falling black horsehair plume, acanthus leaf sprays to sides, large rayed badge bearing post-1816 Royal Arms with regimental title. Lion head ear bosses, plain chinscales.

$1,835 £850

A Victorian officer's lance-cap of The 21st (Empress of India's) Lancers, French blue cloth top, gilt lace mounts and velvet backed chinchain, gilt and silvered badge. $2,040 £850

An officer's Regency style shako of The Yorkshire Dragoons, felt body, leather top and peak, silver lace top band with black rosette and plain button in front, silvered rose badge, chinscales and ear rosettes, black horsehair drooping plume in silvered holder. $2,115 £920

An officer's rare lance-cap of The 12th (Prince of Wales's Royal) Lancers, circa 1856. Black patent leather skull and peak with gilt lace and embroidery, scarlet cloth top measuring 7½in. square, with gilt cord trimmings, good gilt and silvered badge incorporating Battle Honours for 'Egypt, Peninsula, Waterloo and Sevastopol but without South Africa 1851-52-53'. Embroidered boss with 'V.R.', slide behind boss for plume entering through the top. Velvet backed, gilt chinchain and lion head bosses. $2,275 £950

A Household Cavalry helmet, 1814-16, black japanned skull, gilt peak binding, copper gilt ear to ear plate with scallop-shell border, bearing crown and reversed interlaced 'G.R.' cypher, copper gilt ornamental comb with Medusa head finial, gilt leaf holder for sideplume. $1,900 £1,000

A Georgian Yeomanry Tarleton helmet, leather skull, plated peak binding and headband, green turban, plain brass badge comprising 'G.R.' cypher, bearskin fur crest, white over red sideplume. $2,400 £1,000

A Japanese helmet kabuto, 18 plate steel skull with copper gilt pierced plates embossed with flowers and foliage. Silver rimmed peak with copper gilt head of dog of Fo bearing brass kuwagata (restored), 3 black lacquered neck lames, recurving fukigayeshi at front with silver flower heads attached. Original fabric lining. $2,460 £1,025

A helmet, circa 1865, of the 1st Troop of Yeomanry Cavalry, London Canada West, white metal skull, brass binding, oak-leaf head and back bands, 'Albert' type plume mount, badge of crowned 'V.R.' over escutcheon bearing beaver, '1 London CW', within maple wreath and trophies, motto scroll 'Semper paratus' ear rosettes, black horsehair plume and large rosette, leather lining.

$2,420 £1,100

A Victorian officer's black japanned transition helmet of The Denbighshire Yeomanry, circa 1850, silvered badge and mounts comprise: large rayed badge with superimposed Prince of Wales's plume and regimental title, laurel sprays at sides and large lion head bosses with four leaf chinscales and lion paw clasp, acanthus leaf plume mount holding an upright white hair plume supporting a falling white plume with silvered rose finial. Leather lining. $3,000 £1,250

An officer's 1818 Roman pattern helmet of The 3rd or The Prince of Wales's Dragoon Guards, japanned skull and comb, gilt badge, mounts and velvet backed chinscales with lion bosses, original leather and silk lining. $3,000 £1,250

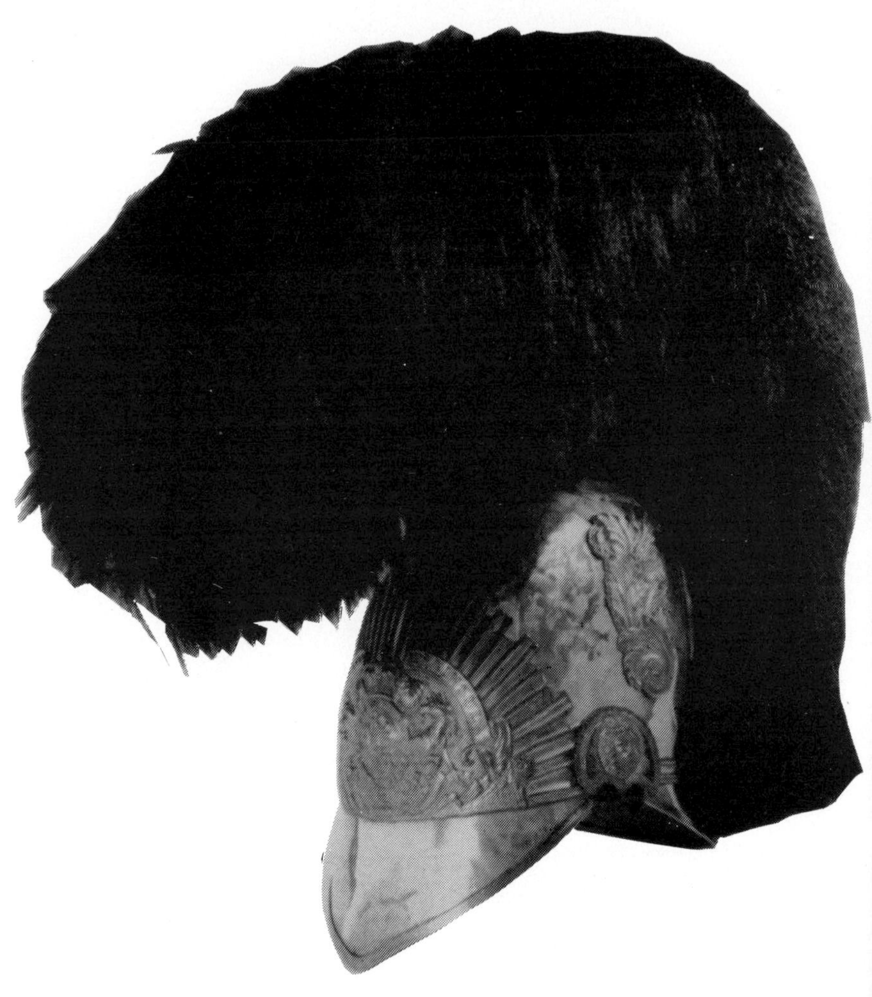

A Household Cavalry officer's 1818 Roman pattern helmet, silver plated skull with gilt peak bindings and some pieces of acanthus decoration, comb with rounded scallop edging, gilt badge on rayed plate, special pattern lion ear bosses and detached section of chinscales, bearskin fur crest. $3,125 £1,300

A Tarleton helmet of The Dorset Volunteer Yeomanry, leather skull and brass bound peak, brass title strip, chain leopardskin headband, bearskin crest, red feather sideplume, linen lining. $3,225 £1,400

A Georgian Tarleton helmet of The Northamptonshire Yeomanry, leather skull with brass peak and side binding, green lined turban and brass chains, ear to ear brass title 'Northamptonshire Yeomanry', white over red feather plume, bearskin fur crest, part of original lining with maker's label 'Goodman & Sons, Patent Saddle Cloth Manufacturers, and Saddlers in General to Northampton . . ' etc. $6,500 £2,700

A decorative painted carved wood Malay kris stand in the form of a standing dancer wearing grotesque mask, on rounded wooden base, overall height 22½in. $60 £25

A painted carved wood Malay kris stand for displaying a single kris, in the form of a male standing dancer, overall height 23in. $85 £40

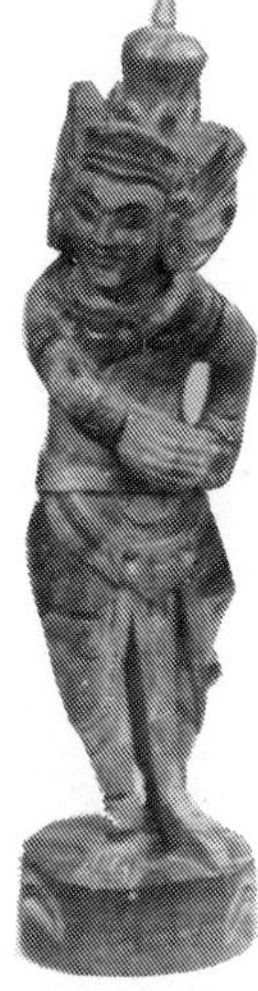

A carved wooden Indonesian kris stand, 19½in., in the form of a male dancer with scroll carved loin cloth and headdress, polychrome decorated overall. $105 £50

A carved painted wood Malay kris stand, in the form of a standing male dancer, on wooden base, height 28in. $105 £50

A decorative painted carved wood Malay kris stand, in the form of a standing male dancer wearing traditional costume, round base, height 19½in. $90 £50

A painted carved wooden Malay kris stand, for displaying a single kris, in the form of a standing dancer, with demon mask, on round base, overall height 23in. $130 £60

A large carved wooden Indonesian kris stand, 23in., in the form of a dancing demon, bulging eyes, flared nostrils, large belly, wearing a loin cloth. $130 £65

A painted wooden Malay kris stand in the form of grotesque standing figure, on base, overall height 24in. $135 £75

A decorative painted carved wood Malay kris stand, in the form of a standing grotesque female demon, height 19in., on round base. $90 £50

Mr Davison's Nile medal 1798, in copper gilt, as issued to Petty Officers. $77 £35

I.G.S. 1854: 1 bar Sikkim 1888, (2395 Pte. G. Bannister, 2nd Bn. Derby Regt.) $95 £40

N.G.S. 1915: 1 bar Persian Gulf 1909-14. $50 £38

Baltic 1854-55, un-named as issued, in its original titled card box. $130 £60

C.B.E. Military division, first type neck badge in gilt and enamels. $145 £60

A.G.S. 1902: 1 bar Kenya (Pte. A. Anderson B.W.). $140 £65

Indian Mutiny: 1 bar Central India (engraved Sowar Mohomed Rheem, Pathan Horse). $135 £70

Sutlej 1845: Moodkee rev. with 3 bars, Feroz, Aliwal, Sobraon. An un-named glass encased gilt specimen. In its velvet lined, close fitted case. $160 £75

China 1900, 1 bar Rel. of Pekin.
$170 £78

A.G.S. 1902: 1 bar Nigeria 1918, (316C Const. Moliki. Pako, Nigerian Police). $185 £90

Ghuznee 1839, un-named as issued.
$195 £90

Empress of India Medal 1877, in silver, lacquered, suspender re-affixed.
$205 £90

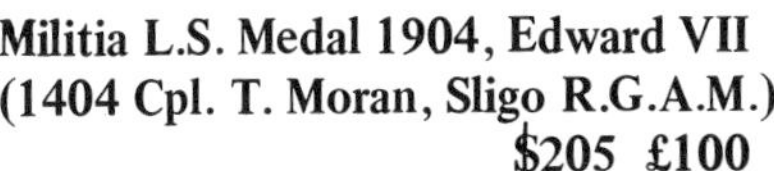

Militia L.S. Medal 1904, Edward VII (1404 Cpl. T. Moran, Sligo R.G.A.M.) $205 £100

A.G.S. 1902: 1 bar Kenya, (Pte. M. Mullins, Glosters), in its original envelope and box. $105 £55

Pair: Crimea, 1 bar Sebastopol, Turkish Crimea (Sardinia issue), with brooch fittings at both riband tops, (C. Ford, 6th Dragoons). $230 £120

Punjab 1849: no bar, Lt. G. F. Hotham, 16th Irregular Cavalry. $260 £120

Indian Mutiny: no bar (Impressed Capt. Jas. Michael, Vol. 2nd Hd. Cavalry). $270 £125

South Africa 1877-79: 1 bar 1879 (E. Porter, A.B. H.M.S. Boadicea). $275 £125

The Most Distinguished Order of St. Michael and St. George, companion's neck badge in gilt and enamel. $305 £125

Pair: China 1900: no bar (J. A. Chandler, Lce Cpl., RM H.M.S. Pique). Shanghai Volunteer Corps silver Long Service Medal. $270 £130

Pair: East and West Africa Medal 1887-1900: 1 bar Witu, Naval Long Service medal, Victorian issue, 1½in. suspension (R. H. Horne, A.B. H.M.S. Brisk and Ldg. Sto. H.M.S. Cambridge). $280 £135

South Africa 1877-79: 1 bar 1879 (220 Pte. J. Jones 1-24th Foot). $310 £140

Three: Crimea: 4 bars; Indian Mutiny: 1 bar, Lucknow; Turkish Crimea: British issue, un-named, with non-original suspension (T. R. Allen, 1st Bn. 20th Regt.) $340 £145

The Royal Humane Society's large silver medal, diam. 2in., engraved 'Peter Ford, A.B. H.M.S. Indefatigable, 11th March & 13th July 1856'. $310 £150

Military Medal, George VI issue, with 'Ind. Imp' (1938-48), (Sjt. W. Brandrick, Suffolk Regt.)
$355 £165

North West Canada 1885: no bar (engraved Lt. W. H. Saunders 95th M.G. (Manitoba Grenadiers). Together with letter from the Public Archives of Canada giving details of recipient. $380 £160

Order of Bath, companion Military neck badge in gilt and enamels.
$445 £185

QSA: no bar (Mr R. M. B. Paxton, 'The Sphere'). This medal was awarded without bars to civilians whose work furthered the war efforts.
$470 £205

A rare Nazi Cross of the Order of the German Eagle, 2nd class, in silver and white enamels. $565 £240

Pair: Air Force Cross, Eliz. II, Eliz. II Coronation 1953. (Both un-named as issued), A.F.C. engraved with date 1967. $595 £290

Waterloo 1815 (Peter Gray, 42nd or Royal Highland Regt. Infantry). $640 £290

Family Group of six, comprising three: Crimea: 3 bars; Meritorious Service; Turkish Crimea Sardinian issue and three 1914-15 star trio. $640 £350

Pair: MGS 1793, 4 bars Sahagun, Vitt, Orthes, Toulouse, Waterloo (Corp. Samuel Stilwell, 15th or King's Reg. Hussars). $1,300 £710

Order of the Bath. (See Below)

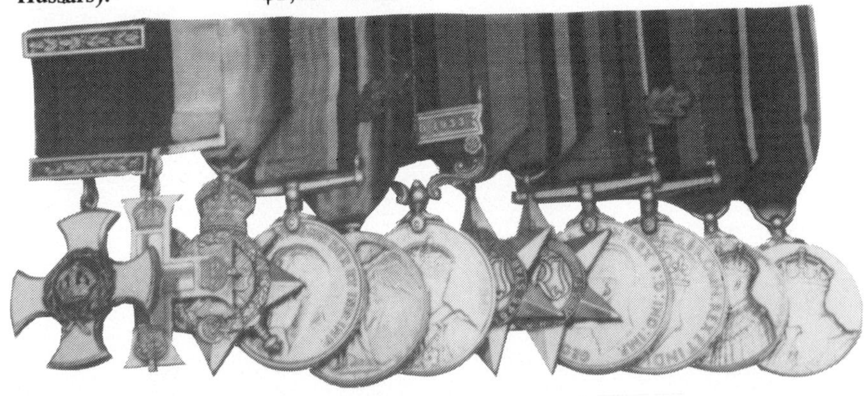

Thirteen: Order of the Bath, Companion's neck badge, military issue; DSO George V, MC George V, 1914-15 star, BWM, Victory with MID, IGS 1908 1 bar Mohmand 1933, 1939-45 star, Burma star, Defence, War with MID, George V Jubilee medal 1935, Coronation 1937. Together with spouses medals: 1939-45 star, Burma star, War. Family biographical details include: MC won on Western Front in 1916, DSO won on the Indian Frontier in 1933, CB won in Burma in 1943. $2,360 £1,025

The Army Gold Medal awarded for Albuhera, 1811. Small size as issued to field officers. In its glazed and gold rimmed case engraved 'Alexr. Willm. Campbell, Lt.-Col.' In a later close fitted velvet lined case. (Major Gordon states only 29 small Army Gold Medals without bars were awarded for Albuhera.)
\$6,000 £2,550

A 32-shot snail drum magazine for the artillery Luger or Bergmanne carbine, No. 223105 with folding lever to assist in loading. $250 £105

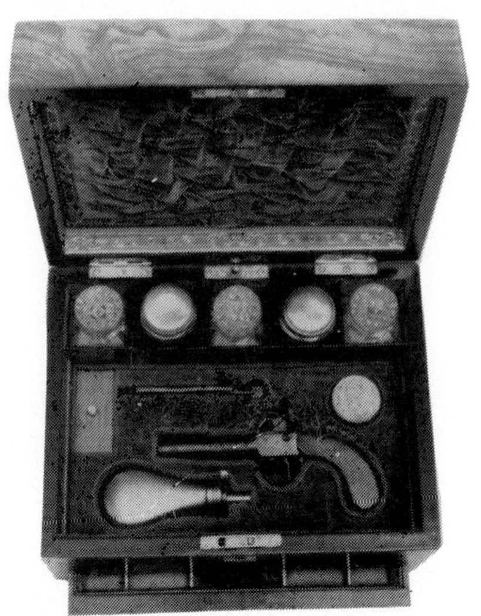

A Victorian walnut veneered vanity case, 12 x 9 x 7in., back with 3 fitted glass bottles and 2 glass jars. Velvet re-lined tray lifts to reveal a percussion boxlock pistol, 7in., and a copper powder flask. $350 £145

6 mounted and 10 foot, German made, solid cast, painted Roman soldiers, in their original box. $45 £22

A Nazi painted porcelain equestrian figure of an S.S. officer on dappled grey horse, made at the S.S. Porcelain factory at Allach, overall height 12in. $740 £360

An officer's 19th century travelling penknife body eating set, comprising: plated fork and spoon, knife 3½in. with rounded tip, by 'Fisher Strand', corkscrew, ivory grips, open 7¾in., with its original leather covered carrying case. $55 £30

A Nazi Kriegsmarine sextant, with Nazi Eagle above 'M. 20300', graded scale, contained in its original wooden carrying case. $560 £260

A 17th century 'Armada' iron chest, the elaborate lock inside the lid with foliate pierced front panels, overall measurements 42½ x 22 x 24in., with lid key. $1,500 £625

An old carved wood native dancing mask, from Kabrok, New Guinea, of oval form, overall 31in. $120 £50

A Victorian scrimshaw drinking horn with H.M. silver rim (1872). The top is carved 'John Sweeney Plumber Glasgow 1856' and the remainder of the horn depicts men-o'-war etc. Inscription ends with 'D. Gourlay Plumber carved me when he was aged seventy'. $240 £100

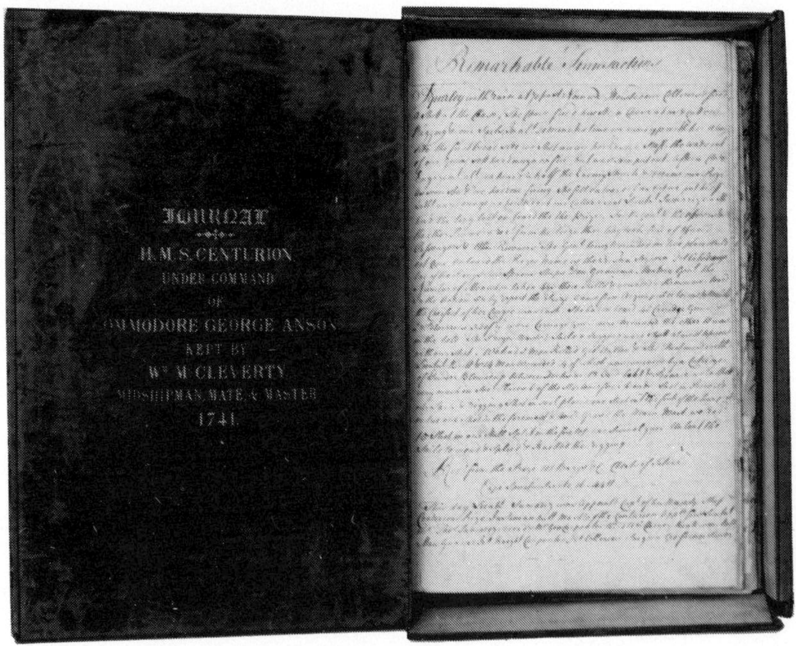

An historic contemporary manuscript journal of Anson's circumnavigation of the globe, 1740-1744, as kept by William McCleverty present on board H.M.S. Centurion, Anson's flagship. $3,720 £1,550

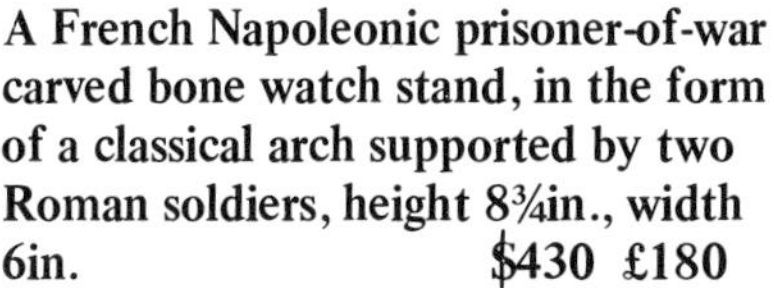

A French Napoleonic prisoner-of-war carved bone watch stand, in the form of a classical arch supported by two Roman soldiers, height 8¾in., width 6in. $430 £180

A 19th century Japanese bronze of a mounted warrior, signed Gioko Saku, overall height 14in., overall length 14½in. The warrior dressed in armour with dragon on Do. $3,670 £1,700

A Georgian rectangular 18ct. gold presentation snuff box, H.M. London 1807. The inner lid inset the plate engraved with inscription 'From the Officers of the 17th Light Dragoons to James Anderson Esqr. their late surgeon. As a memento of their esteem'. Size 3¼ x 2¼in. Weight 6 troy oz. $4,920 £2,050

A Franco-Prussian War commemorative glazed pottery half litre beerstein, decorated in blue and brown glazing.
$170 £80

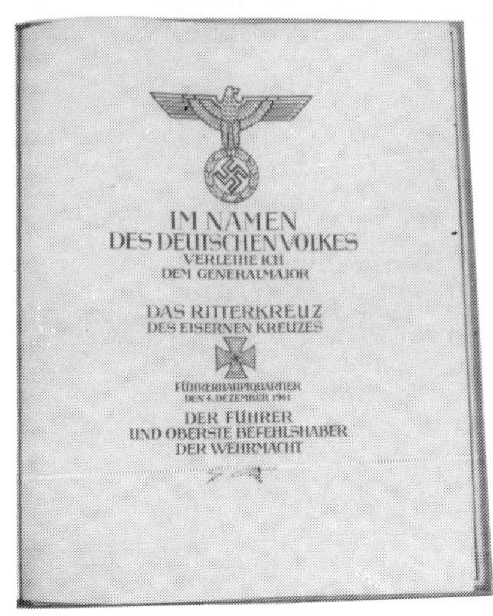

IM NAMEN
DES DEUTSCHEN VOLKES
VERLEIHE ICH
DEM GENERALMAJOR
DAS RITTERKREUZ
DES EISERNEN KREUZES
FÜHRERHAUPTQUARTIER
DEN 4. DEZEMBER 1941
DER FÜHRER
UND OBERSTE BEFEHLSHABER
DER WEHRMACHT

A rare original Nazi citation for the Knight's Cross of The Iron Cross, on vellum, signed by Hitler, Fuhrerhauptquartier 4 December 1941, 13½ x 17½in.
$2,160 £1,000

A half-length portrait, oil on canvas, of an officer of the 41st (Welch) Regt., circa 1850, size 36 x 28in.
$360 £150

A Nazi S.A. bugle of brass, with white metal mounts, the bell mouth with Nazi party eagle-and swastika applied badge, red cord and tassel bound round body, 10½in. $250 £105

A H.M. silver mounted Scottish ram's horn snuff mull (Edinburgh 1888, maker's mark H. & I.), 11in. overall, natural ram's horn on 2 silver ball feet. $690 £300

A standing wooden figure of a Venetian Blackamoor, with arm upraised and standing on the prow section of a gondola, overall height 24½in. $330 £150

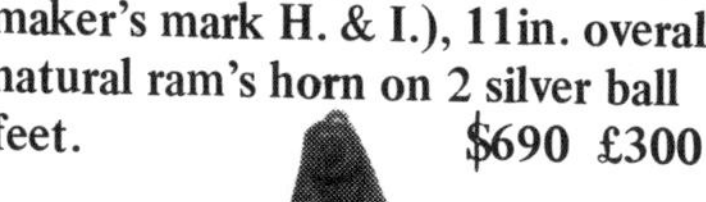

A Victorian wooden framed barometer and temperature gauge, made to commemorate the Duke of Wellington, overall length 56in., width 17½in. $840 £350

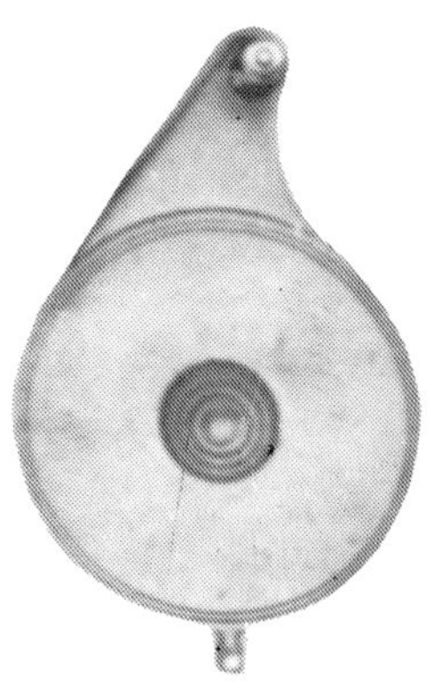

A brass percussion cap dispenser of teardrop form, 3in. overall, circular cover plate unscrews to reveal spring loaded magazine, spring clip at muzzle. $95 £42

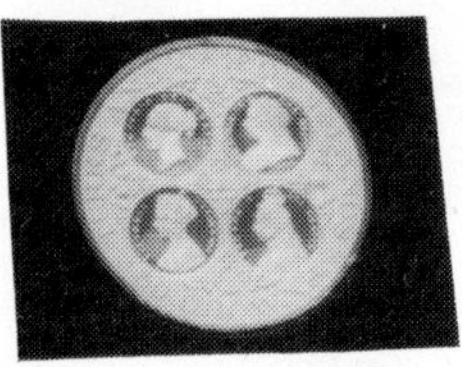

Turks and Caicos Islands: Proof set of coins 1976, comprising AV 100 crowns and AR 50 and 20 crowns (3 coins). In its leather bound presentation case. $115 £60

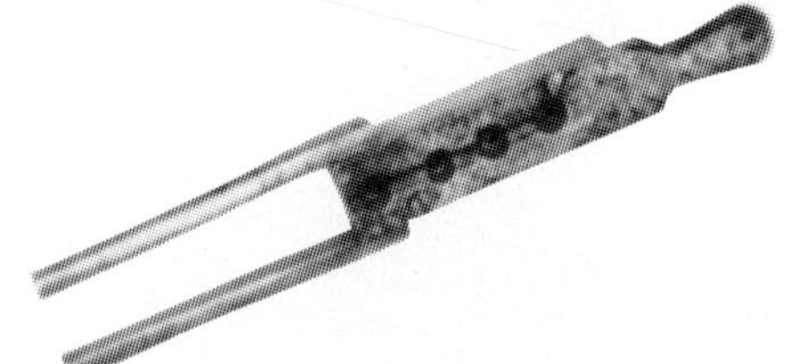

A brass 4 cavity Colt's patent gang mould, 9½in. overall, with steel cut-off, stamped 'Colt's Patent' with W.D. and broad arrow. For casting .38 balls. $85 £35

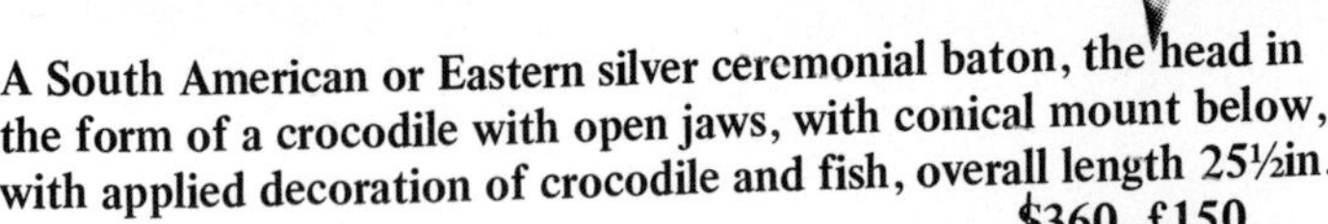

A South American or Eastern silver ceremonial baton, the head in the form of a crocodile with open jaws, with conical mount below, with applied decoration of crocodile and fish, overall length 25½in. $360 £150

A 19th century Indo-Persian all steel 'devil's head' mace, 29in. overall length, pierced mouth, applied horns, hemispherical collar, etched overall with 6 seated sages within foliage. $135 £70

Philippines: AV Proof 5,000 Piso 1977. (2.21 troy oz. in .900 fine gold.) Krause 69. B. Unc. in original case. $855 £450

A pair of Georgian scrimshaw whale's teeth inscribed 'A True and Lamentable Ballad Call'd Billy Taylor shewing the Fatal Effects of Inconsistency'. 7 x 3in. $1,200 £500

An AR medallion commemorating the Spanish Forces victory over the British at Buenos Aires on 12 Aug. 1806. $125 £65

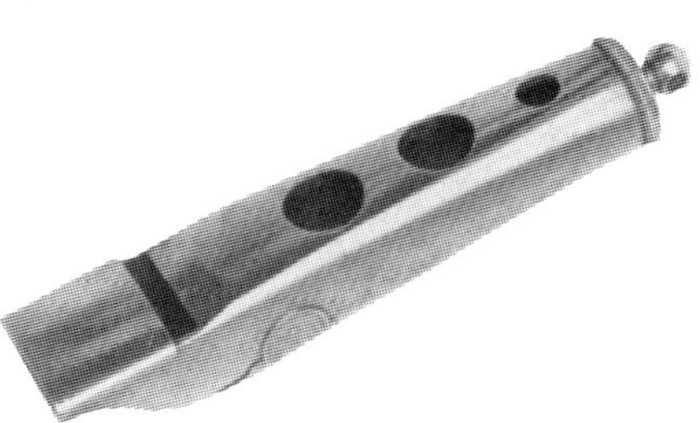

A Victorian white metal 'Field Pipe' with Royal Arms above 'Porteous's Regimental Field Pipe', 4¼in. $90 £48

A Persian 18th century armour armguard Bazu Band, of pressed sheet iron damascened overall with scrolls, chained wristguards and chainmail hand defence backed with leather and brown velvet. $385 £210

An etched and gilt pauldron from a Pisan armour, circa 1580, made up of 5 plates, roped borders. $140 £60

'Royal Salute 1977': a set of 4 'crown-medals' commemorating the Silver Jubilee of 1977 struck in solid platinum. diam. 1½in., in original case. $1,330 £770

A Britain's armoured machine-gun carrier with driver and gunner and a vehicle only, a Tank Corps officer and 6 other ranks, rifles at the trail. $56 £26

A Britain's World War I period motorcycle machine-gun combination with driver and gunner, and a similar solo despatch rider. $60 £28

A Britain's 6-wheel army lorry with driver. $80 £36

A Britain's 2-horse general service waggon, with khaki driver and 2 seated soldiers. $150 £70

A Britain's R.A.M.C. 4-horse covered ambulance waggon, original linen cover, with 2 A.S.C. drivers and 2 seated R.A.M.C. orderlies, all full dress, and R.A.M.C. officer, nurse and stretcher. $175 £80

Britain's Band of the 1st Life Guards, 11 mounted bandsmen, including drummer, in their box No. 101; a Life Guards trooper in cloak. $125 £65

A Britain's Royal Engineers 4-horse carriage and pontoon bridge section, 2 drivers in full dress, wooden pontoon and 2 bridge sections. $365 £170

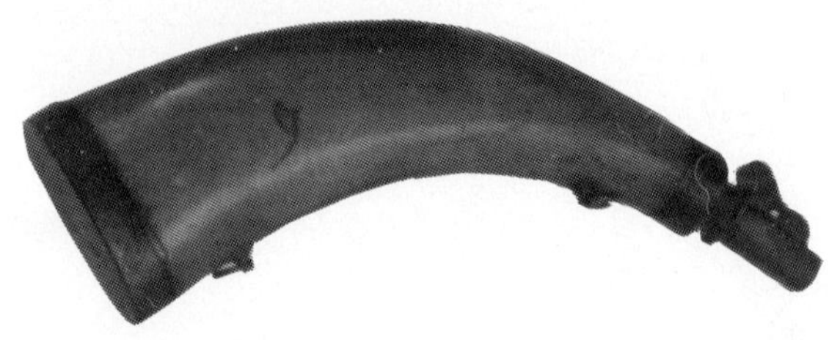

An early 19th century Continental translucent horn flattened curved powder flask, plain brass base plate and plain charger unit and nozzle with detachable twist nozzle cover, 9in. $40 £22

An 18th century Military powder horn, 15in., sprung brass charger, turned brass nozzle cap for use as measure, turned ribbed brass base cap, brass hanging loops, red suspension cord. $80 £34

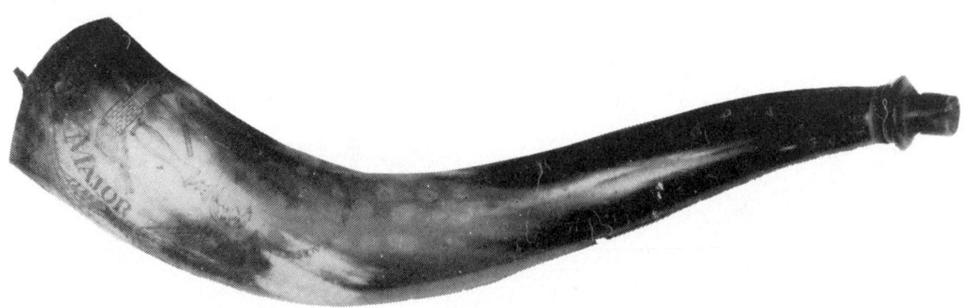

An early 19th century cowhorn powder horn, with contemporary engraving of three-masted man-of-war, thistles, motto 'Nemo Me Impune Lacessit' and 'Alexr. Johnston, Serj Major F.M.', wooden base, 19in. $210 £100

A Volunteer Baker Rifle powder horn, made for the Rifle Section of The Percy Tenantry, raised by the Duke of Northumberland, circa 1798, engraved with coronet over crescent within plain garter, all enclosed within oval. $275 £120

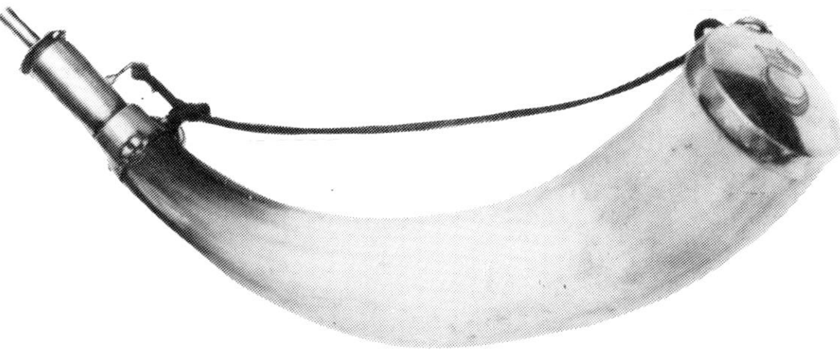

A Volunteer Baker Rifle powder horn, made for the Rifle Section of The Percy Tenantry, 14in., brass end cap engraved with Northumberland crest of coronet over crescent, sprung, shovel charger engraved 'D53', provided with 2 suspension rings. $265 £125

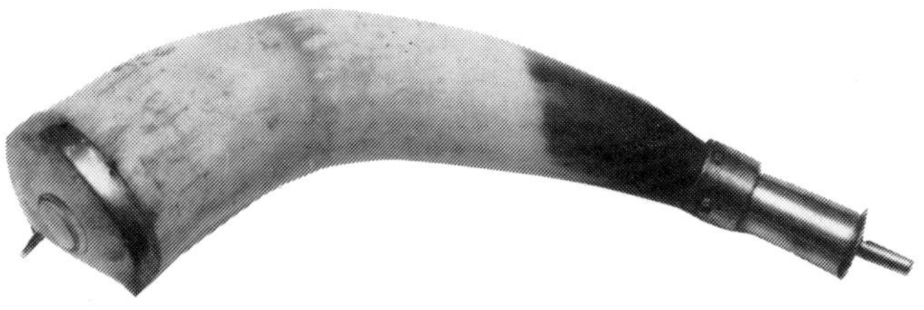

A Volunteer Baker Rifle powder horn, made for the Rifle Section of The Percy Tenantry, 13½in., brass end cap engraved with Northumberland crest of coronet over crescent, sprung, shovel brass charger, 2 suspension rings. $300 £130

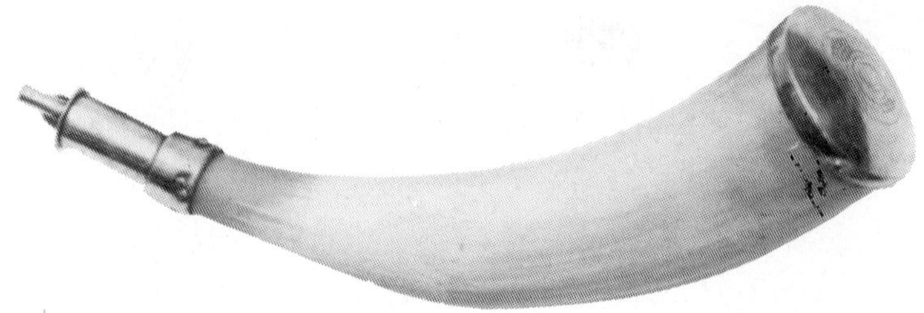

A Volunteer Baker rifle powder horn, made for the rifle section of the Percy Tenantry, circa 1798, end cap engraved with Northumberland crest of coronet over vacant garter around crescent within oval border. $280 £135

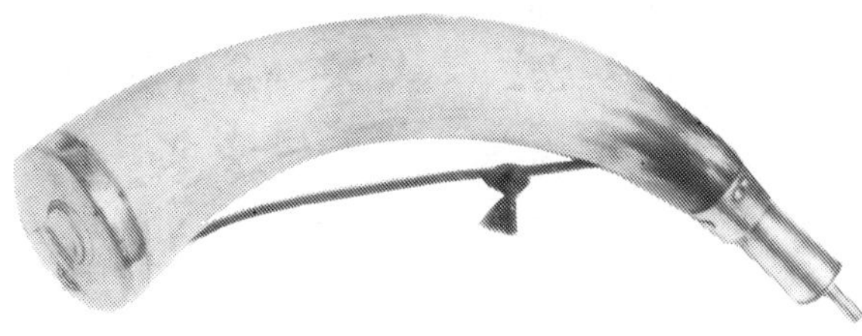

A Volunteer Baker rifle powder horn, made for the rifle section of the Percy Tenantry, raised by the Duke of Northumberland, circa 1798, 14in., brass end cap engraved with Northumberland crest of coronet over crescent, sprung shovel brass charger engraved G39, two suspension rings. $315 £145

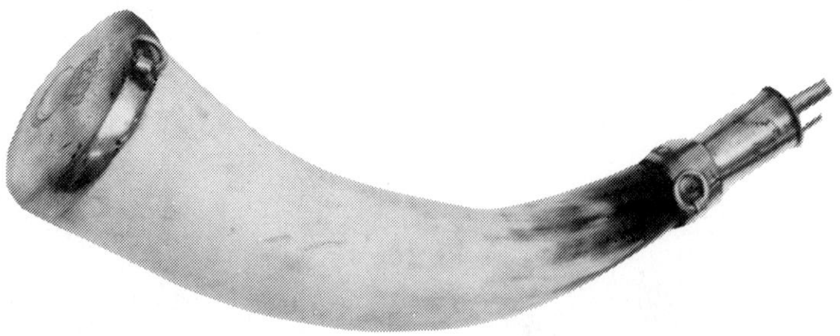

A Volunteer Baker rifle powder horn, made for the rifle section of the Percy Tenantry, raised by the Duke of Northumberland, circa 1798, 13½in., brass end cap engraved with Northumberland crest of coronet over crescent, sprung shovel brass charger, two suspension rings. $550 £225

A Victorian Royal Artillery officer's full dress embroidered sabretache, gilt lace and embroidery, 13½in. x 11in.
$185 £80

A Victorian sabretache of The Queen's Own Royal Staffordshire Yeomanry.
$250 £120

A Victorian sabretache of The Queen's Own West Kent Yeomanry. $350 £170

An early sabretache of The 4th (Royal Irish) Dragoon Guards, size 14in. x 12in.
$410 £200

A Victorian sabretache of The Sherwood Rangers, dark green velvet, gilt lace border. $430 £210

A Victorian officer's full dress embroidered sabretache of The Royal Suffolk Hussars, scarlet cloth with regimental gilt lace border. $475 £225

A Victorian sabretache of The Hungerford (Berkshire) Yeomanry, scarlet cloth, silver lace border. $490 £240

A Victorian sabretache of The Royal Wiltshire Yeomanry (Prince of Wales's Own). $515 £250

A Victorian officer's full dress embroidered sabretache of The 4th (Queen's Own) Hussars. $610 £250

A Victorian sabretache of The 15th (The King's) Hussars, scarlet cloth, gilt regimental lace border. $540 £260

A 19th century Continental officer's embroidered sabretache, probably Austrian, scarlet cloth gilt, silver and coloured embroidered crown over 'FI' or 'FJ' (Francis Imperator or Franz-Joseph). $625 £260

A Victorian officer's full dress embroidered sabretache of The 20th Hussars, scarlet cloth, gilt lace and crimson stripe border, embroidered device, with its foul weather cover. $650 £270

A Victorian officer's full dress embroidered sabretache of The 19th (Prince of Wales's Own) Hussars. $620 £300

A Victorian officer's full dress sabretache of The South Nottinghamshire Yeomanry Cavalry. $650 £300

A Victorian officer's full dress sabretache of The 10th (Prince of Wales's Own Royal) Hussars. $650 £300

A very rare large Georgian full dress sabretache of The 15th (King's) Hussars. $650 £300

A Victorian sabretache of The 20th Hussars, red cloth, gilt regimental lace border. $660 £320

A Victorian officer's full dress sabretache of The Royal Marine Artillery. $715 £330

A Victorian officer's full dress sabretache of The 3rd (King's Own) Hussars, gilt and silver bullion crowned 'V.R.' cypher above garter and motto. $755 £350

A Victorian officer's full dress sabretache of The Queen's Own Oxfordshire Hussars. $780 £360

A Victorian sabretache of The 4th Madras Cavalry. $780 £380

A pre-1855 officer's full dress embroidered sabretache of The King's Dragoon Guards. $860 £390

A Georgian full dress sabretache of a Light Cavalry Regiment (either 13th Light Dragoons or 18th Hussars). $865 £400

A Victorian officer's full dress sabretache of The 13th Hussars, gilt bullion device of crowned 'V.R.' cypher. $885 £410

A Victorian full dress sabretache of The Royal Wiltshire (Prince of Wales's Own) Yeomanry Cavalry. $885 £410

A Victorian officer's full dress embroidered sabretache of The Queen's Own Royal Glasgow Yeomanry Cavalry, 13½ x 10½in., with its foul weather cover. $885 £410

A rare and interesting Georgian sabretache of The 10th Light Dragoons (Hussars). $930 £450

An early Victorian officer's full-dress sabretache of The 12th (Prince of Wales's Royal) Lancers. $1,100 £510

An early Victorian Yeomanry sabretache, possibly Lancashire, maroon velvet, heavy gilt embroidered border, crown, reversed and interlaced 'V.R.', with superimposed gilt and red rose. $1,070 £520

An Indian early 19th century parrying and thrusting weapon, Madu, 23¼in., black buck horns each 15in., with brass caps, overlapping to form grip with steel tips. Circular brass shield with 4 bosses, linear decoration and up-turned rim. $75 £40

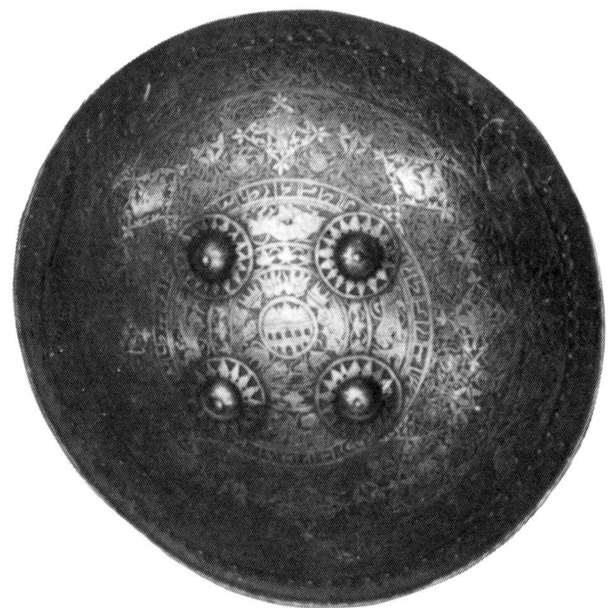

An Indo-Persian metal shield, 4 bosses, the surface chiselled overall with fighting beasts, elephants, foliage, gods etc., heightened in gold, the bosses bordering a circular inscription, 'toothed' outer border, diam. 19in. $140 £70

SHOULDER BELT PLATES

An officer's 1840-81 gilt shoulder belt plate of The 79th (Cameron Highlanders) Regt. $70 £30

A post-1902 officer's gilt and silvered shoulder belt plate of The Royal Scots Fusiliers. $165 £70

An officer's silvered and gilt rectangular shoulder belt plate of the 89th, Royal Aberdeenshire Highlanders (Militia), gilt 'LXXXIX' and title scrolls on plain plate. $155 £75

A Victorian officer's silver plated copper rectangular shoulder belt plate of the 3rd West Yorkshire Militia. $165 £75

A Georgian officer's oval silver shoulder belt plate, hallmarked 1803, engraved crown over 'K.V.' $190 £80

An officer's 1847-55 pattern copper (originally gilt) and silvered shoulder belt plate of The 31st (Huntingdon) Regt. $200 £85

A late Victorian officer's shoulder belt plate of a Militia battalion, H.L.I., with blank Assaye scroll. $210 £90

A officer's gilt and silvered shoulder belt plate of The Royal Scots, design as for cap badge with cloth centre over title scroll. $215 £90

A Georgian rectangular silver (hall-marked 1803) shoulder belt plate of The Exeter Volunteer Infantry, gilt centre device. $225 £95

An officer's shoulder belt plate of The 6th Bn. The Royal Scots, silvered centre. $225 £95

A Georgian officer's gilt and silvered shoulder belt plate of The 2nd West India Regt. $235 £100

A Victorian officer's gilt and silvered shoulder belt plate of The Highland Light Infantry, imperial crown. $235 £100

A Victorian officer's silvered shoulder belt plate of the 1st Aberdeen Rifle Volunteers. $235 £100

An officer's shoulder belt plate of the 4th Volunteer Bn. The Royal Scots. $250 £105

A post-1902 officer's silvered shoulder belt plate of the 5th Volunteer Bn. The Highland Light Infantry. $260 £110

An officer's silvered shoulder belt plate of a Volunteer Bn. The Royal Scots. $280 £120

An officer's shoulder belt plate of the 5th Volunteer Bn. The Royal Scots. $280 £120

An officer's silvered shoulder belt plate of the 3rd Volunteer Bn. The Seaforth Highlanders. $280 £120

A pre-1855 officer's gilt, silvered and enamel shoulder belt plate of The 57th (W. Middlesex) Regt. $275 £125

An officer's silvered shoulder belt plate of a Volunteer Bn. The Gordon Highlanders. $305 £130

A scarce senior NCO's silver shoulder belt plate of the 72nd (Duke of Albany's Own) Highlanders, (hallmarked B'ham 1846) stamped design. $310 £130

An officer's gilt, silvered and enamel shoulder belt plate of The 41st (Welch) Regt. $310 £130

A Georgian officer's copper gilt rectangular shoulder belt plate of The 4th Royal Veteran Battalion. $325 £150

An officer's silvered shoulder belt plate of a Volunteer Bn. The Argyll and Sutherland Highlanders. $355 £150

A scarce Georgian other rank's oval brass shoulder belt plate of the 3rd Bn. The 60th (Royal American) Regt. $370 £155

A scarce Royal Marines officer's rectangular gilt shoulder belt plate, circa 1826-30, $345 £160

A scarce Georgian officer's silvered oval shoulder belt plate of The 33rd (First Yorkshire West Riding) Regt., circa 1800. $350 £160

A good pre-1855 officer's gilt and silvered shoulder belt plate of The 77th (E. Middlesex) Regt., $440 £200

A very rare Georgian officer's gilt oval shoulder belt plate of The Royal Navy, circa 1805. $550 £230

A very rare Georgian officer's gilt oval shoulder belt plate of The Royal Navy, circa 1805. $600 £250

A good post-1902 officer's waistbelt of The Royal Scots Greys, gilt lace of regimental pattern, gilt, silver and enamel plate with badge. $145 £70

A Victorian officer's full dress embroidered pouch of the Clare Artillery, gilt lace, embroidery and mounts. $145 £70

A Victorian officer's special pattern gilt flapped pouch of The 9th (Queen's Royal) Lancers. $180 £75

A Victorian Hussar officer's silver flapped pouch, (hallmarked B'ham 1892). $190 £80

An officer's embroidered pouch of The 7th (Queen's Own) Hussars, scarlet cloth, gilt 'QO' monogram within leaf border, gilt mounts. $205 £85

A Georgian other rank's buff leather shoulder belt and shoulder belt plate of The Ballaghkeen Cavalry, plate engraved with crowned harp, title scrolls above and below. $185 £85

A George V officer's full dress blue velvet shoulder belt and pouch of the Hon. Corps of Gentlemen-at-Arms, with embroidered crowned cypher, gilt lace border, gilt belt with belt buckle, tip and slide. $165 £90

A good post-1902 Royal Artillery officer's full dress shoulder belt and pouch with matching waistbelt and sword slings, and sword knot, contained in their velvet lined tin case. $270 £130

A fine and interesting officer's full dress shoulder belt and pouch of the 22nd Frontier Force (Sam Browne's Cavalry) gilt lace belt, with buckle, tip and slide, black cloth embroidered pouch with crowned 'SBC', title battle honours within wreath, and lace border, complete with its foul weather cover. $325 £135

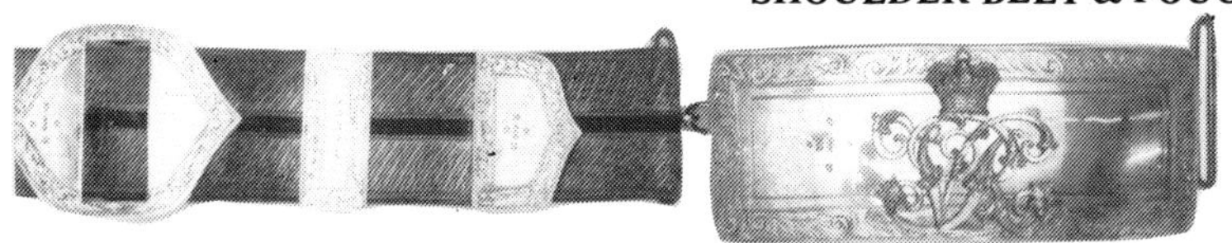

A Victorian officer's full dress shoulder belt and pouch of The 20th Hussars, with silver mounts hallmarked Birmingham 1862, gilt lace belt with crimson stripe, silver prickers set, buckle, tip and slide, red pouch with silver flap and gilt 'VR'. $335 £140

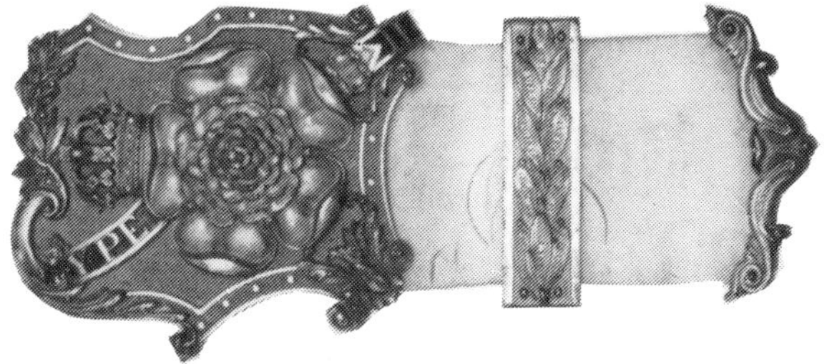

A rare officer's gilt and enamel shoulder belt plate of The 7th (or Royal Fusiliers), complete with regimental slide bearing battle honours and tip, on buff leather belt end. $360 £150

An officer's pouch of the 2nd Bengal Lancers, green leather with solid silvered flap, engraved border, gilt '2.B.L.' monogram on crossed lances. $380 £155

An officer's full dress shoulder belt and silver flapped pouch of the Prince of Wales's Bengal Lancers, gilt lace with central crimson stripe, silver buckle, tip and slide, prickers and chains, boss and holder, hallmarked Birmingham 1886. (Pouch only illustrated) $350 £170

A Victorian officer's full dress black velvet pouch and shoulder belt of the 1st Lincolnshire Rifle Volunteers, bugle device and wreath spray in silver bullion wire and crimson velvet scrolls. $432 £180

An officer's full dress embroidered pouch of The 4th (Royal Irish) Dragoon Guards, blue velvet with silver lace border. $450 £190

A scarce Victorian officer's full dress scarlet cloth pouch of the 8th Royal Irish Hussars, $455 £210

An officer's full dress embroidered pouch of The 4th Bengal Cavalry, blue velvet with embroidered tiger over IV 'BC' monogram and Scinde 1844', within wreath, gilt mounts. $495 £210

A post-1901 officer's full dress shoulder belt pouch and belt of The Bengal Lancers, the pouch with hallmarked silver flap with floral and foliate engraved borders, gilt crowned 'B.L.' entwined device, hallmarked en suite B'ham 1901. $505 £210

A Victorian officer's full dress embroidered pouch of the 4th (Royal Irish) Dragoon Guards, blue velvet, gilt (rubbed) lace border, embroidered star, battle honours within wreath, gilt mounts. $510 £210

A Victorian officer's full dress gilt metal pouch of the 11th (Prince Albert's Own) Hussars. $520 £240

A Victorian officer's shoulder belt and pouch of The 11th (Prince Albert's Own) Hussars, solid copper gilt flapped pouch with silvered regimental badge incorporating battle honours to Sevastopol, hallmarked en suite B'ham 1868. (Pouch only illustrated) $625 £330

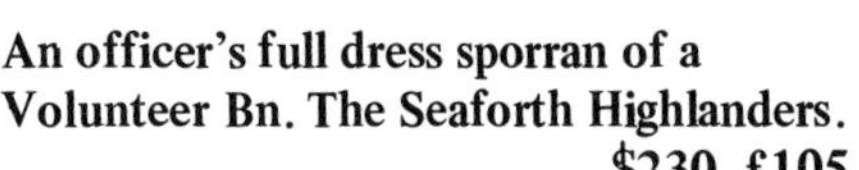

An officer's full dress sporran of a Volunteer Bn. The Seaforth Highlanders. $230 £105

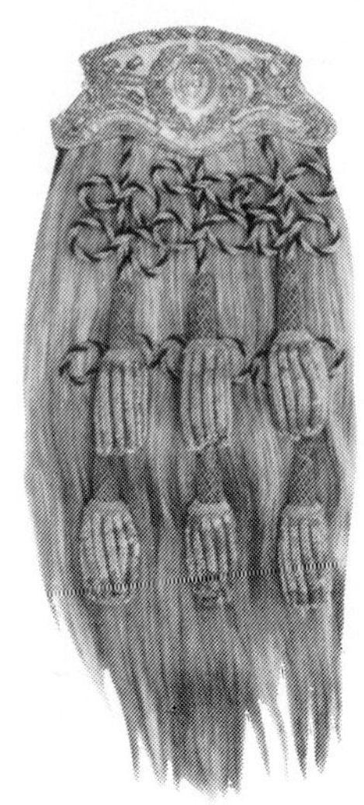

A Victorian officer's full dress sporran of The Queen's Own Cameron Highlanders. $250 £105

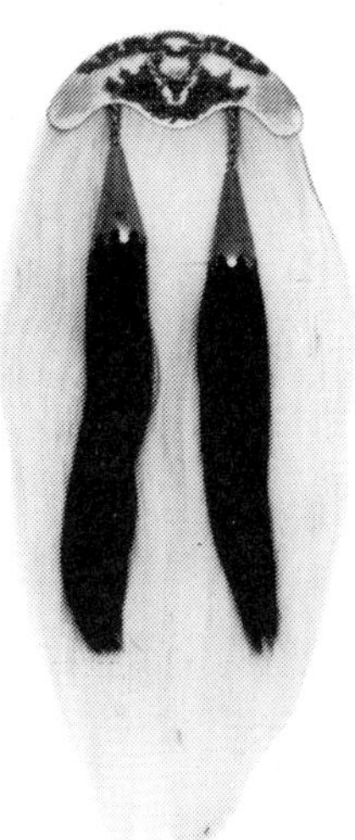

An officer's sporran of The Seaforth Highlanders. $390 £160

An officer's badger sporran of The Argyll & Sutherland Highlanders, complete with badger head and six white goat hair tassles in gilt conical thistle embossed mounts, pouch interior, in its linen bag cover. $410 £190

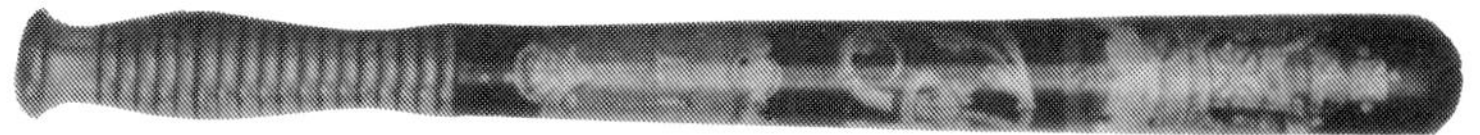

A Victorian painted police truncheon, painted with crown, 'V.R.', 'Police', etc., turned wooden hilt stamped 'Parker Holborn', 17½in. $75 £40

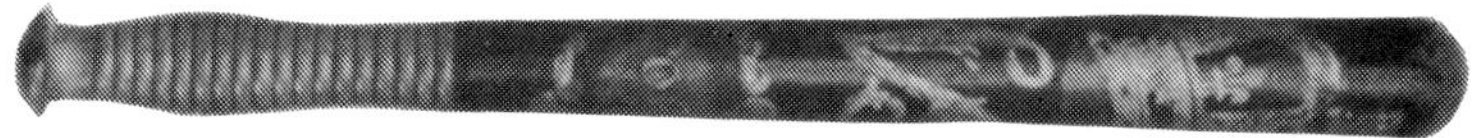

A Victorian painted police truncheon, painted with crown, 'V.R.', 'Police', etc., turned wood hilt stamped 'Field, 233 Holborn', 17in. $80 £45

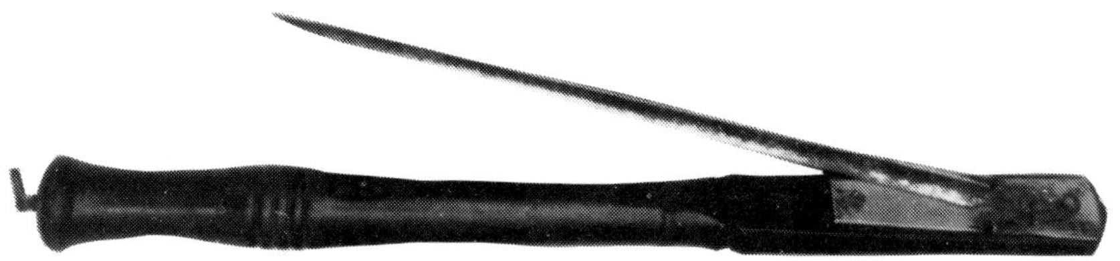

A 19th century watchman's wooden truncheon bayonet, the flattened head mounted with triangular bayonet, 14½in., hinged and secured by a steel lug affixed to a brass plate numbered '6', turned grip with small trigger lug, overall 21in. $145 £65

A George IV painted police truncheon of the City of Bath, 14in., painted with town arms. Turned wood grip. $140 £70

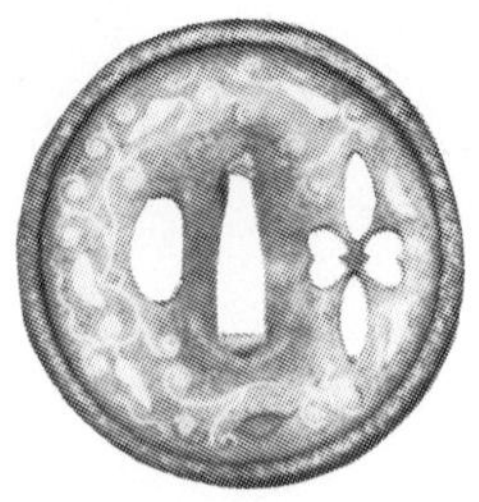

A large circular Japanese iron tsuba, 8cm., with single ruibitsu and heart-shaped piercings with leaves. $50 £22

A Japanese pierced iron Wakizashi tsuba, mumei, 6½cm., composed of concentric rings silhouettes and 3 panels of woven basketwork. $75 £35

A large circular Japanese iron tsuba, 8¼cm., surface chiselled with low relief basketweave design. $85 £38

A Japanese circular iron tsuba, 6¾cm., the thick chiselled rim (1¼cm.), in the form of bamboo. One shakudo plugged ruibitsu. $85 £38

A Japanes oval iron sukashi tsuba, 6¾cm., mumei, with 'pie-crust' infill. $85 £40

A Japanese katana sized circular iron tsuba, 9cm. chiselled in low relief as a single stylised chrysanthemum. $90 £42

A Japanese pierced iron katana tsuba of circular form, 8cm., signed Masakawa Saku. $120 £55

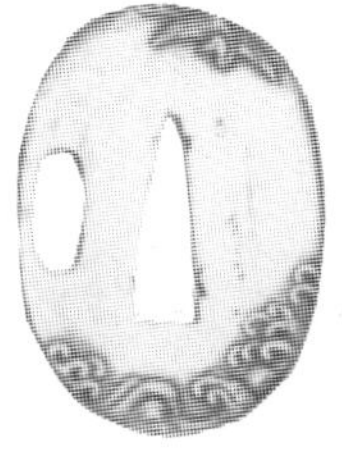

An oval silver tanto tsuba, mumei, 5½cm., chiselled in low relief with flying crane above waves. $115 £60

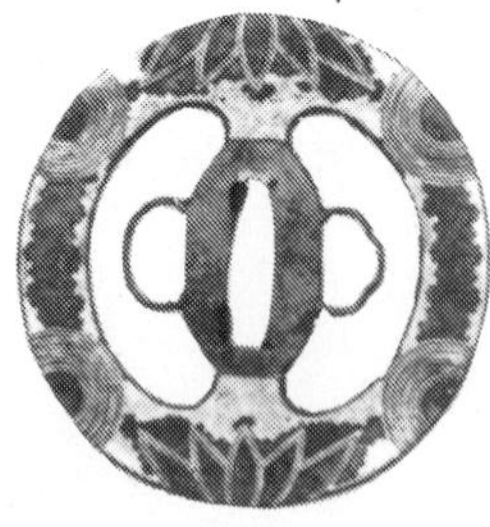

A Japanese katana sized circular pierced iron tsuba, the broad rim inlaid with brass circles, iron silhouette ruibitsu. $130 £60

A large oval shakudo ishime katana tsuba, 8¼cm., with sentuko rim and pierced with sentuko inlaid cherry blossom. $150 £70

A cast bronze mirror-maker's tsuba, 8¼cm., signed Yamashiro Nokuni Kaneyasu Rokujusan Kakihan. $150 £70

A circular Japanese iron tsuba, 8¼cm., inlaid overall with a brass geometric diaper pattern. $168 £75

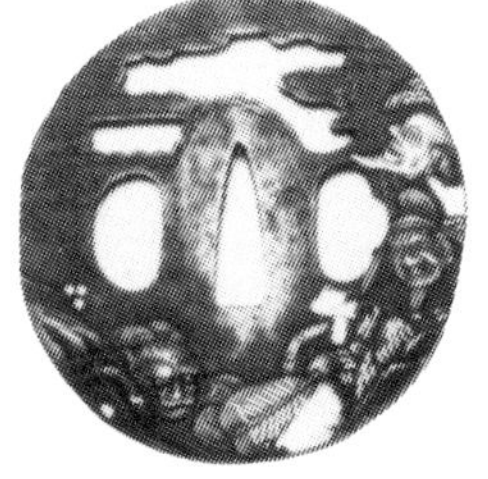

A Japanese pierced iron tsuba, 7cm., inlaid with 2 sages and a tiger in gold, silver, shakudo and shibuichi. $180 £80

A Japanese circular iron tsuba, 7¼cm., chiselled with a Daimyo and one of his retainers espying an incoming ship. $185 £85

A sentuko tsuba, 7cm., signed Masakazu Saku, chiselled in relief with eagle perched in prunus, eyeing chidori. $190 £90

A Japanese oval iron tsuba, 7¾cm., mumei, inlaid with gilt copper dogs playing on foliage covered rocks near silver waterfall. $190 £90

A Japanese iron tsuba of squared form, 7cm. signed Yoshikiyo with Kakihan chiselled in relief. $190 £90

A shakudo nanako goto wakizashi tsuba, 6½cm., mumei, depicting 2 ken tailed dragons entwined through the plate. $190 £100

A good, rare boy's size coatee of a gentleman cadet of The Royal Military Academy at Woolwich, blue cloth, scarlet facings and edging, slashed cuffs, gilt Royal Artillery crown, 3-gun and 'Ubique', buttons, single twisted shoulder cords, $165 £75

A rare, possibly unique, officer's coatee of an ADC to Queen Adelaide, wife of William IV (1830-1837), scarlet cloth, blue facings, gilt roped embroidery to collar and 4 shallow chevrons to cuffs and waist, fine gilt buttons bearing collar 'R' arms and arms of Saxe Meiningen, blue cloth epaulettes, bullion tassels.

$240 £110

An officer's short double-breasted coatee of the 1st Regiment N. Yorks Local Militia, raised 1807, disbanded 1816, scarlet cloth with black velvet facings, 2 rows of silvered, very slightly convex buttons to chest, straight cuffs with 4 buttons, slashed skirts with buttons, white turnbacks and embroidered device, one silver bullion epaulette. $451 £200

A post-1902 Lieutenant's full dress uniform of the Royal Artillery, comprising: tunic with embroidered collar badges, gilt buttons and trimmings, good ball-topped blue cloth helmet, gilt badge, mounts and velvet backed chinchain; gilt lace shoulder belt and black leather binocular case containing small pair of binoculars by Negretti and Zambra, London. $485 £210

A Victorian Squadron Sergeant Major's full dress part uniform of the Westmoreland and Cumberland Yeomanry, comprising jacket with white facings, silvered loops to chest, 3 rows buttons, embroidered rank badge and marksman's badge, busby with scarlet bag, silvered cockade and cap lines, and a white over red horsehair plume in white metal holder, gilt and crimson barrel sash. $530 £230

A Victorian Volunteer Artillery Major's full dress uniform, comprising: tunic with embroidered grenade collar badges, silver lace trim and heavily braided cuffs, silvered buttons; blue cloth ball-topped helmet, silvered badge, mounts and velvet backed chinchain; shoulder belt and pouch, embroidered pouch of Sussex Artillery Volunteers, waistbelt and sword slings. $715 £310

A Victorian Squadron Sergeant Major's full dress tunic and helmet of the Queen's Own Royal Yeomanry (Staffordshire), scarlet facings, silvered buttons, trimmings and rank badge; helmet with white metal badge, mounts and leather backed chinchain, white horsehair plume and white metal rosette. $760 £330

A post-1902 full dress uniform of a Lieutenant, Royal Horse Artillery, comprising: jacket with embroidered collar badges, heavy gilt loops to chest, domed buttons, busby with scarlet bag, gilt busby lines and a 9in. egret plume, both in their tin cases, gilt lace shoulder belt and embroidered pouch with foul weather cover, gilt mounts. $875 £380

An other rank's brass waist belt clasp of The Huntington Rifle Vols.
$50 £20

An officer's silvered waist belt clasp of The 1st Vol. Bn. The Royal Lancaster Regt., enamel rose.
$95 £40

A Victorian officer's special pattern silvered and enamel waist belt clasp of The 2nd Vol. Bn. The Derbyshire Regt. $100 £40

An officer's gilt and silvered waist belt clasp of The Middlesex Regt.
$105 £44

An officer's silvered waist belt clasp of The 36th Cheshire (Crewe) Vol. Rifles. $110 £50

An officer's gilt and silvered waist belt clasp of The Royal North British Fusiliers, pre-1877. $120 £51

An officer's silvered waist belt clasp of The South Devon Regt. of Militia.
$120 £55

A pre-1881 officer's gilt and silvered waist belt clasp of The 16th (Bedfordshire) Regt. $155 £60

PERCUSSION & CARTRIDGE WEAPONS

BLUNDERBUSS

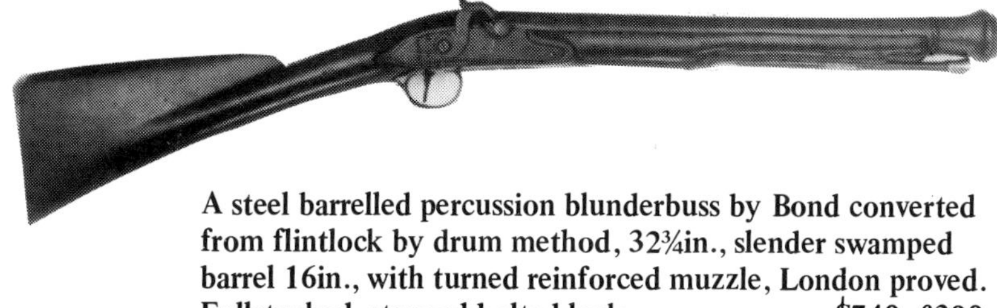

A steel barrelled percussion blunderbuss by Bond converted from flintlock by drum method, 32¾in., slender swamped barrel 16in., with turned reinforced muzzle, London proved. Fullstocked, stepped bolted lock. $740 £390

CARBINES

A 16-bore 1844 pattern percussion Yeomanry carbine of The Ayrshire Yeomanry Cavalry, 36in., barrel 20in., Tower proved with fixed rearsight. Fullstocked, lock engraved with crowned 'V.R.'Tower, 1845'. Regulation brass mounts. $165 £75

A .56in. rifled percussion Paget Yeomanry carbine, 32in., barrel 16in., Tower proved with 3 leaf rearsight, fullstocked, border engraved lockplate stamped with 'Tower' and 'V.R.', regulation brass mounts. $330 £150

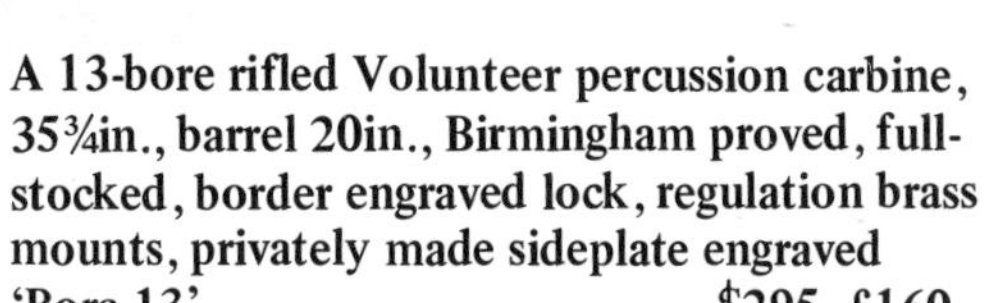

A 13-bore rifled Volunteer percussion carbine, 35¾in., barrel 20in., Birmingham proved, full-stocked, border engraved lock, regulation brass mounts, privately made sideplate engraved 'Bore 13'. $295 £160

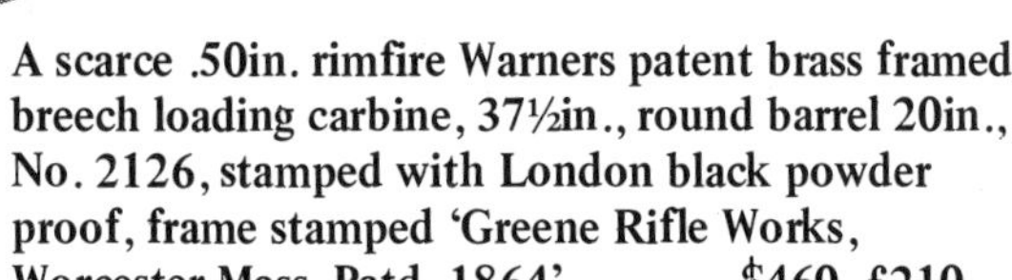

A scarce .50in. rimfire Warners patent brass framed breech loading carbine, 37½in., round barrel 20in., No. 2126, stamped with London black powder proof, frame stamped 'Greene Rifle Works, Worcester Mass. Patd. 1864'. $460 £210

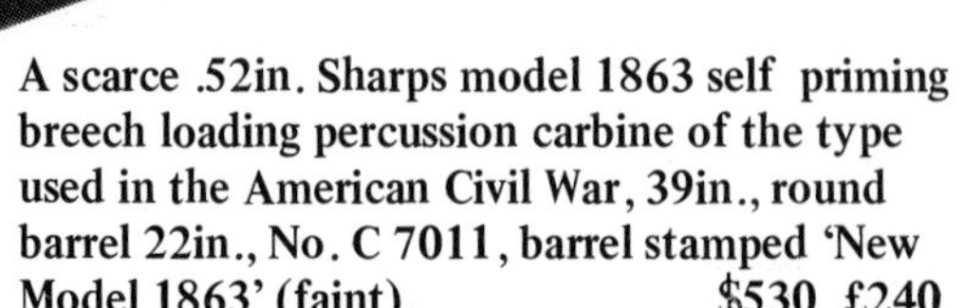

A scarce .52in. Sharps model 1863 self priming breech loading percussion carbine of the type used in the American Civil War, 39in., round barrel 22in., No. C 7011, barrel stamped 'New Model 1863' (faint). $530 £240

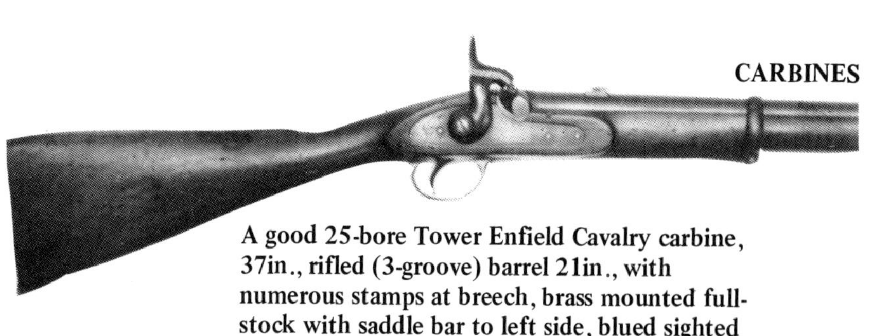

A good 25-bore Tower Enfield Cavalry carbine, 37in., rifled (3-groove) barrel 21in., with numerous stamps at breech, brass mounted full-stock with saddle bar to left side, blued sighted barrel captive rammer. $685 £280

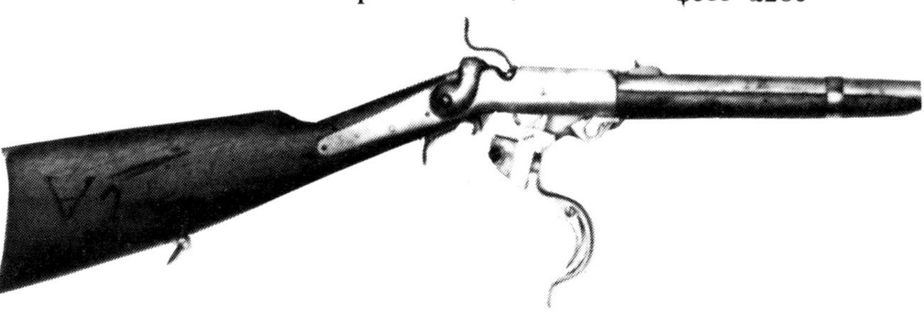

A 28-bore Burnside's patent breech loading percussion Cavalry carbine No. 6952, 40in., barrel 21in. stamped 'Cast-Steel 1864', hinged rearsight to 500 yards, breech stamped. $730 £305

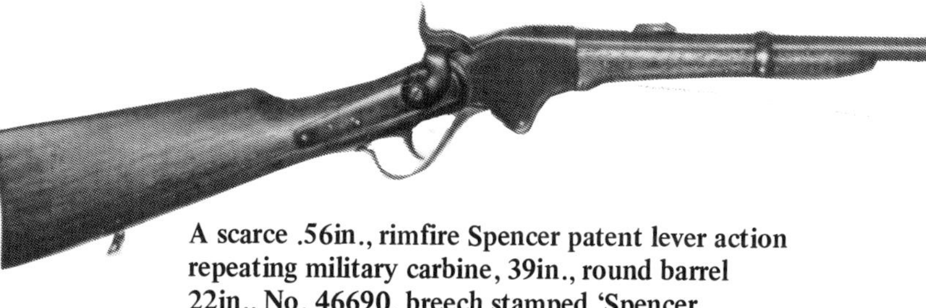

A scarce .56in., rimfire Spencer patent lever action repeating military carbine, 39in., round barrel 22in., No. 46690, breech stamped 'Spencer Repeating Rifle Co. Boston Mass. Patd. March 6 1860', the butt plate stamped 'U.S. 8'. $680 £310

A good 16-bore 1844 pattern percussion Yeomanry carbine, 36in., barrel 20in., Tower proved, full-stocked, border engraved lock with crowned 'V.R. Tower 1844', regulation brass mounts. $690 £320

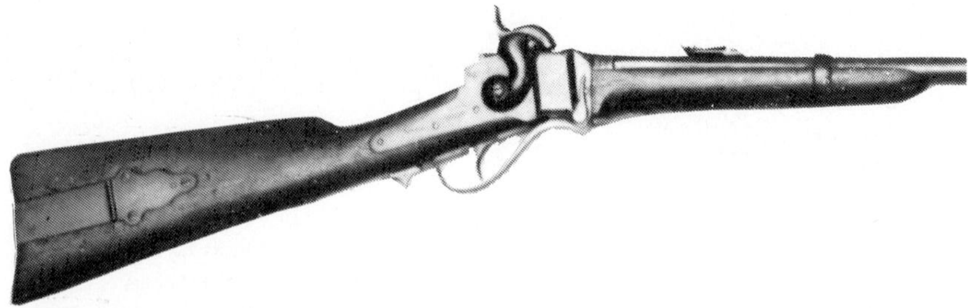

A good scarce .52in Sharps model 1863 self priming breech loading percussion carbine, 39in., round barrel 22in. No. 70194, barrel stamped 'New Model 18' on left side of breech 'C Sharps Pat/Sept 12th 1848', lock stamped 'C Sharps' Pat. Oct. 5th 1852' and by pellet primer 'R.S. Lawrence Pat./April 12th 1859' walnut stock with iron crescent shaped butt plate. $740 £360

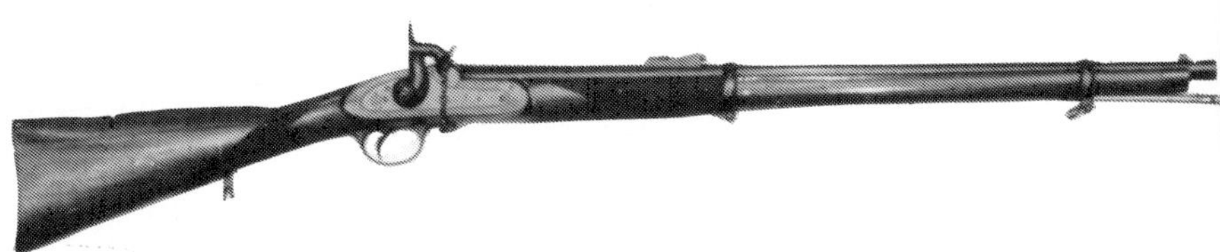

A good .577 Enfield type 2 hand Volunteer percussion carbine, 45in., blued rifled barrel 28¾in., Tower and Birmingham proved, ladder rearsight to 1100 yards, stamped 'P.W. & S.', fullstocked, twin line border engraved lock with crowned VR and 1860 Tower ordnance mark, blued steel furniture with government inspectors marks. $830 £360

A very fine custom made double barrelled back action percussion Jacobs carbine by Swinburn & Sons, 40½in. overall, barrels 24in., 30-bore left hand deep 4 groove rifled barrel, 16-bore smooth bore right hand barrel, 3 leaf rearsights to 300 yards, thereafter ladder rearsight to 2000 yards, halfstocked, locks engraved 'Swinburn & Son patent 1861', steel furniture. $1,380 £600

DERRINGERS

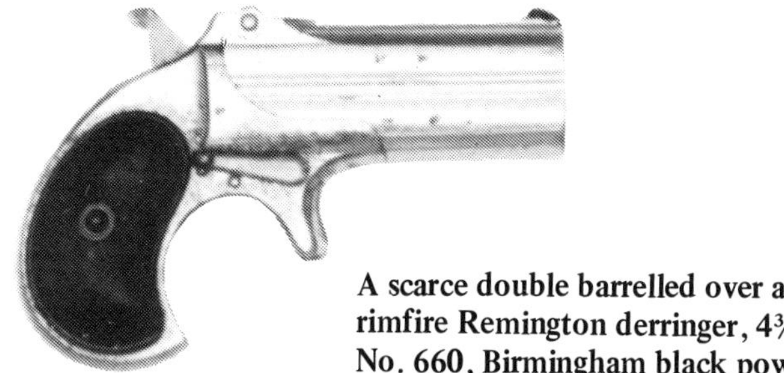

A scarce double barrelled over and under .41in. rimfire Remington derringer, 4¾in., barrels 3in., No. 660, Birmingham black powder proof, barrel rib stamped 'Remington Arms Co. Ilion NY', small moulded grip inserts to bird's head butt. $205 £85

A good 2-shot .41 rimfire Remington over and under derringer, 4¾in., barrels 3in. No. 634, barrel stamped 'Remington Arms Co. Ilion, NY'., moulded composition grips to bird's head butt, iron frame with spur trigger. $455 £190

EPROUVETTES

A brass powder tester eprouvette, circa 1800, 6¼in. overall, round brass frame stamped 'Woolley', brass wheel graduated '1-7', hand ignited, round beech grip. $95 £40

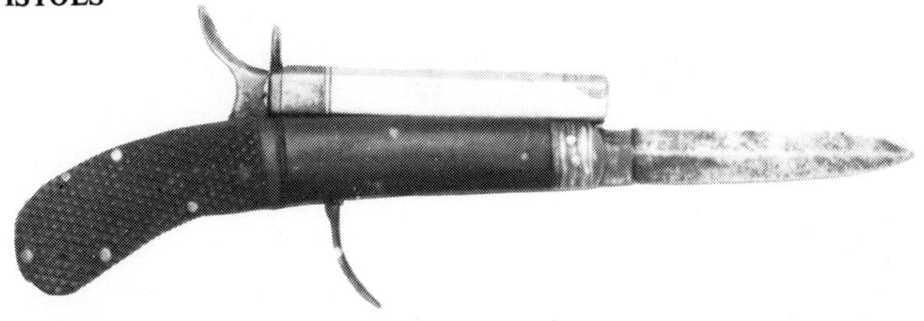

An interesting .25in. rimfire Unwin & Rodgers patent knife pistol, 10¼in. with blade extended, barrel 5 5/8in., barrel stamped 'Unwin & Rodgers Patentees' Sheffield', with 'Non & XLL' whitemetal grip strap with cartridge trap, folding trigger, heavy hammer and eared extractor, chequered horn grips to knife body. $115 £55

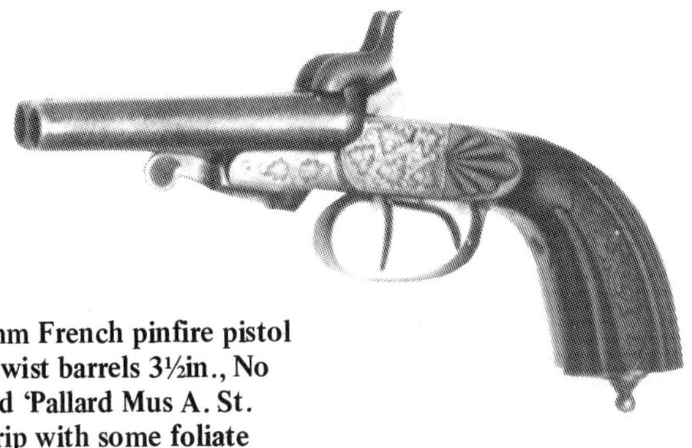

A double barrelled 12mm French pinfire pistol by Pallard 8in., round twist barrels 3½in., No Vis No., barrels stamped 'Pallard Mus A. St. Louis', fluted ebony grip with some foliate carving, steel butt plate. $240 £100

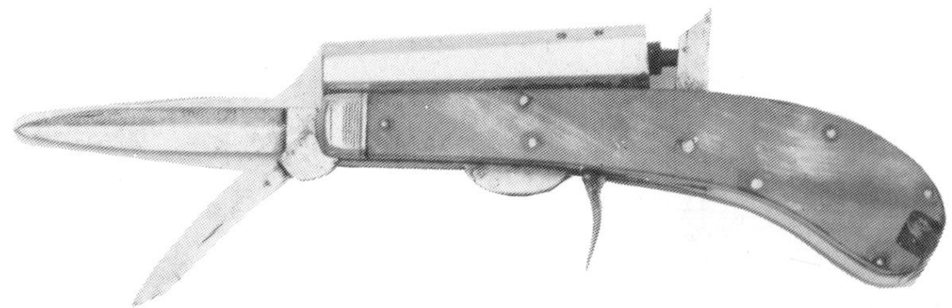

A .32 boxlock percussion combination knife pistol, 6½in., white metal octagonal barrel 3½in., Birmingham proved, plain horn grip sides, hinged trigger, knife blades 3¼in. and 2½in., stamped 'James Rodgers, Sheffield' (faint), white metal backstrap with hinged trap for balls. $200 £105

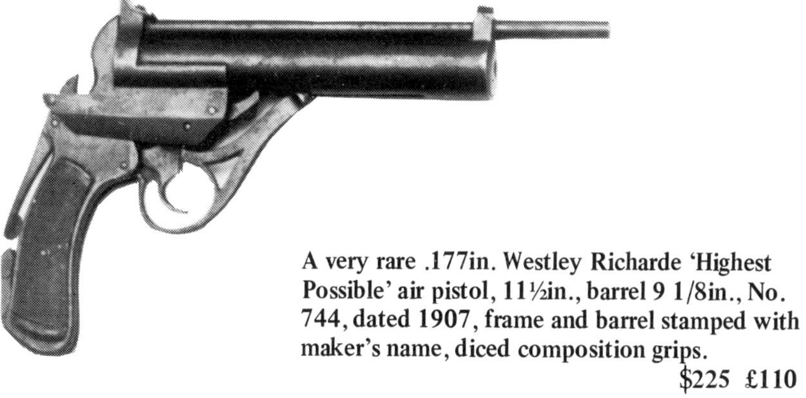

A very rare .177in. Westley Richarde 'Highest Possible' air pistol, 11½in., barrel 9 1/8in., No. 744, dated 1907, frame and barrel stamped with maker's name, diced composition grips.
$225 £110

An interesting 5-shot .32in. extra short rimfire Remington-Rider magazine pistol, 5½in., octagonal barrel 3in., No Vis No., barrel stamped 'E. Remington & Sons, Ilion, NY, Riders Pat. Aug. 15th 1871', 2-piece plain walnut grips. $310 £130

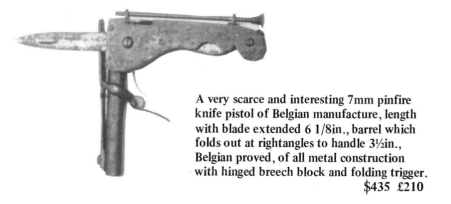

A very scarce and interesting 7mm pinfire knife pistol of Belgian manufacture, length with blade extended 6 1/8in., barrel which folds out at rightangles to handle 3½in., Belgian proved, of all metal construction with hinged breech block and folding trigger.
$435 £210

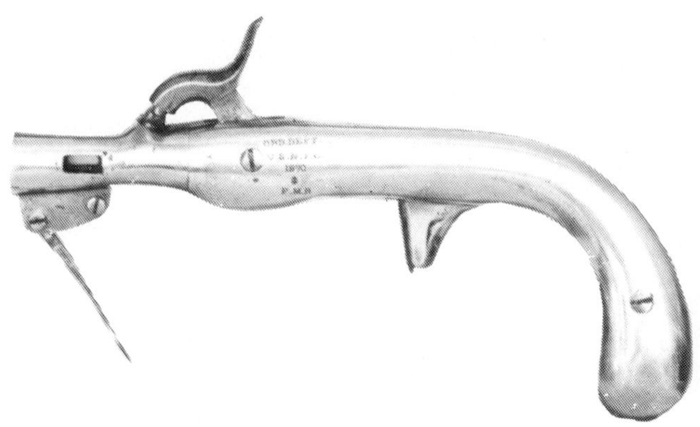

A rare American Naval bronze boxlock percussion pyrotechnic pistol date 1870, 9in., frame stamped 'Ord Dept. U.S.N.Y.W. 1870 F.M.R.' with small anchor mark, sheathed trigger, swollen long grip, steel lever retains pyrotechnic cartridge. $530 £220

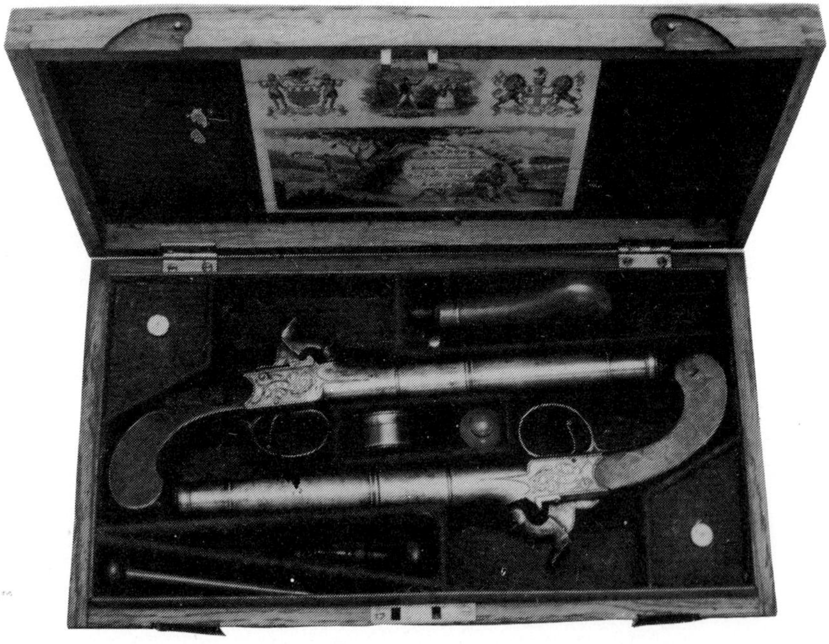

A pair of 26-bore cannon barrelled boxlock percussion pistols by Barbar, converted from flintlock, 12½in., turn-off barrels 5¾in., Tower proved, border and foliate engraved frames with 'Barbar, London' within banners. $960 £400

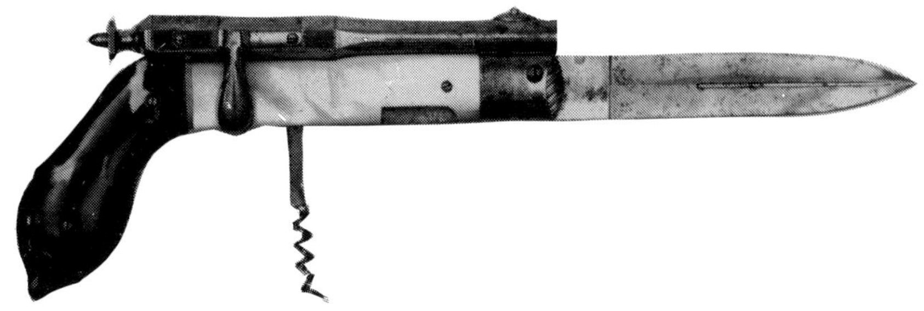

An extremely fine and rare single shot .22in. bolt action needle fine knife pistol by Berthod of Paris, length overall with blade extended 11in., smooth bored barrel in two stages 3in., down turned tulip shaped pistol grip with tortoiseshell side plates and white metal back strap.

$1,140 £475

A scarce Sharps .32 falling block breech loading disc primed single shot pistol No. 701, 10½in., round rifled barrel 6½in. to falling breech, framed stamped 'C. Sharps & Co's Rifle Works Phila. PA' and 'C. Sharps Patent 1848-52', hinged trigger guard linked to falling breech. $1,670 £695

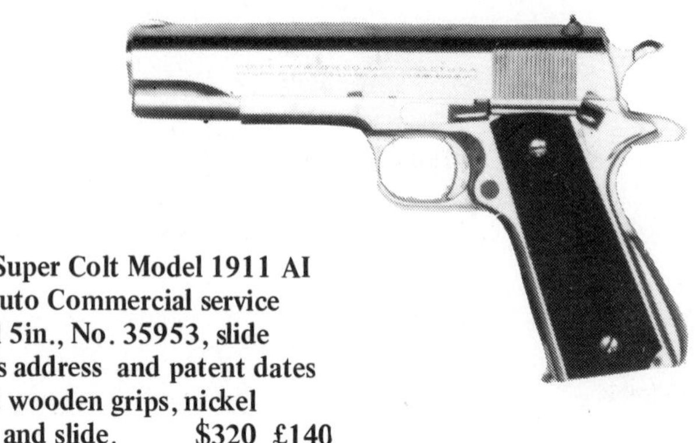

A good 8-shot .38 Super Colt Model 1911 AI Government semi auto Commercial service pistol, 8½in., barrel 5in., No. 35953, slide stamped with Colt's address and patent dates to 1913, chequered wooden grips, nickel plated frame barrel and slide. $320 £140

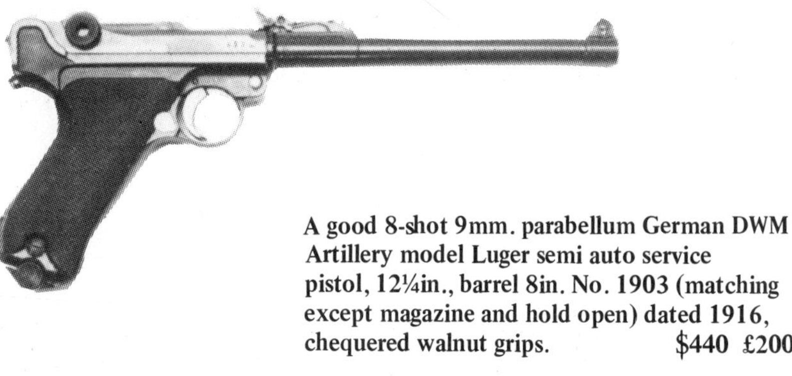

A good 8-shot 9mm. parabellum German DWM Artillery model Luger semi auto service pistol, 12¼in., barrel 8in. No. 1903 (matching except magazine and hold open) dated 1916, chequered walnut grips. $440 £200

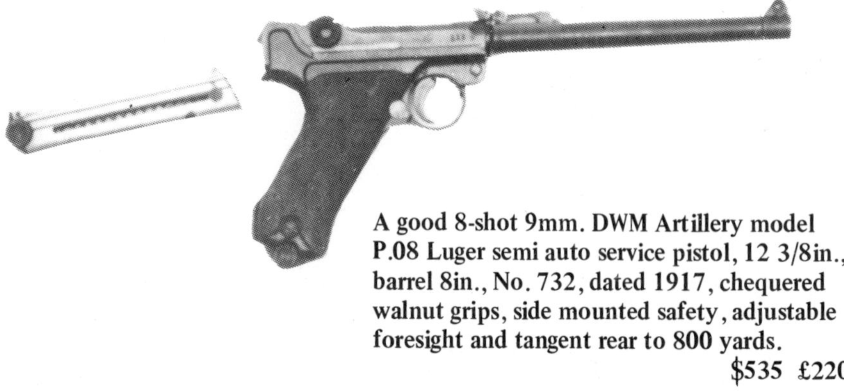

A good 8-shot 9mm. DWM Artillery model P.08 Luger semi auto service pistol, 12 3/8in., barrel 8in., No. 732, dated 1917, chequered walnut grips, side mounted safety, adjustable foresight and tangent rear to 800 yards. $535 £220

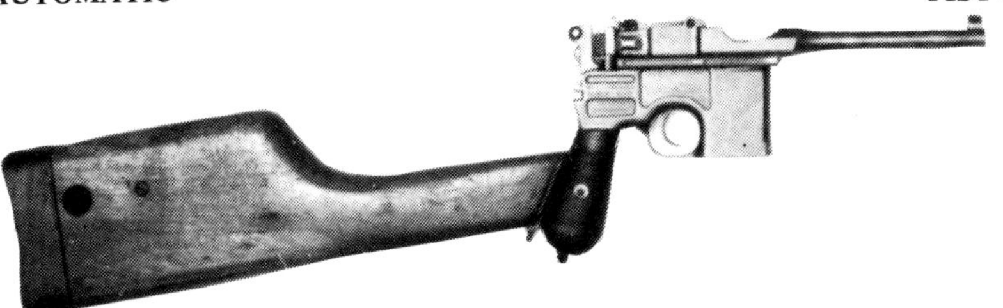

A 10-shot 7.63mm. Oberndorf Mauser Commercial semi auto pistol, 11in., barrel 5½in., No. 255060 matching, ribbed wooden grips, fitted lanyard ring, thumb safety which lifts up to lock, box magazine integral with frame, barley corn fore sight. $625 £260

A good 7-shot .455in. Colt Model 1911 Government semi auto service pistol, 8 3/8in., barrel 5in., No. W29119 slide with maker's and address and patent dates to August 19 1913, and calibre, chequered wooden grips side safety an slide hold open, grip safety. Contained in a case carved with 'R.F.C.' wings, badge, motto and owner's initials. $660 £300

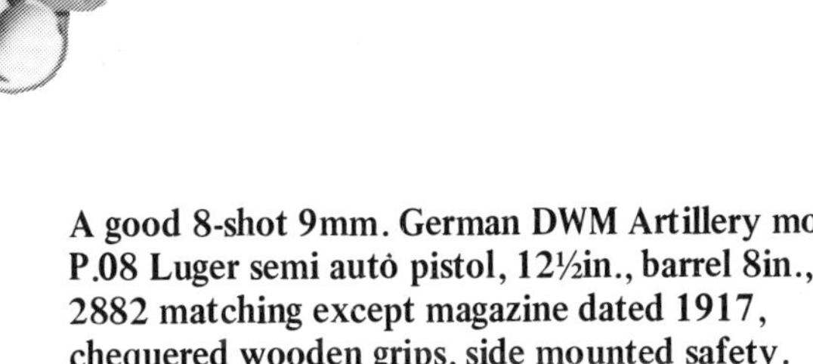

A good 8-shot 9mm. German DWM Artillery model P.08 Luger semi autò pistol, 12½in., barrel 8in., No. 2882 matching except magazine dated 1917, chequered wooden grips, side mounted safety. $825 £350

A good quality double barrel boxlock sidehammer percussion turnover belt pistol by Smith of London, 8in., turn-off deeply rifled barrels 3in., London proved, foliate and border engraved frame and hammer, sliding safety bolt, concealed trigger, top strap engraved 'Smith London'. $465 £190

A very fine 10-bore boxlock backaction sidehammer percussion 'Manstopper' belt pistol by J. Beattie, 11½in., browned octagonal twist barrel 6in., engraved J. Beattie, Regent St., London', foliate and shell engraved breech, London proved, blued lower rib for swivel ramrod.
$540 £250

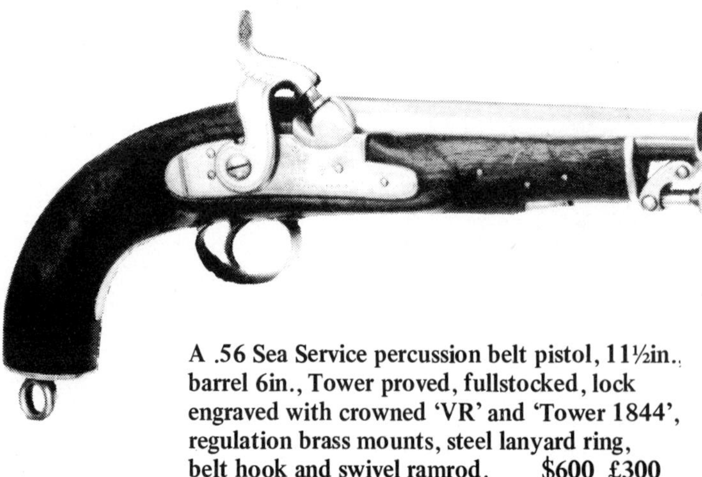

A .56 Sea Service percussion belt pistol, 11½in., barrel 6in., Tower proved, fullstocked, lock engraved with crowned 'VR' and 'Tower 1844', regulation brass mounts, steel lanyard ring, belt hook and swivel ramrod. $600 £300

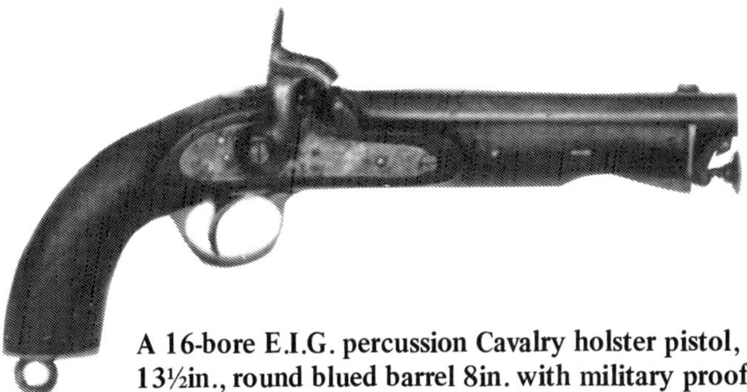

A 16-bore E.I.G. percussion Cavalry holster pistol, 13½in., round blued barrel 8in. with military proof marks, walnut fullstock stamped 'Joseph Smith' with brass buttcap with fitted lanyard ring, trigger guard and fore-end cap/rammer thimble. $430 £180

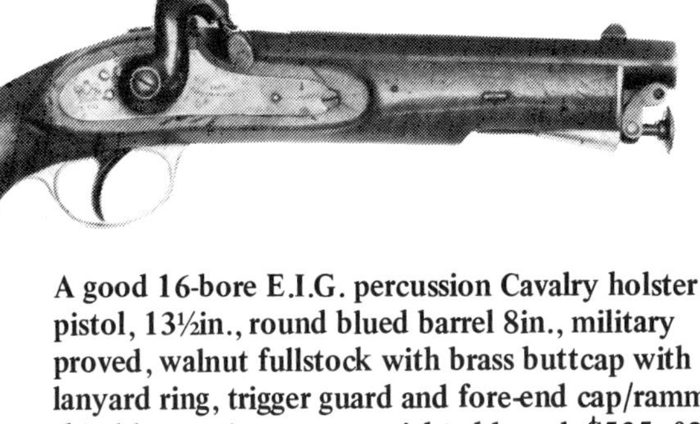

A good 16-bore E.I.G. percussion Cavalry holster pistol, 13½in., round blued barrel 8in., military proved, walnut fullstock with brass buttcap with lanyard ring, trigger guard and fore-end cap/rammer thimble, captive rammer, sighted barrel. $535 £220

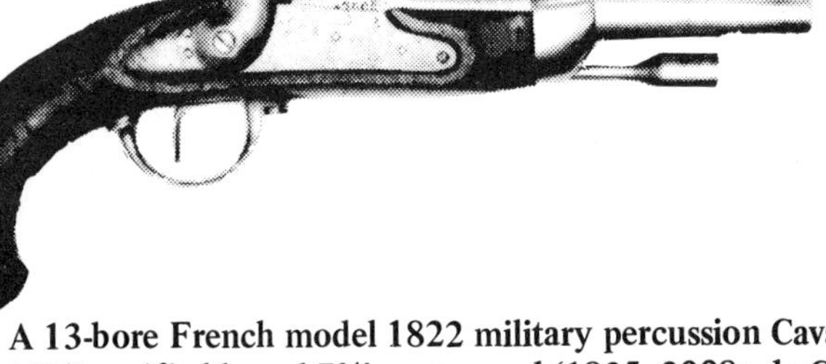

A 13-bore French model 1822 military percussion Cavalry pistol, 13¾in., rifled barrel 7¾in., stamped '1825, 2008c de C*M'. barrel engraved 'Mle 1822 bis', halfstocked, lock engraved 'Mre Rle de Mutzig', regulation brass mounts struck with factory marks, anchor struck on buttcap denoting naval requisition, steel lanyard ring and shovel ended ramrod. $620 £310

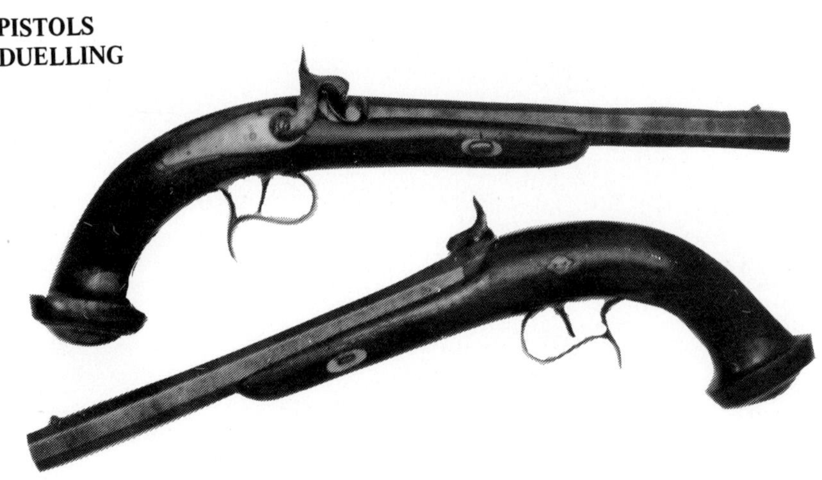

An unusually large pair of 20-bore Belgian rifled backaction percussion duelling pistols, 16¼in., heavy octagonal barrels 10in. with etched twist pattern, fixed sight, halfstocked, plain locks with detented actions and adjustable set triggers, plain steel furniture, pineapple finialled spurred trigger guards, oval buttcaps, chequered grips, oval white metal barrel wedge plates. $960 £400

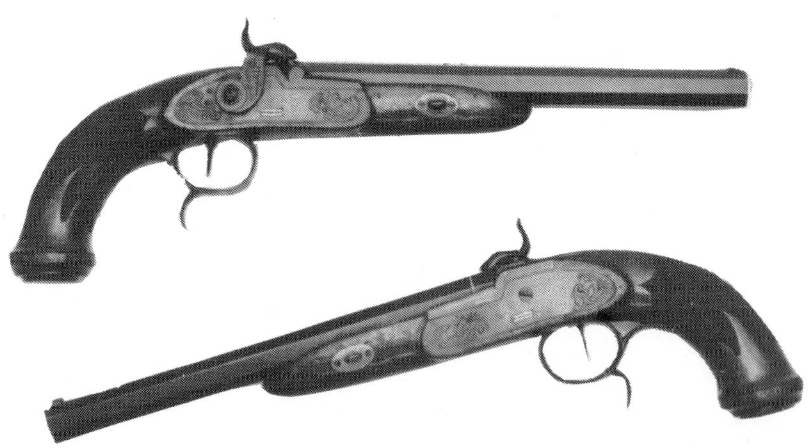

A fine quality pair of German 40-bore rifled percussion duelling pistols by C. Rehbichler of Munich, 16¼in., browned octagonal deeply rifled barrels, 10in., gold inlaid 'C. Rehbichler in Munchen', with twin gold breech lines, halfstocked, lockplates inlaid with gold poincons 'Rehbichler' and on side-plates 'In Munchen'. $2,400 £1,000

A most unusual pair of 22-bore Bohemian double shot superimposed loading rifled percussion duelling pistols by M. Fiala of Bistrici, 16in. overall, octagonal barrels 10in. engraved 'M. Fiala W Bistrici', foliate engraved breeches inlaid in gold 1 and 2, with adjustable rearsights, halfstocked, foliate and border engraved locks with 'M. Fiala W Bistrici'. $3,600 £1,500

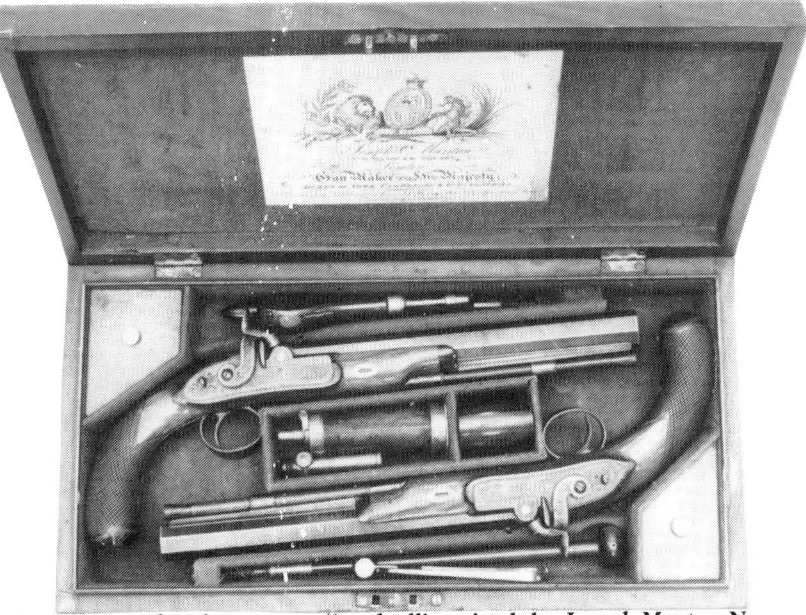

A good pair of 52-bore percussion duelling pistols by Joseph Manton No. 1978, 15in., octagonal twist browned barrels 10in. with fixed sights, half-stocked, detented bolted case colour hardened locks engraved 'Joseph Manton London', with borders, foliage and dolphin hammers, silver safety plugs, engraved blued steel furniture. $5,125 £2,100

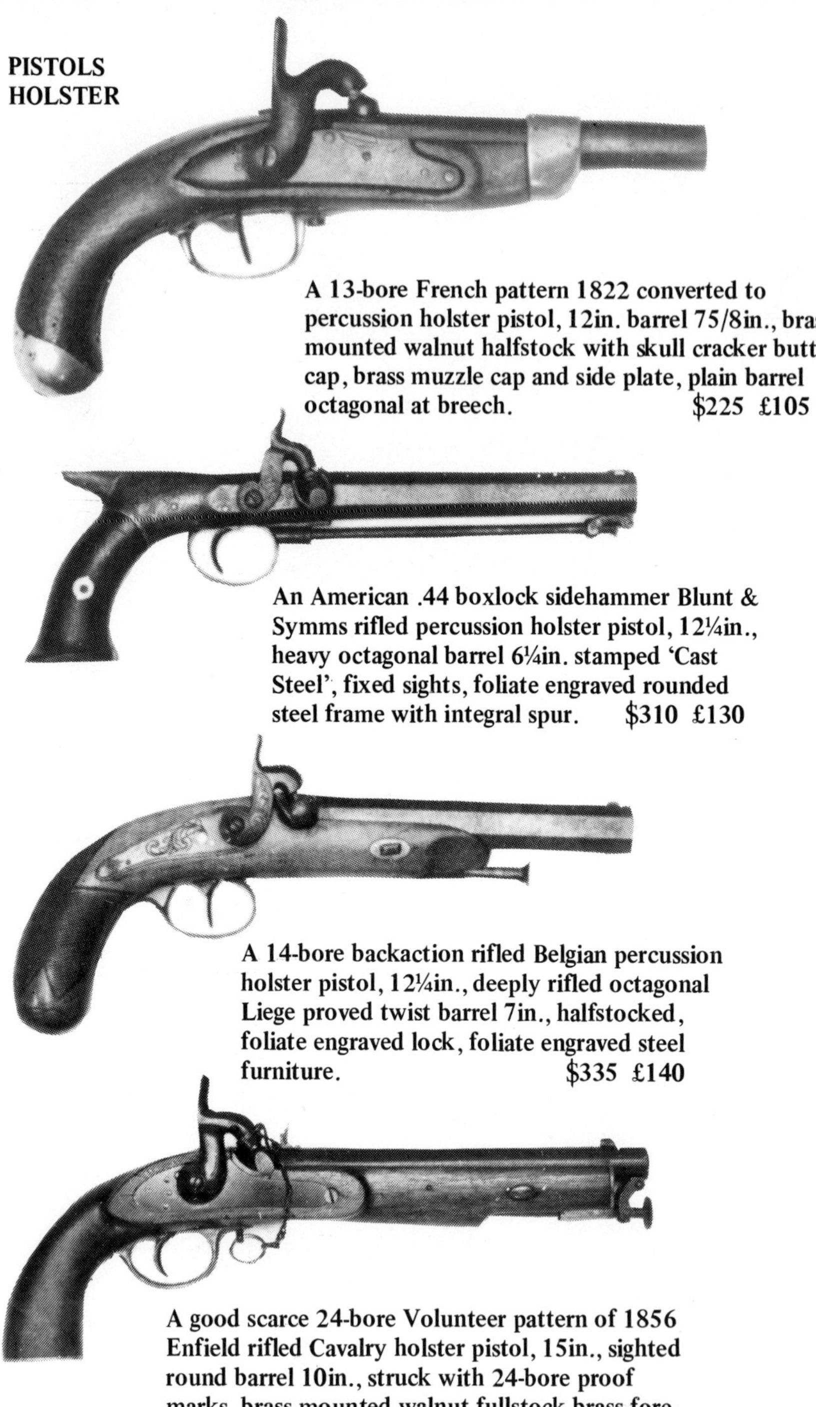

A 13-bore French pattern 1822 converted to percussion holster pistol, 12in. barrel 75/8in., brass mounted walnut halfstock with skull cracker butt-cap, brass muzzle cap and side plate, plain barrel octagonal at breech. $225 £105

An American .44 boxlock sidehammer Blunt & Symms rifled percussion holster pistol, 12¼in., heavy octagonal barrel 6¼in. stamped 'Cast Steel', fixed sights, foliate engraved rounded steel frame with integral spur. $310 £130

A 14-bore backaction rifled Belgian percussion holster pistol, 12¼in., deeply rifled octagonal Liege proved twist barrel 7in., halfstocked, foliate engraved lock, foliate engraved steel furniture. $335 £140

A good scarce 24-bore Volunteer pattern of 1856 Enfield rifled Cavalry holster pistol, 15in., sighted round barrel 10in., struck with 24-bore proof marks, brass mounted walnut fullstock brass fore-end cap combination ramrod pipe. $335 £150

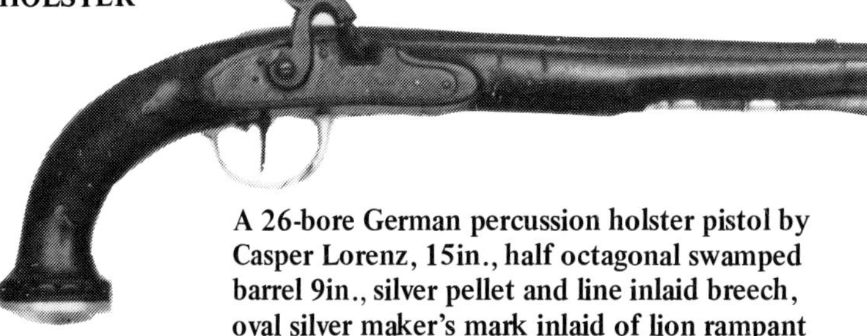

A 26-bore German percussion holster pistol by Casper Lorenz, 15in., half octagonal swamped barrel 9in., silver pellet and line inlaid breech, oval silver maker's mark inlaid of lion rampant above 3 bars, silver foresight. $370 £160

A 16-bore percussion holster pistol by Scudamore, 13¾in., octagonal twist barrel 8¼in., engraved 'Scudamore', fullstocked, foliate engraved bolted lock with 'Scudamore', foliate engraved steel trigger guard, swivel ramrod. $430 £180

A good .56 Sea Service percussion holster pistol, 12in., barrel 6in., Tower proved, fullstocked, regulation lock engraved with crowned VR Tower 1847, regulation brass mounts, swivel ramrod and lanyard loop. $480 £200

A 12-bore percussion trade holster pistol, 14in., round barrel 8in.,, struck with London proofs, walnut fullstock with brass mounts including buttcap with lanyard ring, trigger guard and fore-end cap. $480 £200

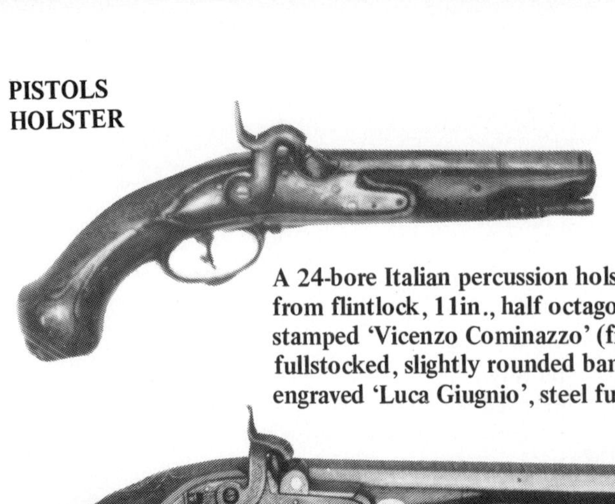

A 24-bore Italian percussion holster pistol converted from flintlock, 11in., half octagonal barrel 6in. stamped 'Vicenzo Cominazzo' (first name faint), fullstocked, slightly rounded banana shaped lock engraved 'Luca Giugnio', steel furniture. $505 £210

A 30-bore percussion holster pistol by Blissett, converted from flintlock, 15in., octagonal rebrowned twist barrel 9in., re-engraved 'I. Blissett, Leadenhall St., London, maker to H.R.H. The Duke of Sussex', halfstocked, stepped bolted detented lock engraved with foliage, I. Blissett and dolphin hammer. $510 £210

A large 14-bore Belgian over and under backaction rifled percussion holster pistol, 12¾in., browned damascus twist barrels 7in., Liege proved, swivel ramrod to size, vine foliage engraved locks, hammers and steel furniture. $555 £270

A scarce 18-bore Swedish Military percussion holster pistol, 18¼in., barrel 11in., stamped 49 at breech, halfstocked, lockplate 'H. 1851. 309', regulation brass mounts, buttcap struck '309-49 RS', chequered grip, steel backstrap slotted for detachable shoulder stock. $650 £270

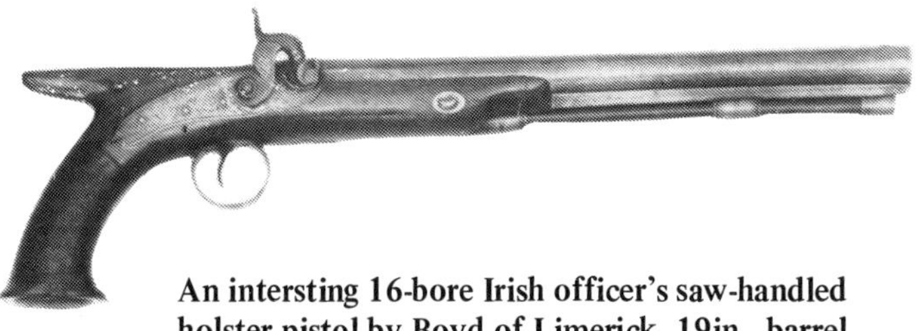

An intersting 16-bore Irish officer's saw-handled holster pistol by Boyd of Limerick, 19in., barrel 12in., London proved, engraved 'London', with silver spider foresight, halfstocked well foliate and border engraved back-action lock with 'Boyd Limerick' in script, dolphin hammer. $730 £300

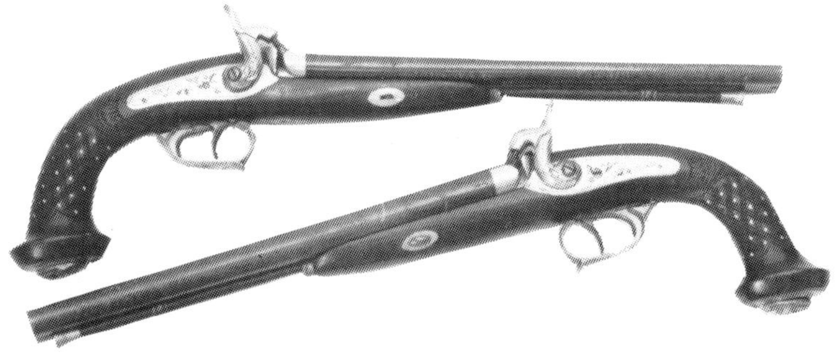

A good late pair of 14-bore Belgian double barrelled back-action percussion holster pistols, 17½in., browned barrels 11in. with false twist, top ribs faintly gold damascened with 'Troxados de Ac?', twin eagles roll engraved above plated breeches, halfstocked in ebonised wood. $1,040 £440

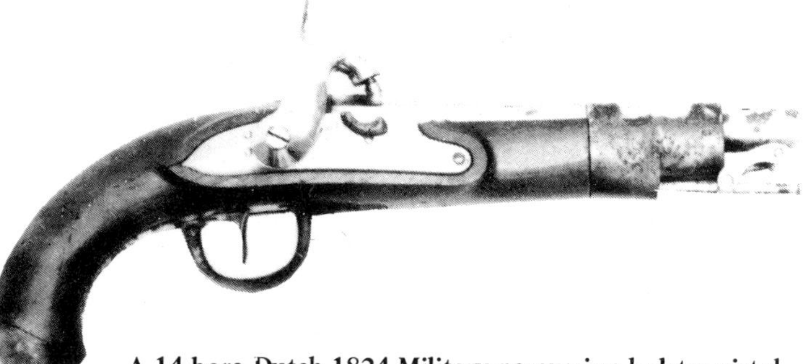

A 14-bore Dutch 1824 Military percussion holster pistol, converted to percussion in 1845, 14½in., barrel 8¼in., fullstocked, regulation brass mounts, steel trigger plate, backstrap and swivel ramrod. $1,000 £485

A pair of double barrelled 12-bore percussion holster pistols, 12in., browned twist barrels 6¾in., engraved 'Maybury & Sons, 15 St. Mary's Square, Birmingham' on top ribs, silver safety plugs, foliate and border engraved bolted locks, with 'Maybury & Sons', fullstocked, foliate engraved steel mounts, pineapple finialled trigger guards. $950 £500

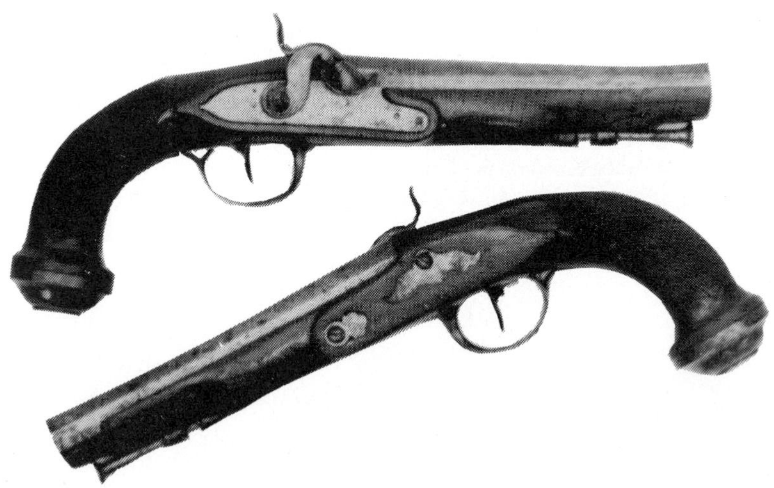

A pair of 12-bore French officer's percussion holster pistols by Piliol of Versailles, circa 1825, 13in. overall, swamped octagonal barrels 7½in., St. Etienne proved, with fixed raised rearsight, fullstocked, one lock engraved 'Piliol a Versailles' in script, scrolled cap fences, steel furniture. $1,220 £500

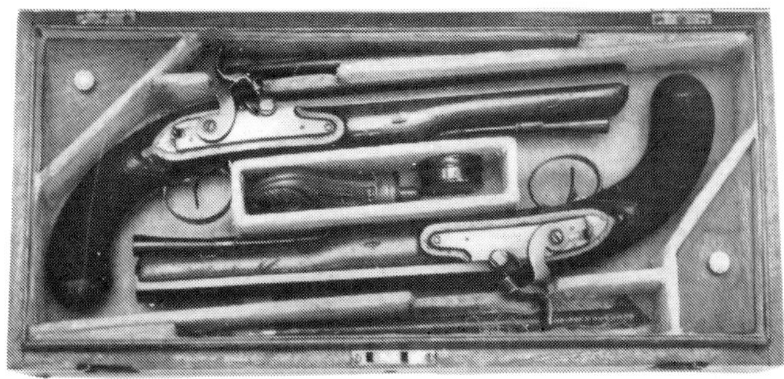

A pair of 16-bore percussion holster pistols by Twigg, circa 1790, 14½in., octagonal barrels 9½in., London proved, engraved 'London' on top flats, fullstocked, bolted locks engraved 'Twigg', pineapple finialled steel trigger guards with Britannia shield centred trophies on bows, deeply chequered rounded grips, horn tipped wooden ramrods with steel worms. $1,320 £550

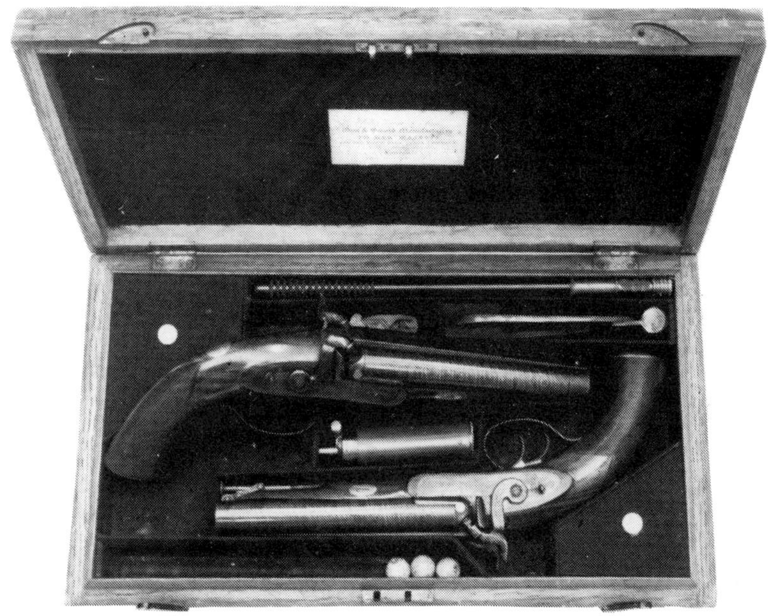

A good desirable pair of 14-bore double barrelled percussion holster pistols by H. James, London, 13in., browned twist barrels 6½in., engraved 'London' on top rib, silver safety plugs and bead foresights, fullstocked, foliate and border engraved bolted detented colour hardened locks with 'H. James'.

$3,800 £1,650

PISTOLS
MUFF

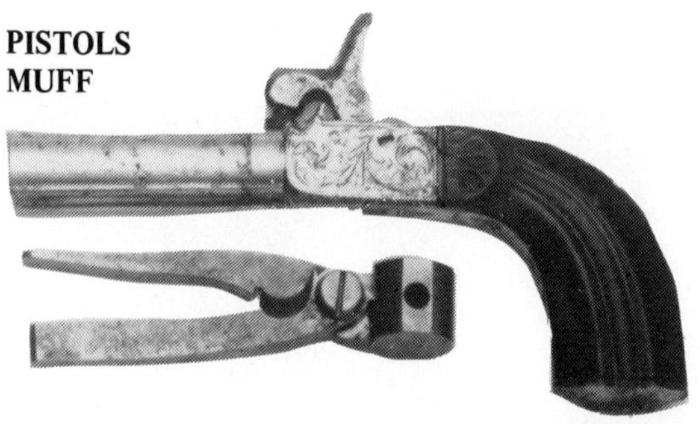

An unusual French boxlock percussion rifled muff pistol by J. Fournet, 4½in. overall, turn-off barrel 1¾in. numbered 79 to breech and key, deep 16 groove rifling, foliate engraved frame, hammer off-set for sighting, fluted bolster, concealed trigger. $225 £110

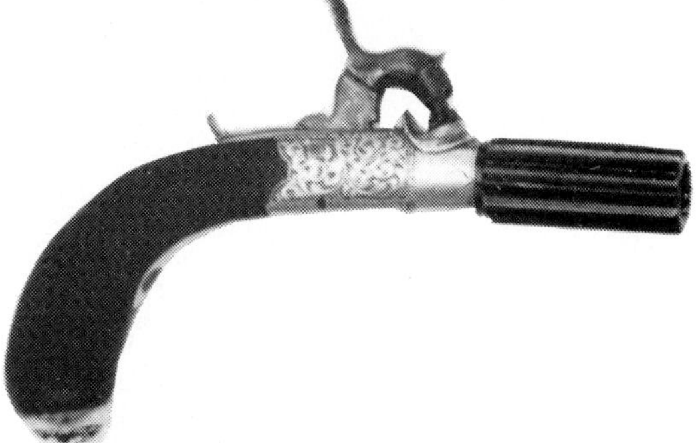

A fine quality 60-bore percussion muff pistol, 4 7/8in., overall, screw-off fluted barrel 1½in., finely scroll engraved rounded German silver frame signed in copper plate script around nipple bolster 'D. Egg, 4 Pall Mall, London', London proved. $610 £250

OVERCOAT

A Belgian .44in. rifled boxlock percussion overcoat pistol, 7¾in., half octagonal turn-off barrel 3¼in. with knurled bands, foliate engraved frame stamped 'B.C.', concealed trigger, hammer off-set for sighting, rounded walnut grip. $160 £65

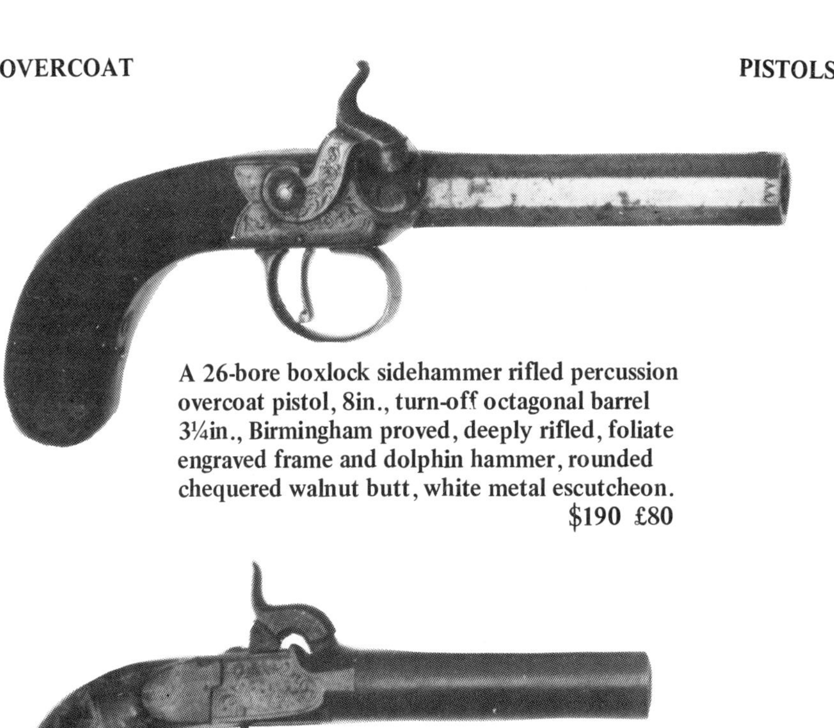

A 26-bore boxlock sidehammer rifled percussion overcoat pistol, 8in., turn-off octagonal barrel 3¼in., Birmingham proved, deeply rifled, foliate engraved frame and dolphin hammer, rounded chequered walnut butt, white metal escutcheon.
$190 £80

A 12-bore Belgian boxlock percussion 'man stopper' overcoat pistol, 8in. overall, turn-off multi-groove rifled twist barrel 3¾in., Liege proved, foliate and border engraved frame, concealed trigger, round bird's eye maple butt with foliate engraved hinged white metal cap trap, shield shaped white metal escutcheon.
$205 £85

A 12-bore French percussion military holster pistol, converted from flintlock, 12½in., round barrel 6½in., dated 1813, walnut halfstock with heavy skull cracking brass buttcap, brass trigger guard, sideplate and fore-end cap/ barrel band, the lock with rounded tail with traces of engraved maker's name, the stock struck with various issue marks. $275 £115

An unusual 70-bore German boxlock percussion pocket pistol, 6in., turn-off octagonal barrel 2½in., steel trigger guard, square frame, long topstrap spur, rounded walnut grip inlaid with scroll silver wire with floral and foliate dcsign.. $160 £75

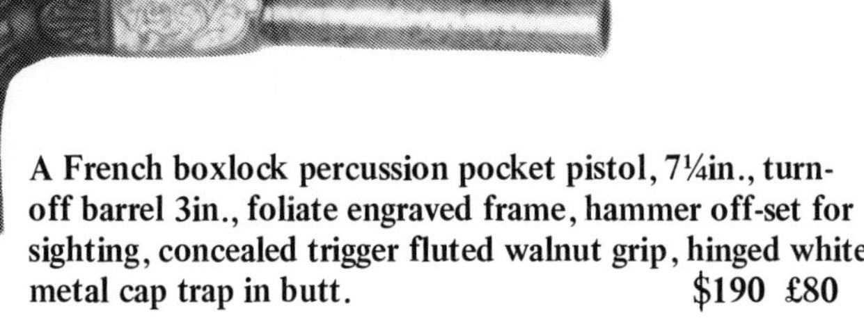

A French boxlock percussion pocket pistol, 7¼in., turn-off barrel 3in., foliate engraved frame, hammer off-set for sighting, concealed trigger fluted walnut grip, hinged white metal cap trap in butt. $190 £80

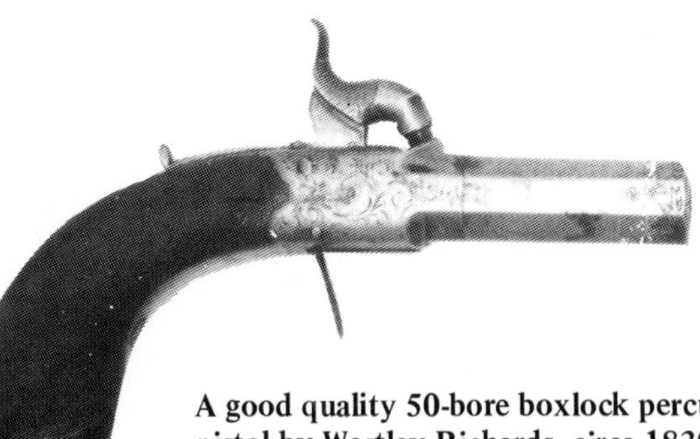

A good quality 50-bore boxlock percussion pocket pistol by Westley Richards, circa 1830, 5¾in., turn-off octagonal barrel 1¾in., Birmingham proved, engraved 'Westley Richards, London', fern tip engraved muzzle, foliate and floral engraved round frame with foliate borders, concealed trigger. $280 £115

A good Continental sidehammer boxlock percussion pocket pistol, 8in., screw-off fluted barrel 3¾in., fluted ebony grip with white metal buttcap, containing compartment for caps, folding trigger, scroll engraved frame and hammer, the top plate inlaid in gold with initials 'J.K.', fine twist sighted barrel with Belgian proof.
$275 £140

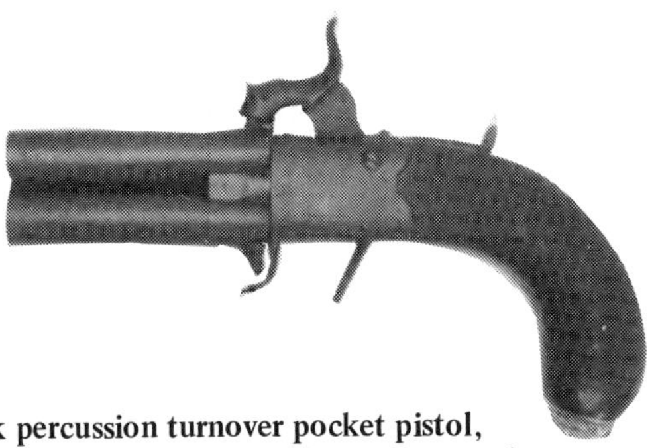

A double barrelled boxlock percussion turnover pocket pistol, 6½in., turn-off barrels 2in., Birmingham proved, foliate engraved frame with F.P. Hopper – Wednesday, sliding top thumb safety with concealed trigger, rounded chequered walnut grip.
$275 £145

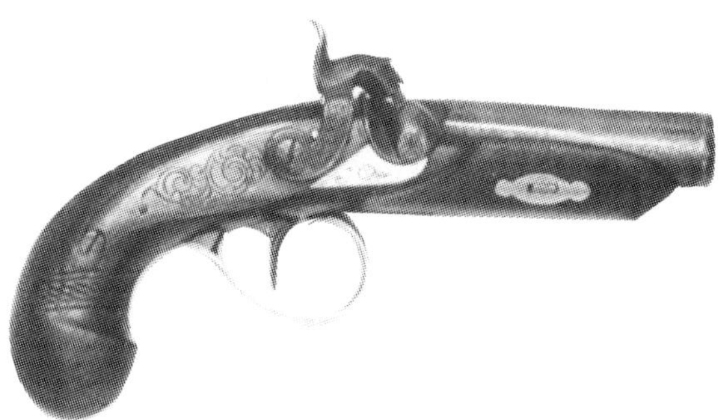

A 60-bore American derringer rifled percussion pocket pistol 6¼in., deeply rifled barrel 3¼in. stamped 'Derringer' at breech, fullstocked, foliate engraved back-action lock, foliate engraved white metal furniture. $410 £200

A pair of .36in. Belgian boxlock percussion pocket pistols 6in., turn-off deeply rifled barrels 2in., rocaille and foliate engraved frames, hammers off-set for sighting, concealed triggers, rounded chequered ebony grips.
$535 £220

A good quality pair of Belgian boxlock percussion pocket pistols, 5¼in., turn-off rifled damascus twist barrels 2in., Liege proved with crowned R931, frames engraved with scrolling foliage and borders, acanthus and chequered engraving over trigger areas, concealed triggers. $410 £215

A boxlock percussion double barrelled turnover pocket pistol, 7½in., turn-off barrels 2½in., Birmingham proved, foliate engraved frame, topstrap engraved 'B. Woodward & Son London', rounded chequered walnut grip with oval white metal escutcheon. $300 £125

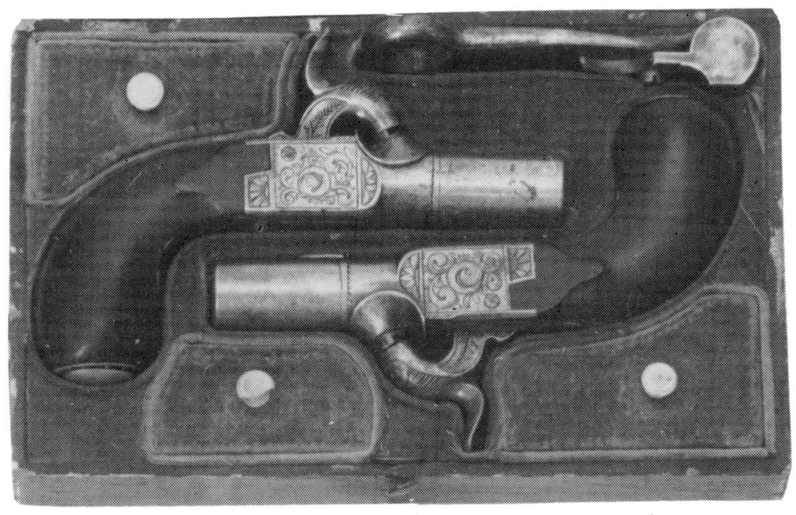

A pair of boxlock percussion pocket pistols by Lepage of Paris, 5¼in., turn-off multi-groove rifled barrels 1¾in., foliate engraved frames, dolphin hammers, concealed triggers, contained in their close fitted velvet lined leather covered case with coloured hardened ball mould. $990 £420

A rare and good quality .22in., American underhammer percussion bootleg target pistol, 14in., octagonal barrel 9in., two-piece polished bone walnut grips each set with three diamond shaped white metal escutcheons, bronze frame and grip straps. $355 £150

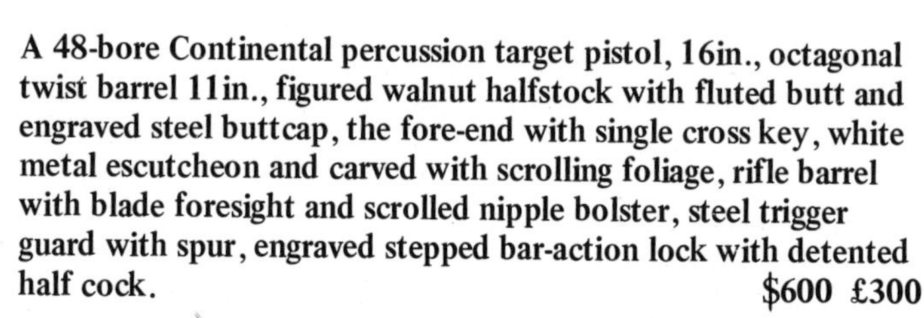

A 48-bore Continental percussion target pistol, 16in., octagonal twist barrel 11in., figured walnut halfstock with fluted butt and engraved steel buttcap, the fore-end with single cross key, white metal escutcheon and carved with scrolling foliage, rifle barrel with blade foresight and scrolled nipple bolster, steel trigger guard with spur, engraved stepped bar-action lock with detented half cock. $600 £300

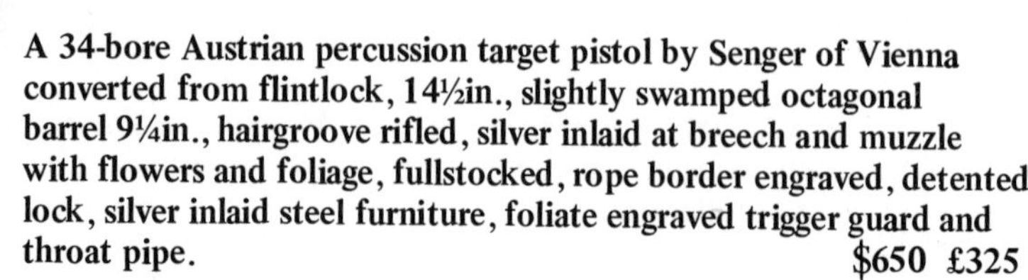

A 34-bore Austrian percussion target pistol by Senger of Vienna converted from flintlock, 14½in., slightly swamped octagonal barrel 9¼in., hairgroove rifled, silver inlaid at breech and muzzle with flowers and foliage, fullstocked, rope border engraved, detented lock, silver inlaid steel furniture, foliate engraved trigger guard and throat pipe. $650 £325

A boxlock percussion travelling pistol fitted with spring bayonet, 7½in., turn-off barrel 2½in., engraved 'Knights Norwich' (worn), foliate and border engraved frame, sliding top thumb safety catch, sliding trigger guard releases 2in. triangular roller bearing sprung bayonet, slab walnut grip, oval silver escutcheon. $215 £100

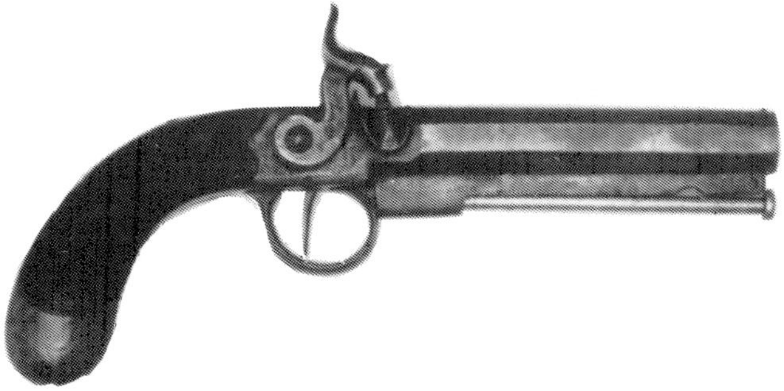

A 34-bore boxlock sidehammer percussion travelling pistol, 9¼in., octagonal barrel 4¼in. engraved 'J.D. Dougall Glasgow' on top flat, Birmingham proved, swivel ramrod, foliate and border engraved frame, trigger guard and hammer, rounded chequered walnut butt with white metal escutcheon. $215 £100

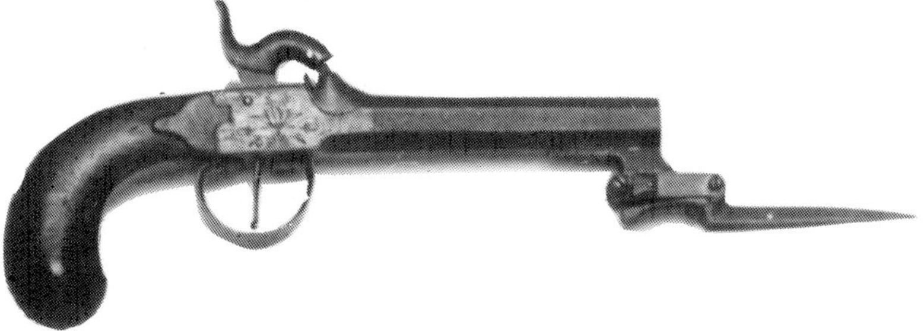

A 38-bore Belgian boxlock percussion travelling pistol by Albert Francotte of Liege fitted with spring bayonet, 9in., turn-off octagonal barrel 4in. stamped with crowned AF, roller bearing sprung triangular bayonet 4in. released by sliding trigger guard. $215 £105

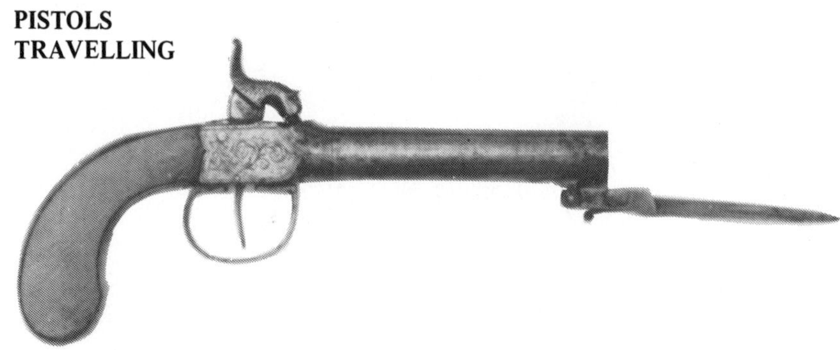

A boxlock percussion travelling pistol fitted with spring bayonet, 8¼in., turn-off barrel 3¾in., Birmingham proved, 4in. sprung triangular bayonet released by sliding trigger guard, foliate engraved frame, dolphin hammer, slab walnut butt with white metal escutcheon. $275 £120

A 28-bore Irish back-action percussion travelling pistol by Colgan of Limerick, 7½in., octagonal deep damascus twist barrel 3¾in., engraved 'Limerick' in script, fullstocked foliate engraved lock with 'Colgan' in script, dolphin hammer. $390 £160

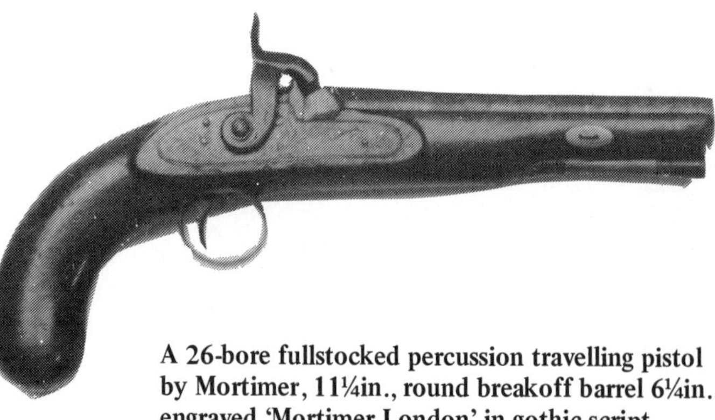

A 26-bore fullstocked percussion travelling pistol by Mortimer, 11¼in., round breakoff barrel 6¼in., engraved 'Mortimer London' in gothic script, silver bead foresight, plain walnut stock with rounded grip, iron furniture. $405 £220

A 28-bore double barrelled boxlock percussion travelling pistol by Moore & Woodward, 9½in., barrels 4¼in., London proved, top rib engraved 'Moore & Woodward, St. James St., London', swivel ramrod on lower rib, foliate engraved frame, hammers and steel furniture, one-piece chequered walnut grip with vacant silver escutcheon. $505 £220

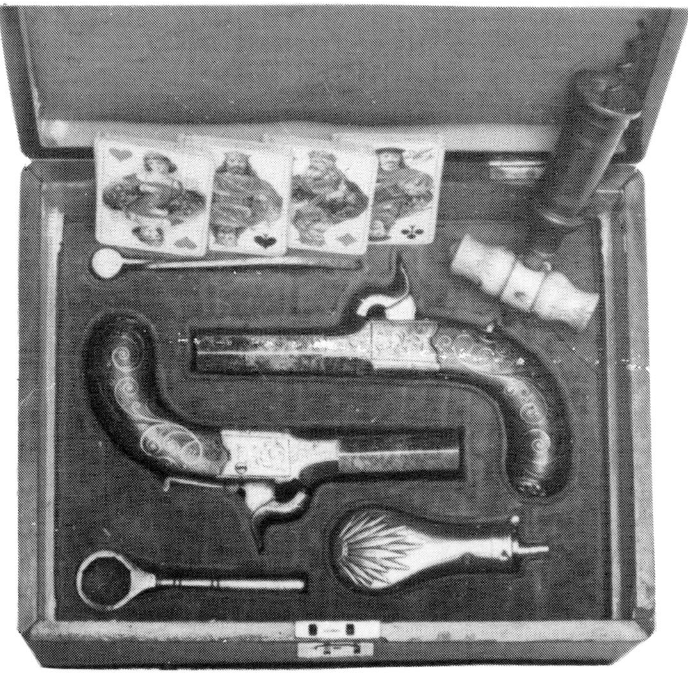

A large pair of 16-bore boxlock percussion travelling pistols, 8in., turn-off octagonal barrels, 2½in., Birmingham proved, foliate and border engraved frames, concealed triggers, sliding top thumb safetys, rounded walnut buttcaps (not hallmarked), oval silver escutcheons engraved 'H', (some silver wire inlay missing), contained in rosewood veneered velvet lined vanity case. $475 £220

A pair of 24-bore boxlock sidehammer percussion travelling pistols, 9½in., round blued barrels 5in., Birmingham proved, swivel ramrods, foliate engraved frames and dolphin hammers, steel trigger guards, rounded chequered walnut grips, white metal lion's head buttcaps. $590 £310

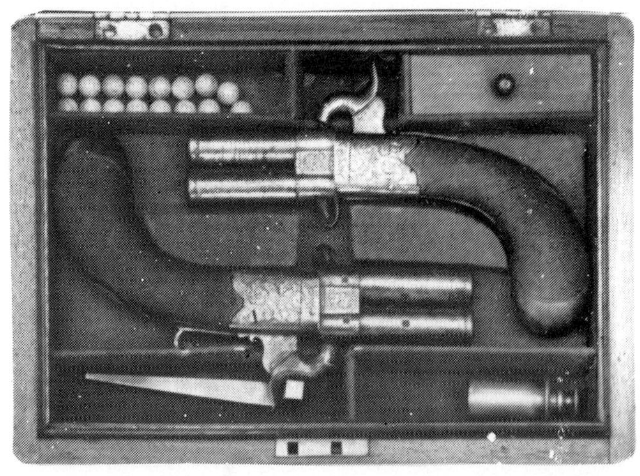

A pair of Irish double barrelled turnover boxlock percussion travelling pistols by Wilson of Dublin, 6¾in., turn-off barrels 2in., Birmingham proved foliate engraved frames, concealed triggers, dolphin hammers, sliding top thumb safety catches, contained in their green beize lined mahogany case with barrel key, brass bottle and balls. $990 £450

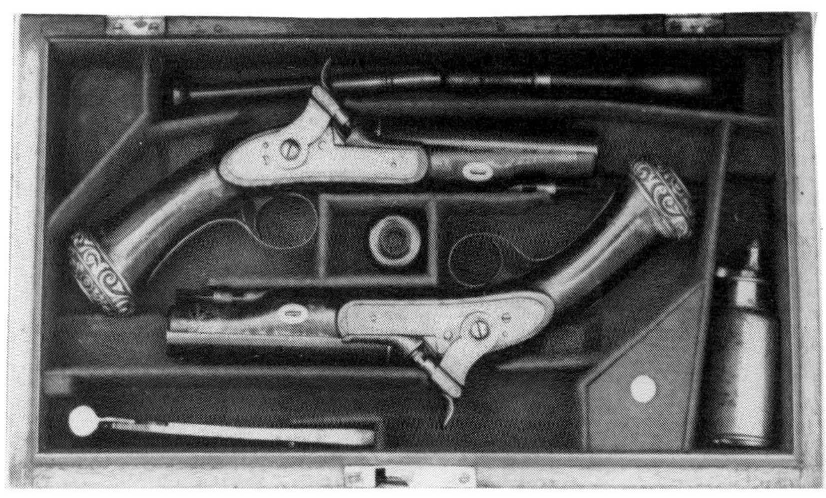

An unusual pair of 50-bore percussion travelling pistols by G. Sturman of London, 9in., browned twist barrels 4in., with top sighting flats, three gold inlaid breech lines with gold foresights, fullstocked in maplewood, foliate and border engraved locks with 'G. Sturman 25 East Road, City Road, London', flattened engraved early style hammers, silver furniture. $1,510 £700

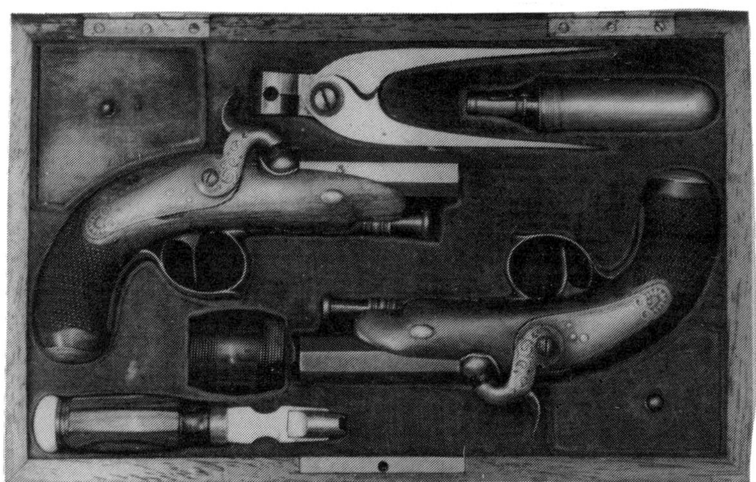

A pair of 20-bore French back-action percussion derringer style travelling pistols, 7in., octagonal multi-groove rifled damascus twist barrels 3in., one struck with crowned 'LF' mark of Le Faucheaux, threequarter stocked, border engraved lock with foliate engraved hammers, foliate and floral engraved white metal furniture. $1,800 £750

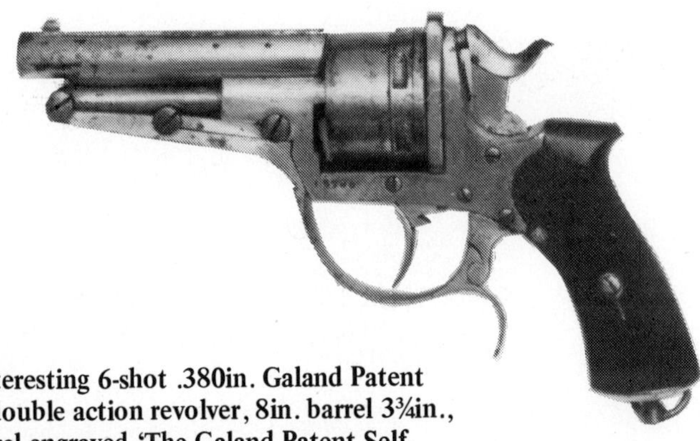

A scarce and interesting 6-shot .380in. Galand Patent self extracting double action revolver, 8in. barrel 3¾in., No. 15786, barrel engraved 'The Galand Patent Self Extractor', chequered walnut grips with lanyard ring, plated frame barrel and cylinder. $195 £95

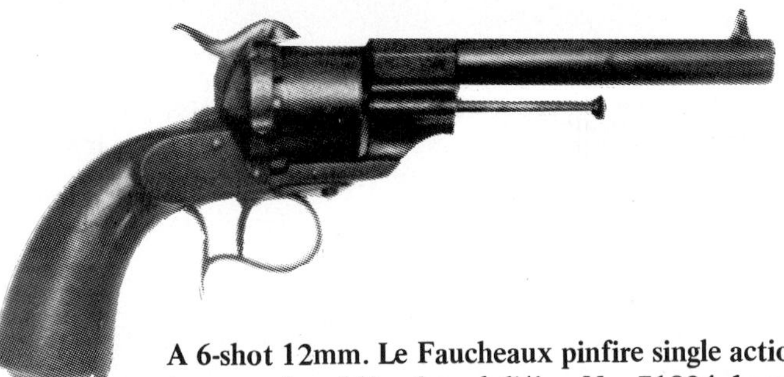

A 6-shot 12mm. Le Faucheaux pinfire single action Military type revolver 11in., barrel 6¼in., No. 71894, barrel engraved 'Invtn E. Le Faucheaux Brte. Scdg. A Paris', walnut grips, iron butt plate with lanyard ring, spurred trigger guard, gate loading and rod ejection. $255 £125

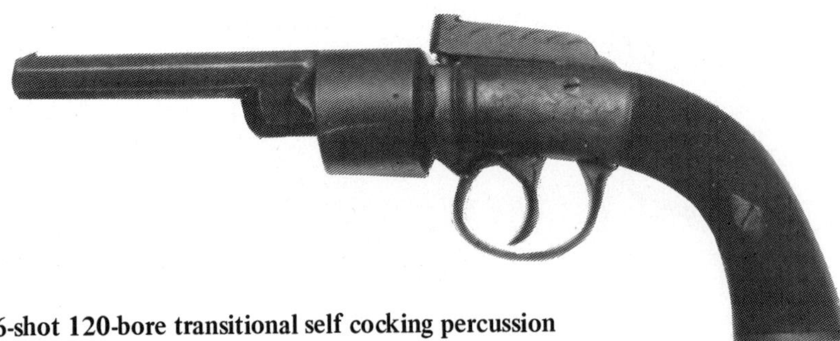

A 6-shot 120-bore transitional self cocking percussion revolver, 9in., octagonal barrel 3½in., Birmingham proved, foliate engraved round frame, husk engraved bar hammer, foliate engraved steel grip strap and mounts, 2-piece chequered walnut grip. $265 £125

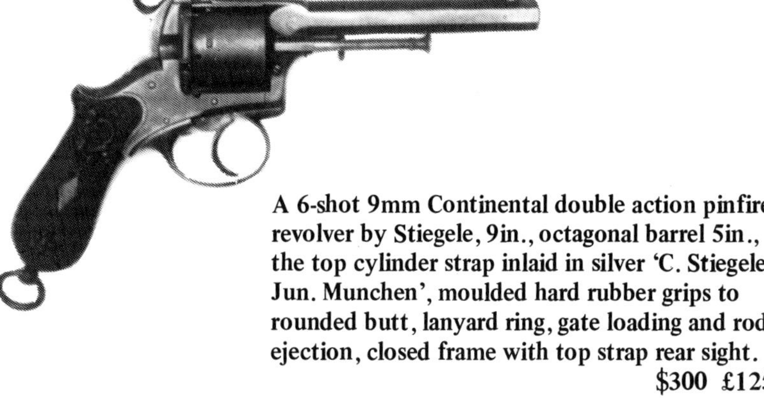

A 6-shot 9mm Continental double action pinfire revolver by Stiegele, 9in., octagonal barrel 5in., the top cylinder strap inlaid in silver 'C. Stiegele Jun. Munchen', moulded hard rubber grips to rounded butt, lanyard ring, gate loading and rod ejection, closed frame with top strap rear sight.
$300 £125

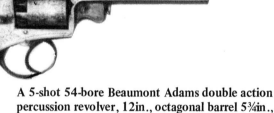

A 5-shot 54-bore Beaumont Adams double action percussion revolver, 12in., octagonal barrel 5¾in., engraved 'H. Blake 18 Swan Stt Minories' on top strap, white metal rear and foresights, sidelever rammer, foliate engraved cylinder safety bolt.
$290 £135

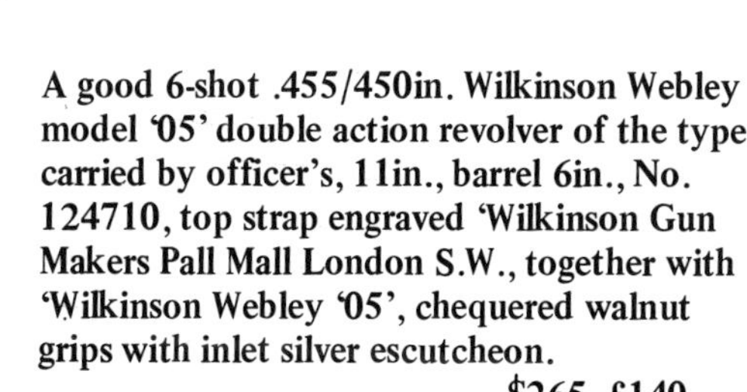

A good 6-shot .455/450in. Wilkinson Webley model '05' double action revolver of the type carried by officer's, 11in., barrel 6in., No. 124710, top strap engraved 'Wilkinson Gun Makers Pall Mall London S.W., together with 'Wilkinson Webley '05', chequered walnut grips with inlet silver escutcheon.
$265 £140

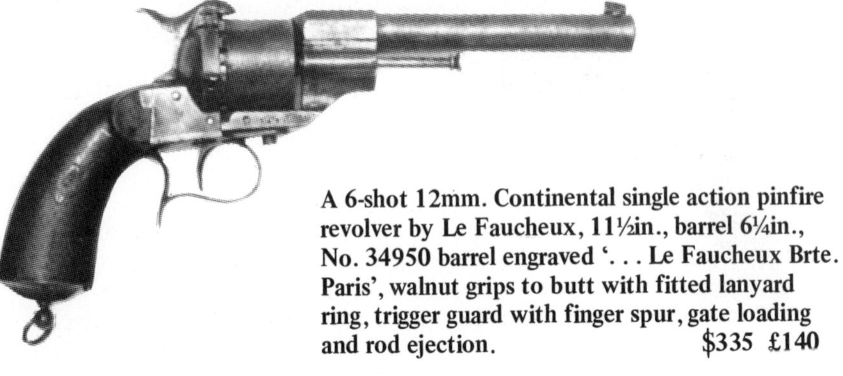

A 6-shot 12mm. Continental single action pinfire revolver by Le Faucheux, 11½in., barrel 6¼in., No. 34950 barrel engraved '. . . Le Faucheux Brte. Paris', walnut grips to butt with fitted lanyard ring, trigger guard with finger spur, gate loading and rod ejection. $335 £140

A 5-shot 54-bore Kerr's patent double action revolver No. 1191 by the London Armoury, 11in., octagonal barrel 5½in., London proved, frame engraved 'Kerr's Patent 1191, back-action lock engraved 'London Armoury', underlever rammer, external hammer, sprung catch retains cylinder axis pin, steel lanyard ring on buttcap, one-piece chequered walnut grip. $345 £150

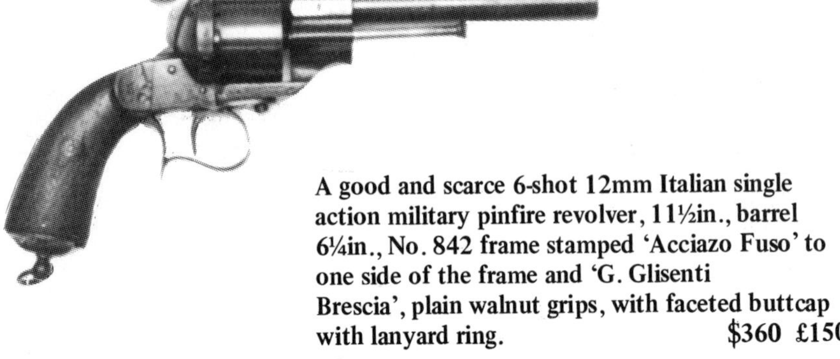

A good and scarce 6-shot 12mm Italian single action military pinfire revolver, 11½in., barrel 6¼in., No. 842 frame stamped 'Acciazo Fuso' to one side of the frame and 'G. Glisenti Brescia', plain walnut grips, with faceted buttcap with lanyard ring. $360 £150

A 5-shot 54-bore Beaumont Adams double action percussion revolver, 11½in., octagonal barrel 5¾in., London proved and stamped L.A.C., barrel engraved 'Robert Adams, 76 King William Street London', chequered walnut grip with steel buttcap, line border engraved frame, side lever rammer, blade foresight. $360 £150

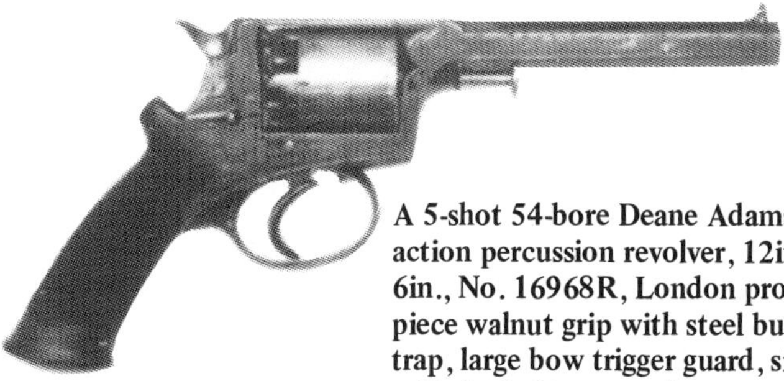

A 5-shot 54-bore Deane Adams & Deane double action percussion revolver, 12in., octagonal barrel 6in., No. 16968R, London proved, chequered one-piece walnut grip with steel buttcap with hinged trap, large bow trigger guard, side mounted cylinder bolt, sprung hammer safety to left side. $360 £150

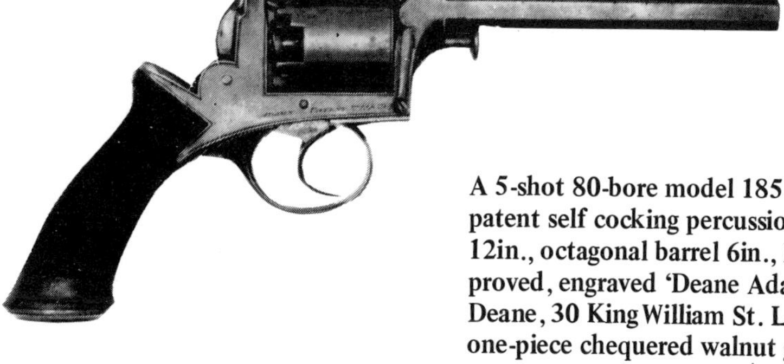

A 5-shot 80-bore model 1851 Adams patent self cocking percussion revolver, 12in., octagonal barrel 6in., London proved, engraved 'Deane Adams & Deane, 30 King William St. London', one-piece chequered walnut grip. $360 £150

A 5-shot 54-bore Beaumont Adams double action percussion revolver, 11½in., octagonal barrel 5¾in., London proved, engraved 'Deane & Son, 30 King William Street, London Bridge' on top flat, engraved 'WT from MDT' on side and stamped L.A.C. with stamp for London Armoury Company. $305 £160

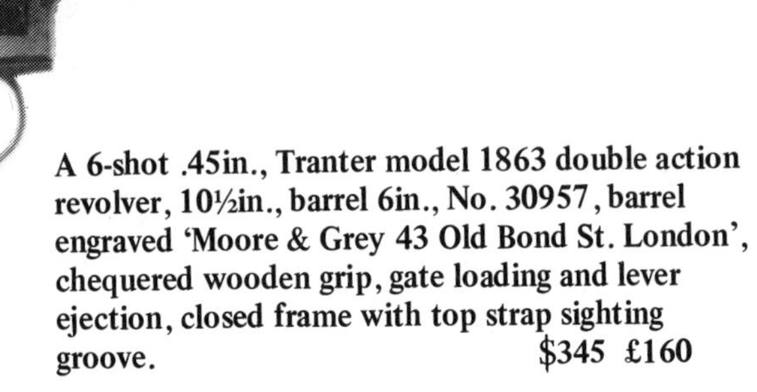

A 6-shot .45in., Tranter model 1863 double action revolver, 10½in., barrel 6in., No. 30957, barrel engraved 'Moore & Grey 43 Old Bond St. London', chequered wooden grip, gate loading and lever ejection, closed frame with top strap sighting groove. $345 £160

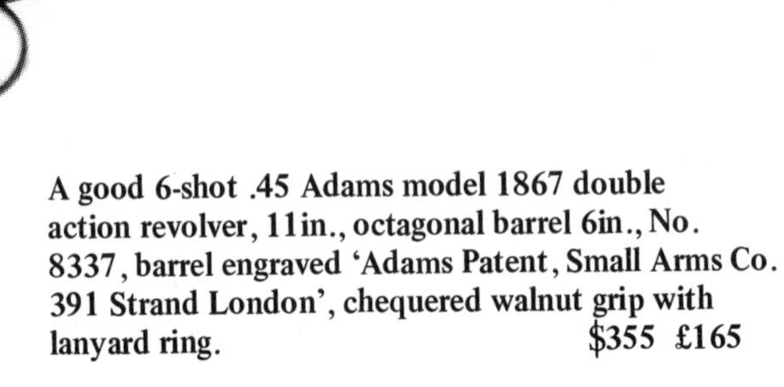

A good 6-shot .45 Adams model 1867 double action revolver, 11in., octagonal barrel 6in., No. 8337, barrel engraved 'Adams Patent, Small Arms Co. 391 Strand London', chequered walnut grip with lanyard ring. $355 £165

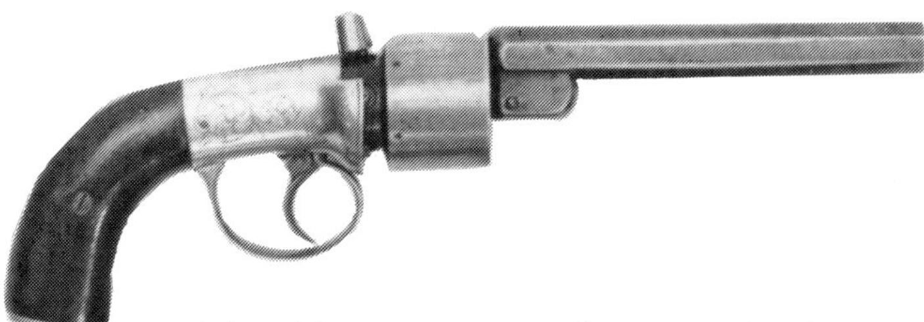

A 6-shot .36in. top snap, open frame transitional percussion revolver, 11½in., octagonal barrel 5½in., Birmingham proved, with traces of blued finish, white metal rounded frame and grip strap, foliate border engraved, steel hammer and trigger guard, 2-piece polished walnut grip. $325 £170

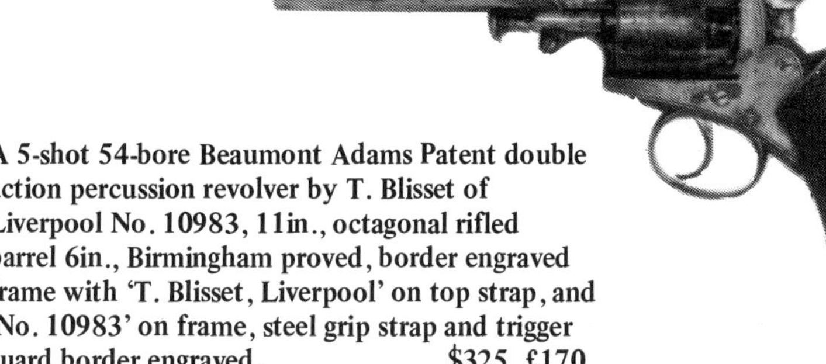

A 5-shot 54-bore Beaumont Adams Patent double action percussion revolver by T. Blisset of Liverpool No. 10983, 11in., octagonal rifled barrel 6in., Birmingham proved, border engraved frame with 'T. Blisset, Liverpool' on top strap, and 'No. 10983' on frame, steel grip strap and trigger guard border engraved. $325 £170

A 5-shot 54-bore Beaumont Adams double action percussion revolver No. 40153, 12in., octagonal barrel 5¾in., London proved, engraved 'William Bishop 170 New Bond St. London' on top strap, border engraved frame with 'Adams Patent No. 40153', sidelever rammer, sliding cylinder safety bolt to side of frame. $390 £180

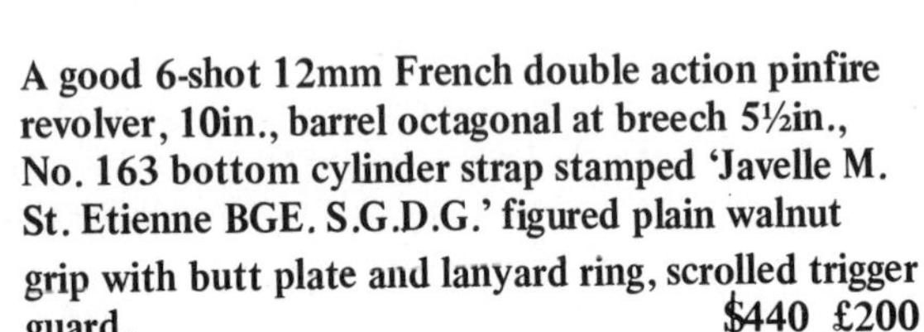

A good 6-shot 12mm French double action pinfire revolver, 10in., barrel octagonal at breech 5½in., No. 163 bottom cylinder strap stamped 'Javelle M. St. Etienne BGE. S.G.D.G.' figured plain walnut grip with butt plate and lanyard ring, scrolled trigger guard. $440 £200

A good 6-shot .45in. Boxer Colt model 1878 double action service revolver, 10in., barrel 5½in., No. 8130, barrel with Colt's London address (faint), chequered walnut grips to bird's head butt with lanyard ring, gate loading rod ejection, circular sideplate to left side, blade foresight top strap groove rear, retaining much original blue finish overall. $495 £210

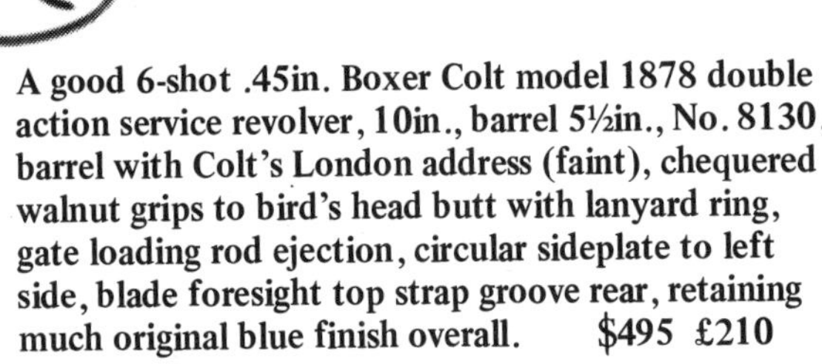

A scarce 5-shot 38-bore self cocking 1851 pattern Adams Dragoon percussion revolver No. 4884, 13¼in., octagonal barrel 7¾in., London proved, engraved 'Hollis & Sheath makers to H.M.H. Board of Ordnance London', London proved cylinder, frame engraved 'Patent No. 4884', one-piece chequered walnut grip, sprung cap trap in butt. $485 £220

A scarce 6-shot .44in. Allen & Wheelock Lip-Fire single action Army revolver, 12½in., part round, part octagonal barrel 7½in., No. 324, barrel stamped 'Allen & Wheelock Worcester M.S.U.S. Allens Pat's Sept. 7 Nov. 9 1858'. polished walnut grips to angular butt, rounded frame with integral recoil shield and loading gate to right side, trigger guard double as ejector lever to remove fired cases.
$528 £220

A rare .55in. 5-shot Austrian Mann's Patent double action percussion revolver No. 1073 modelled upon the Beaumont Adams 12in., octagonal barrel 6¼in stamped 'S. Mann – Scheinigg Tokring Z Wien' with imperial Austrian eagle stamp, side-lever rammer, cylinder with pointed pillar breeches, steel trigger guard and lanyard ring, 2-piece chequered wooden grips. $600 £250

A good 6-shot .44in Remington New Model single action percussion revolver, 13½in., octagonal barrel 8in., No. 105984, barrel stamped 'Patented Sept 14 1858'. maker's name and address and 'New Model', 2-piece walnut grips with inspector's stamp, brass trigger guard. $530 £280

A 6-shot .455in. Webley Fosbery automatic revolver, 10½in., ribbed barrel 6in., stamped 'Army & Navy C.S.L.', No. 1691, diced composition grips with fitted lanyard ring, thumb safety to left side, tip-down barrel for loading, auto ejection, the cylinder with machined zig-zag to facilitate rotation. $650 £300

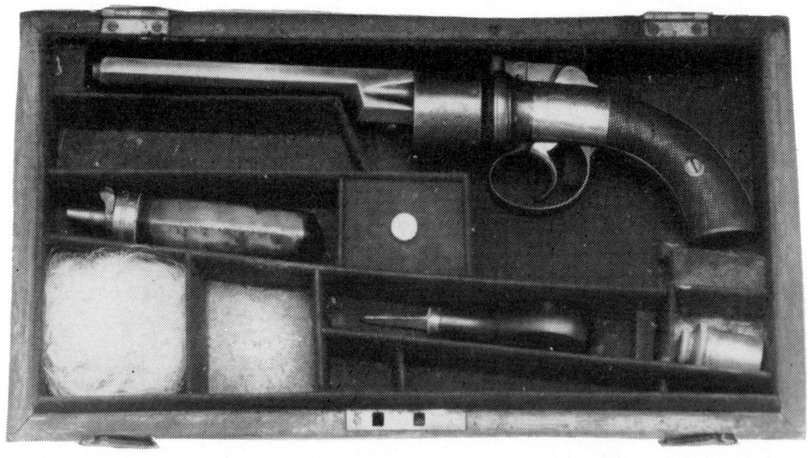

A 6-shot 60-bore bar hammer transitional percussion revolver, 12½in., octagonal barrel 6in., Birmingham proved, chequered walnut grips, round action body with some scroll engraving, bar hammer with sliding top safety which when in position blocks hammer, screw retained sighted barrel. Contained in green baize lined and fitted mahogany case. $840 £350

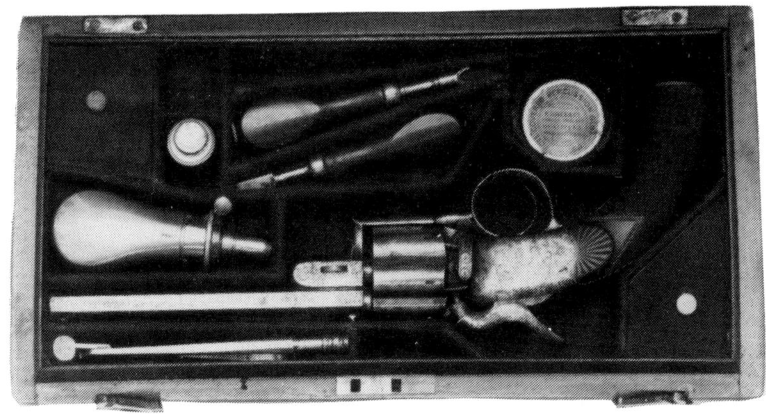

A 6-shot 65-bore J. Beattie patent reciprocating cylinder single action transitional percussion revolver, 12in., octagonal barrel 6in., London proved, barrel engraved 'J. Beattie, 205 Regent St., London', finely chequered walnut grip with steel cap with spring lidded trap, blank silver escutcheon, rounded action body with off-set hammer, fully church steeple fluted cylinder, wedge retained barrel. Contained in its green baize lined and fitted mahogany case. $1,020 £425

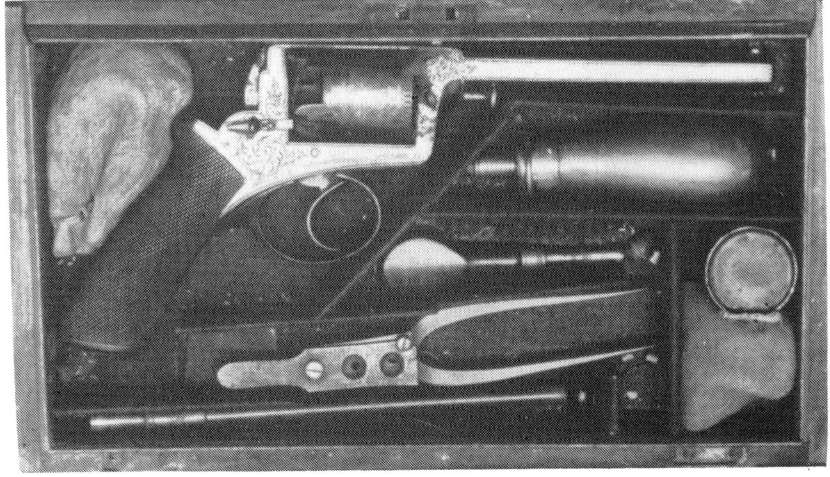

A 5-shot 54-bore Deane Adams & Deane pattern 1851 self-cocking percussion revolver, 12in., octagonal barrel 6 1/8in., No. 15466R, barrel engraved 'Deane Adams & Deane, No. 30 King William St., London Bridge', London proved. Contained in its original green baize lined and fitted oak case. $785 £430

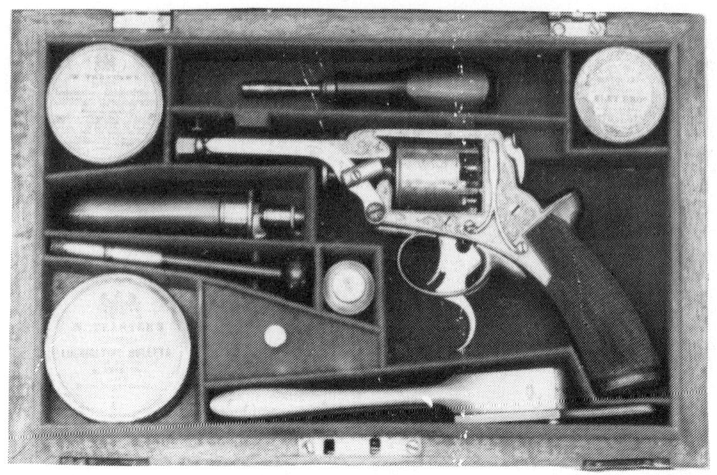

A 5-shot 120-bore double trigger Tranter's patent percussion revolver, No. 19292 T, 8½in., octagonal barrel 4in., Birmingham proved, top flat engraved 'T. Conway, Blackfriars St., Manchester', with foliate border, side lever rammer and trigger stamped 'Tranter's Patent'. One-piece chequered walnut grip with foliate engraved buttcap. Retained in its green baize lined fitted mahogany case with all original accessories. $1,340 £550

A 5-shot 54-bore self-cocking sidehammer percussion revolver by Westley Richards, No. 301, 12in., octagonal barrel 6in., Birmingham proved, cylinder and frame numbered 301. Foliate engraved frame, sidehammer with sprung safety bar, cammed bar secured top strap which can lift to allow removal of barrel. 'Creeping' side lever rammer, one-piece chequered walnut grip, chipped at web spur. $1,370 £570

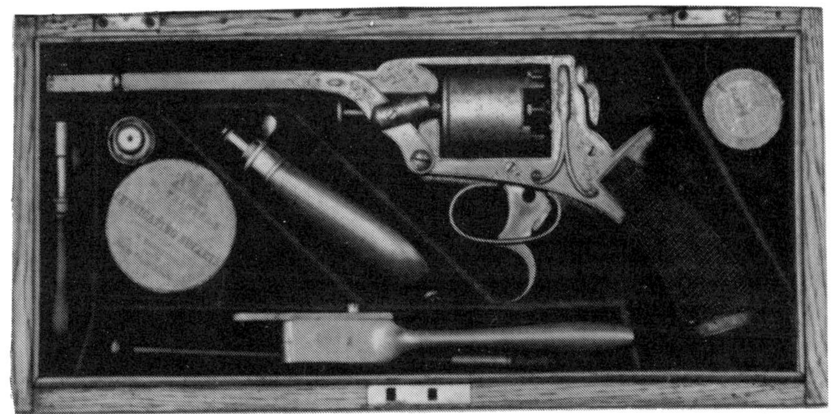

A 5-shot 38-bore Tranter 3rd model double trigger self-cocking Dragoon percussion revolver, 14in., octagonal barrel 7½in., No. 12803T. Chequered one-piece walnut grip with engraved steel fitting along back for shoulder stock attachment and steel butt plate, trigger guard slotted to allow for cocking trigger which is stamped 'Tranter's Patent'. Sprung hammer half cock stop to left side of frame, side lever rammer stamped 'Tranter's Patent'. Plain Birmingham proved cylinder with roped forward border, dovetailed bead fore-sight, hammer bolster rear 'V' notch, in its original green baize lined and fitted oak case bearing the trade label of Edward Whistler, 11 Strand, Trafalgar Square, London and with engraved brass lid escutcheon 'W.A.E. 17th Lancers.'

$1,440 £600

A fully gold damascened 5-shot 54-bore Beaumont Adams double action percussion revolver built on the improved frame and retailed by Wilkinson & Son, and fitted with Brazian's Patent rammer, 11½in., barrel 5 5/8in., No. 34191T, London proved. Contained in a green baize lined and fitted mahogany pistol box with pistol sized flask by Hawksley. $1,560 £650

A 6-shot .44in. Rodgers & Spencer single action Army percussion revolver, No. 3764, 13in., octagonal barrel 7½in., top strap stamped 'Rodgers & Spencer Utica N.Y.'. Colour hardened rammer and hammer. Two-piece wooden grips with government inspector's initials 'R.P.B.'. Backstrap engraved 'Death to Traitors' above rearing snake. $1,405 £650

A 5-shot 54-bore Beaumont Adams double action percussion revolver, for the British Army, No. 24620 R, 12in., octagonal barrel 5¾in., London proved, engraved 'London Armoury' on top flat. Side lever rammer, steel furniture, one-piece chequered walnut grip. In its flat top leather holster, together with a leather accessories pouch. $1,730 £800

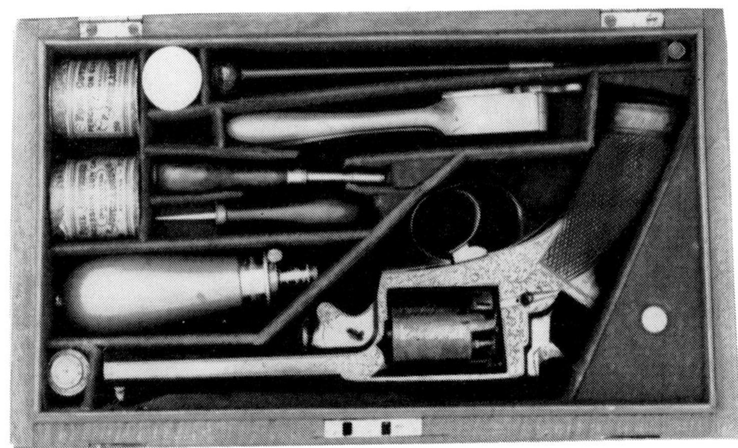

A 5-shot 54-bore Beaumont Adams presentation engraved double action percussion revolver, No. 21002R, 12in., octagonal barrel 5¾in., London proved, engraved 'Deane & Son, No. 30 King William St., London Bridge' on top strap. Cylinder, muzzle, trigger guard and buttcap borders strapwork engraved. Contained in its green baize lined fitted mahogany case. $1,945 £900

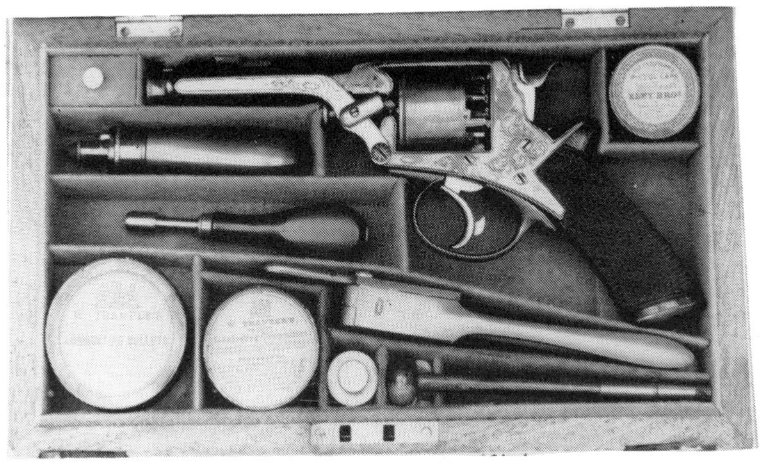

A 5-shot 80-bore Tranter's patent double action percussion revolver, No. 16820T, 9½in., octagonal barrel 4½in., Birmingham proved, engraved 'R. R. Rodda & Co., Gun Makers by Appointment' on top flat. In its green baize lined fitted mahogany case with Dixon flask etc. $2,050 £950

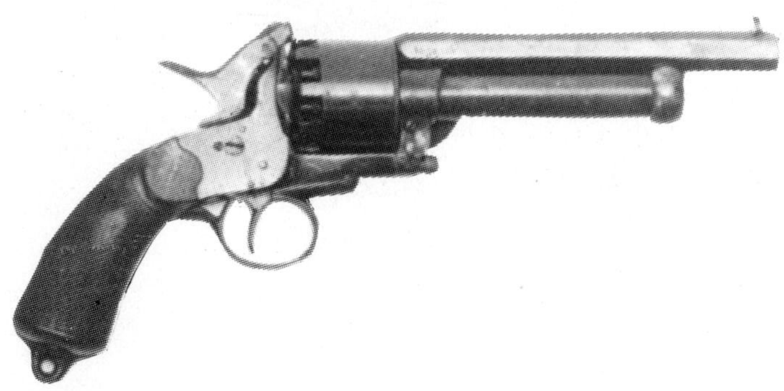

A 10-shot .41in. Le Mat grape shot pistol combination single action percussion revolver, 13in., rifled octagonal revolver barrel 6 5/8in., 16-bore grape shot barrel 6¾in., No. 1754 (matching), barrel engraved in script 'Col. Le Mat Bte. S.G.D.G. Paris', chequered walnut grip with lanyard loop integral with buttcap.

$2,440 £1,000

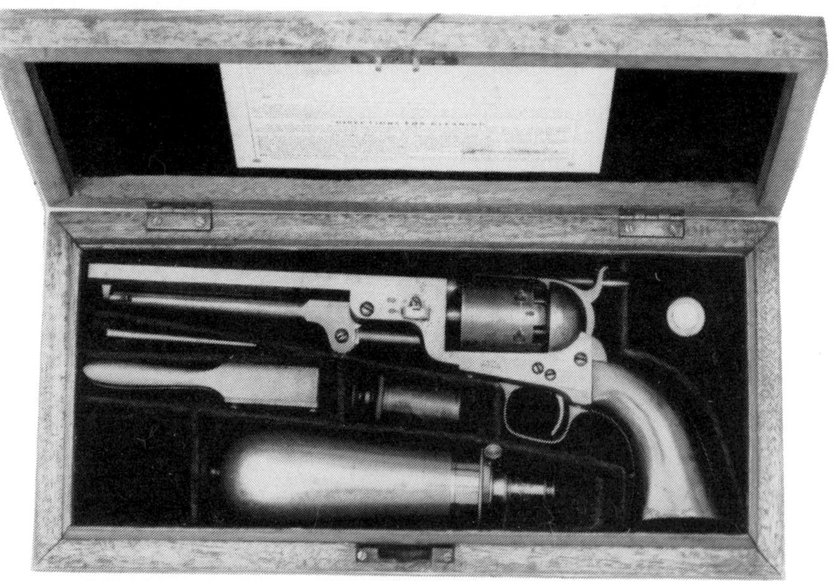

A 6-shot .36in. London Colt Navy single action percussion revolver, No. 30854, 13in., octagonal barrel 7½in., stamped 'Address Col. Colt London' (one line), London proved. Underlever rammer, London proved cylinder roll engraved with Navy scene. Contained in its blue velvet lined fitted mahogany case.

$2,615 £1,210

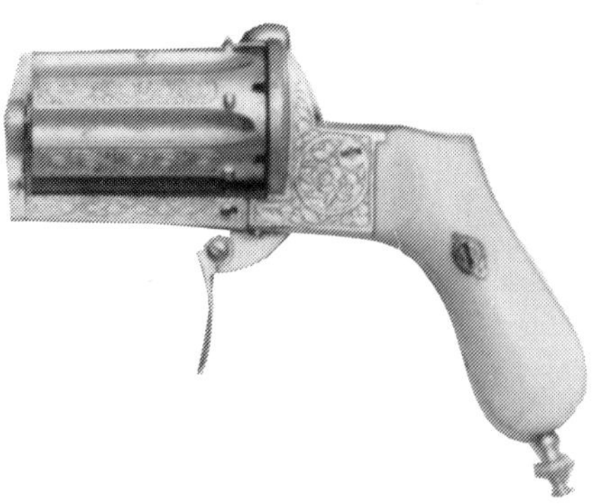

A 6-shot 7mm. pin-fire Continental self-cocking pepperbox revolver, 4¾in., fluted barrels 2in., No. 2212, polished ivory grips to bag-shaped butt with screw-out ejector rod, folding trigger, gate loading, scroll foliate engraved frame and barrel group, the whole pistol gold plated overall. $95 £45

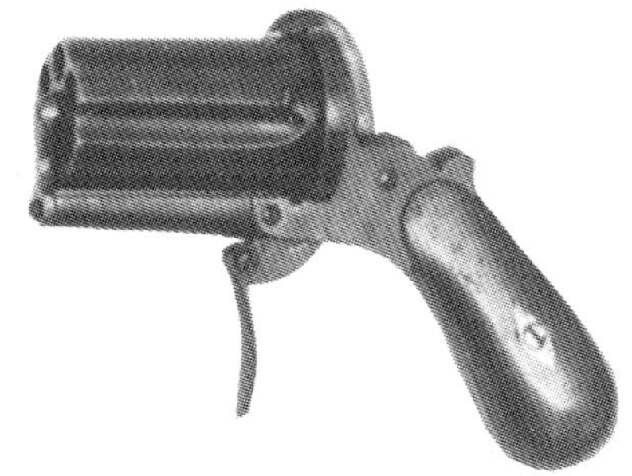

A 6-shot 7mm. Continental pin-fire self-cocking pepperbox revolver, 4 5/8in., barrels 1 7/8in., wooden grips to bag-shaped butt, gate loading folding trigger, smooth-bored barrels with long flutes. $125 £52

A 6-shot 80-bore underhammer ring trigger Cooper's patent percussion pepperbox revolver, 8in., fluted barrel 3¾in., Birmingham proved, frame engraved 'J.R. Cooper's Patent', plain grips to bag-shaped butt, rounded engraved action body, with capping channel to right side. $265 £120

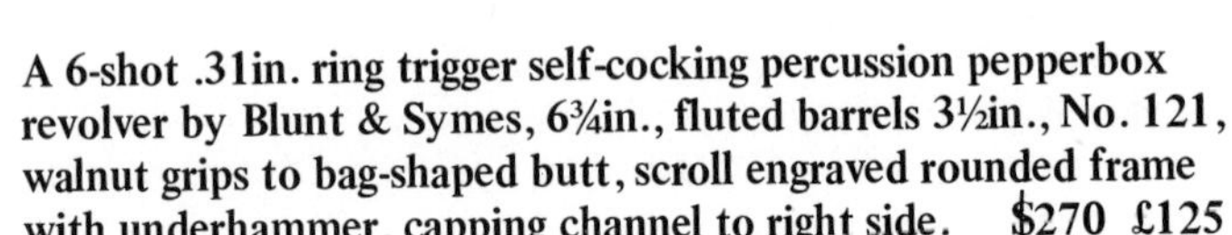

A 6-shot .31in. ring trigger self-cocking percussion pepperbox revolver by Blunt & Symes, 6¾in., fluted barrels 3½in., No. 121, walnut grips to bag-shaped butt, scroll engraved rounded frame with underhammer, capping channel to right side. $270 £125

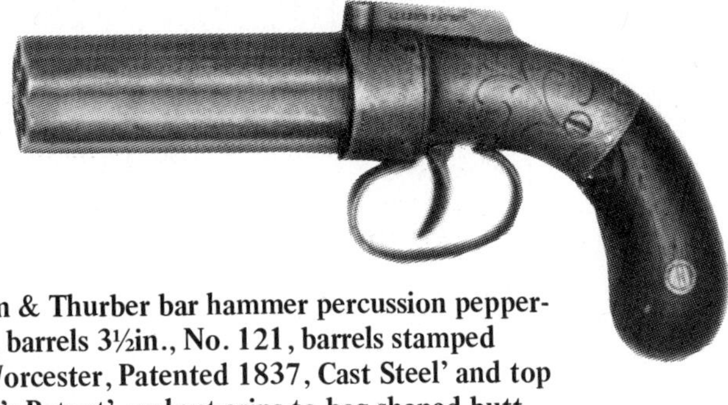

A 6-shot .31in. Allen & Thurber bar hammer percussion pepperbox revolver, 7½in., barrels 3½in., No. 121, barrels stamped 'Allen & Thurber, Worcester, Patented 1837, Cast Steel' and top snap hammer 'Allen's Patent', walnut grips to bag-shaped butt, rounded scroll engraved action body, detachable flash shield, semi-fluted barrels. $300 £125

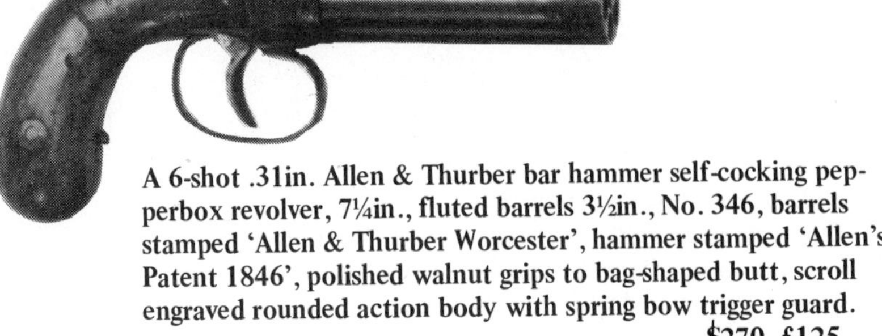

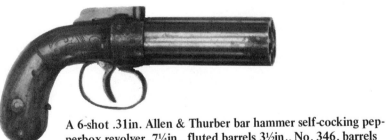

A 6-shot .31in. Allen & Thurber bar hammer self-cocking pepperbox revolver, 7¼in., fluted barrels 3½in., No. 346, barrels stamped 'Allen & Thurber Worcester', hammer stamped 'Allen's Patent 1846', polished walnut grips to bag-shaped butt, scroll engraved rounded action body with spring bow trigger guard. $270 £125

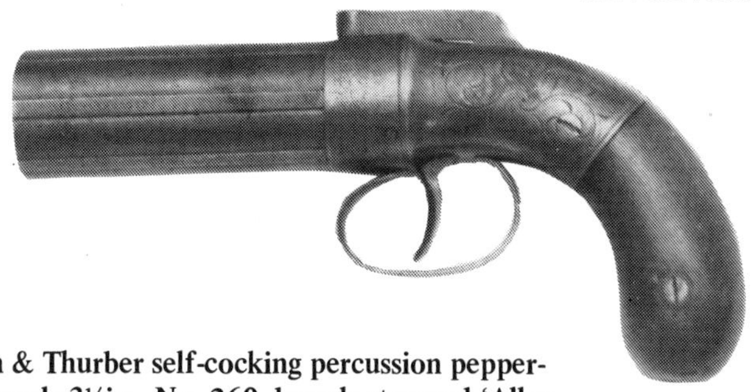

A 6-shot .31in. Allen & Thurber self-cocking percussion pepperbox revolver, 7in., barrels 3½in., No. 260, barrels stamped 'Allen & Thurber Worcester Patented 1837 Cast Steel', polished walnut grips to bag-shaped butt, rounded scroll engraved action body and nipple shield, spring bow trigger guard, bar hammer stamped 'Allen's Patent', fluted barrel group. $270 £130

A 6-shot .31in. Allen's patent bar hammer self-cocking percussion pepperbox revolver, 7in., fluted barrel 3½in., No. 811, barrel stamped 'Patented 1837, Cast Steel', bar hammer stamped 'Allen's Patent', two-piece polished walnut grip with inlet oval white metal escutcheons, round scroll engraved frame, with etched nipple shield, spring steel trigger guard. $305 £130

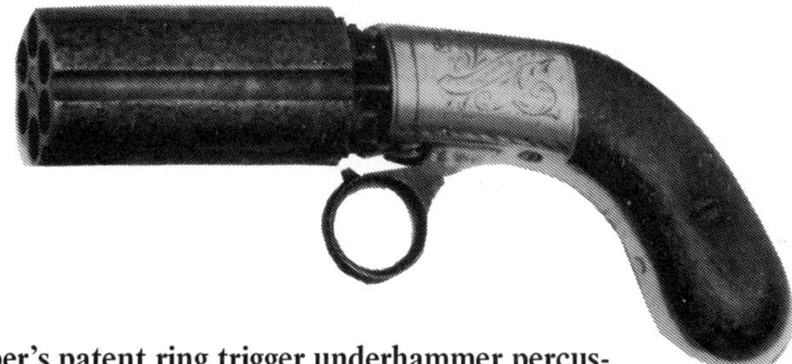

A 6-shot 80-bore Cooper's patent ring trigger underhammer percussion pepperbox revolver, 7½in., fluted barrels 3 3/8in., frame engraved 'J. R. Cooper's Patent', rounded walnut grips to white metal backstrap, rounded white metal action body with border and scroll engraving. $320 £140

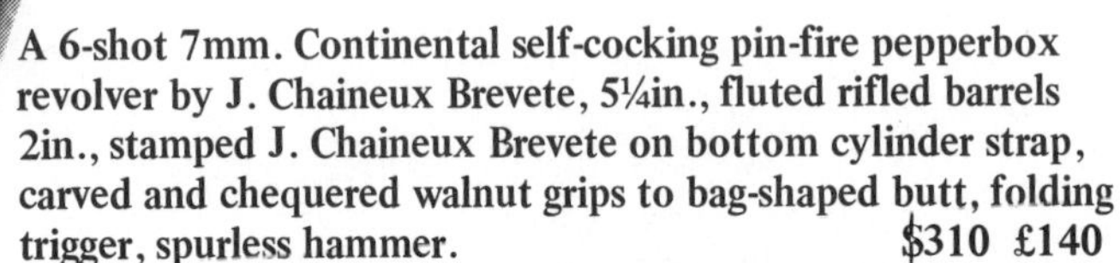

A 6-shot 7mm. Continental self-cocking pin-fire pepperbox revolver by J. Chaineux Brevete, 5¼in., fluted rifled barrels 2in., stamped J. Chaineux Brevete on bottom cylinder strap, carved and chequered walnut grips to bag-shaped butt, folding trigger, spurless hammer. $310 £140

A 6-shot 120-bore self-cocking bar hammer percussion pepperbox revolver by Fenton of London, 7¼in., fluted barrels 2½in., Birmingham proved, foliate tip engraved muzzles. Scroll and foliate engraved squared frame with 'Fenton', 'London' within banners. Foliate engraved hammer and trigger guard. Finely chequered rounded walnut grip with vacant oval escutcheon. $350 £145

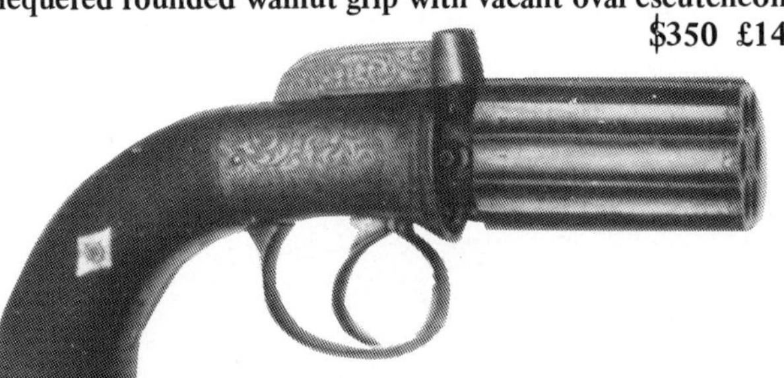

A 6-shot 120-bore self-cocking top snap engraved percussion pepperbox revolver by William Lee, 7½in., fluted cylinder 3in., Birmingham proved. Round frame foliate engraved upon confined stippled ground en suite with hammer, buttcap, trigger guard and grip strap with 'William Lee, Maker', two-piece chequered walnut grips. $315 £146

A 6-shot 80-bore bar hammer percussion self-cocking pepperbox revolver, 7¾in., fluted white metal barrels 3in., Birmingham proved, plain walnut grips to white metal frame, rounded white metal action body with some border and scroll engraving, large bow trigger guard. $330 £150

A 6-shot 34-bore percussion bar hammer pepperbox self-cocking revolver, 7 1/8in., barrel 3in., Birmingham proved, chequered walnut grips, scroll engraved rounded action body, fluted barrels. $390 £160

A 6-shot 120-bore bar hammer percussion pepperbox revolver by J. Beattie, 7in., fluted barrels numbered 1-6 2½in., struck with London proof marks, finely chequered walnut grip with scroll engraved butt trap, blank oval escutcheon, rounded action body scroll engraved with 'J. Beattie, 205 Regent St., London' within oval top, thumb sliding safety. $365 £170

A 6-shot .31in. Allen & Thurber bar hammer self-cocking pepperbox revolver, 7in., semi-fluted barrels 3½in., No. 118, rounded walnut grips to bag-shaped butt, rounded frame with acanthus leaf scroll engraving, roll engraved nipple shield, bar hammer stamped 'Allen's Patent 1845'. $435 £190

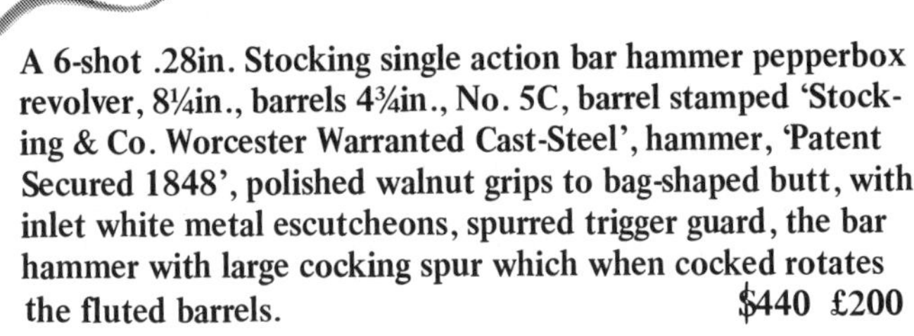

A 6-shot .28in. Stocking single action bar hammer pepperbox revolver, 8¼in., barrels 4¾in., No. 5C, barrel stamped 'Stocking & Co. Worcester Warranted Cast-Steel', hammer, 'Patent Secured 1848', polished walnut grips to bag-shaped butt, with inlet white metal escutcheons, spurred trigger guard, the bar hammer with large cocking spur which when cocked rotates the fluted barrels. $440 £200

A 6-shot 80-bore bar hammer percussion pepperbox revolver, 7¼in., barrel 3in., frame engraved 'Rowntree Bd. Castle', plain polished walnut grips, roped border and scroll engraved white metal frame with integral nipple shield, engraved bar hammer with collar, fluted barrels, Birmingham proved. $535 £220

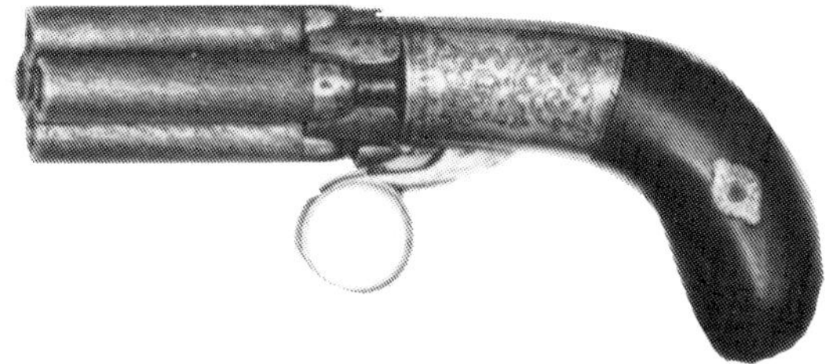

A 4-shot .32in. trigger self-cocking Mariette patent percussion pepperbox revolver, 5¾in., turn-off damascus twist barrels 2in., Liege proved. Rounded foliate engraved frame, stamped 'Mariette Brevete' on grip strap. Two-piece bag-shaped ebony grips. $650 £230

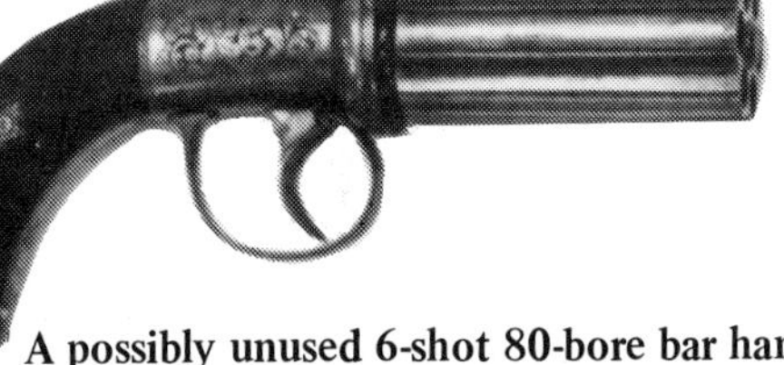

A possibly unused 6-shot 80-bore bar hammer percussion pepperbox revolver, 8in., fluted case-hardened barrels 3in., with Birmingham proofs, rounded butt with chequered walnut grips, and colour hardened trap for caps, rounded action body with integral nipple shield and scroll foliate engraved decoration, engraved back strap and bar hammer. $790 £360

A 60-shot .22in. shot Remington zig-zag revolving pepperbox derringer, 4¼in., barrel group 3¼in., No. 286, framed stamped 'Elliot's Patents, Aug. 17, 1858/May 29, 1860' and 'Manufactured by Remington's, Ilion, N.Y.', plain hard rubber grips, ring type trigger, the barrel cluster with 6 sights, deeply fluted with zig-zag grooves at breech end to facilitate revolution.
$880 £360

A fine and probably unique 24-bore 6-shot Italian self-cocking concealed hammer percussion pepperbox revolver by G. Pilla, PRa Di Avelina Di Pesco, circa 1860, overall length 10¾in., twist barrels 4¼in., inlaid in gold 1-6 en suite with breech, foliate engraved breech plate. Foliate engraved round steel frame gold inlaid 'G. Pilla PRa Di Avelina Di Pesco'. Engraved trigger guard with finger spur. Finely chequered root walnut one-piece rounded grip, carved with foliage at butt. White metal hinged cap trap on butt with lion couchant in relief. $2,400 £1,000

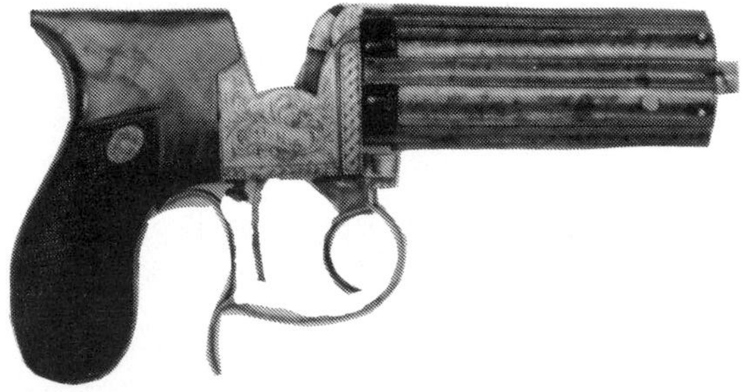

A rare and probably unique 6-shot 55-bore Irish double action percussion pepperbox revolver by W. Norman of Dublin, circa 1860, overall length 8½in., fluted cylinder 4in., released from axis by press stud at muzzle, foliate engraved breeches, silver bead foresights. Strapwork and husk border engraved frame with 'Wm. Norman Dublin' within banners upon foliate scrolls. Topstrap of grip engraved 'Maker & Inventor'. Two-piece chequered walnut grips of 'saw-handled' form with steel grip frame and large trigger guard with finger spur. $2,760 £1,150

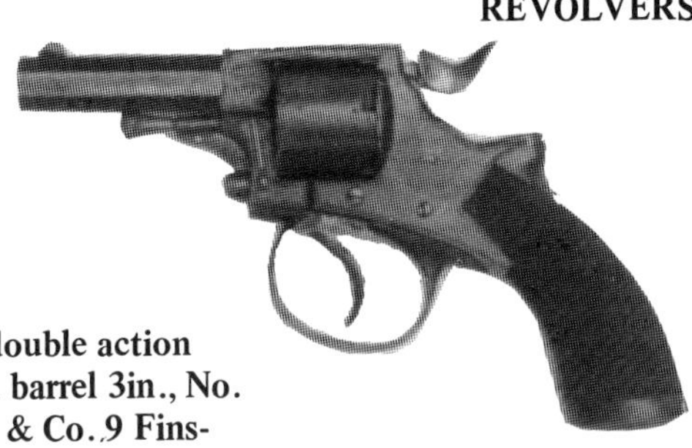

A 5-shot .320in. Tranter patent double action pocket revolver, 7¼in., octagonal barrel 3in., No. 5668, top strap engraved 'Adams & Co.,9 Finsbury Place South London', chequered wooden grip, gate loading and rod ejection, plain Birmingham proved cylinder. $55 £30

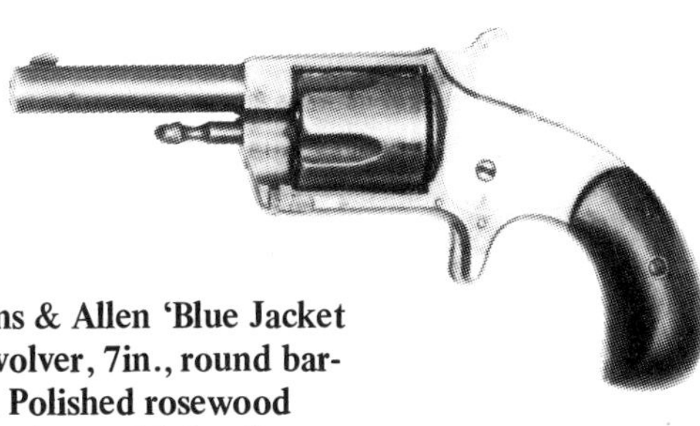

A 5-shot .32in. rimfire Hopkins & Allen 'Blue Jacket No. 2' single action pocket revolver, 7in., round barrel 2¾in. Birmingham proved. Polished rosewood grips to bird's head butt, spur trigger, side loading, closed frame, blade foresight, hammer bolster rear. $100 £50

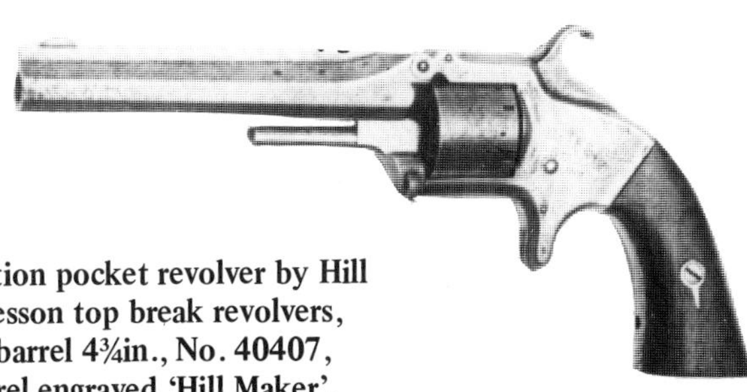

A 6-shot .32in. single action pocket revolver by Hill modelled on Smith & Wesson top break revolvers, 8½in., octagonal ribbed barrel 4¾in., No. 40407, Birmingham proved, barrel engraved 'Hill Maker', 'Patent No. 40407', plain walnut grips to angular butt, spur trigger, tip-up barrel for cylinder removal and loading, spring top strap cylinder stop, brass blade foresight. $180 £75

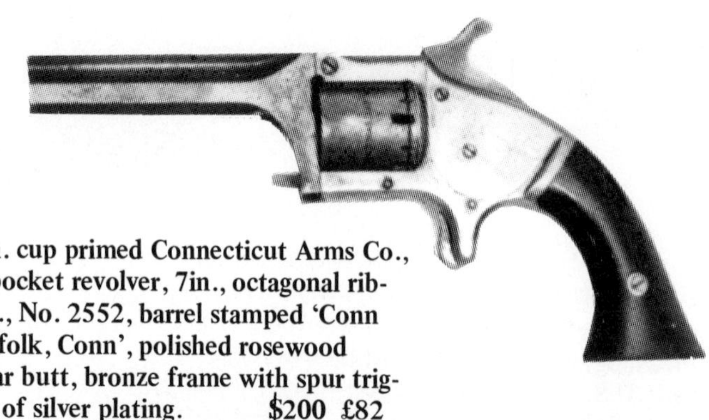

A 6-shot .28in. cup primed Connecticut Arms Co., single action pocket revolver, 7in., octagonal ribbed barrel 3in., No. 2552, barrel stamped 'Conn Arms Co, Norfolk, Conn', polished rosewood grips to angular butt, bronze frame with spur trigger and traces of silver plating. $200 £82

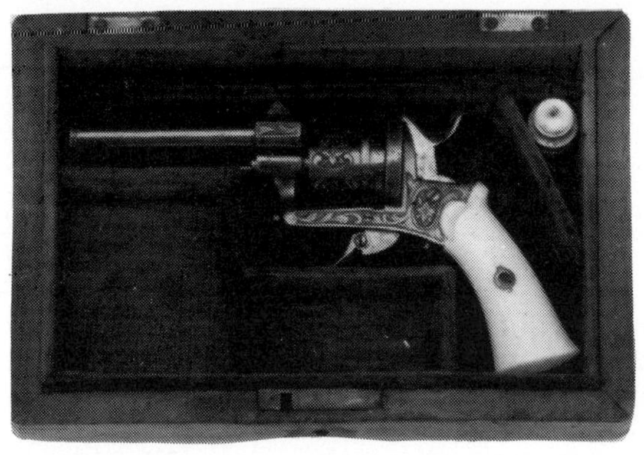

A 6-shot 7mm. Continental double action pin-fire pocket revolver, 7in., round barrel 3½in., ivory grips to angular butt, folding trigger, gate loading and rod ejection, sighted barrel, the frame, cylinder and barrel rear well scroll foliate engraved against a stippled ground. Contained in an associated red velvet lined and fitted case, containing oil bottle. $215 £90

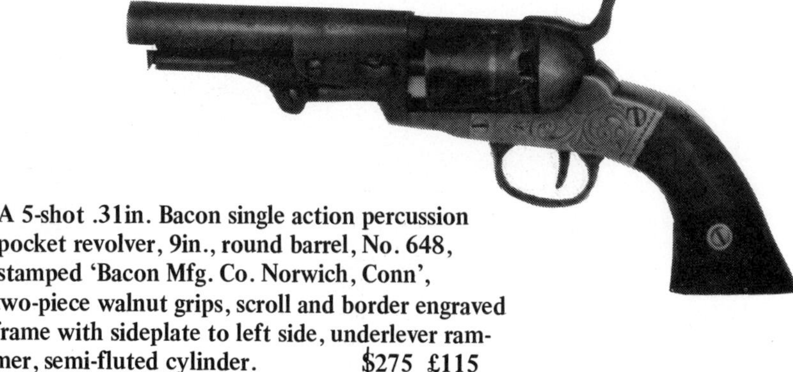

A 5-shot .31in. Bacon single action percussion pocket revolver, 9in., round barrel, No. 648, stamped 'Bacon Mfg. Co. Norwich, Conn', two-piece walnut grips, scroll and border engraved frame with sideplate to left side, underlever rammer, semi-fluted cylinder. $275 £115

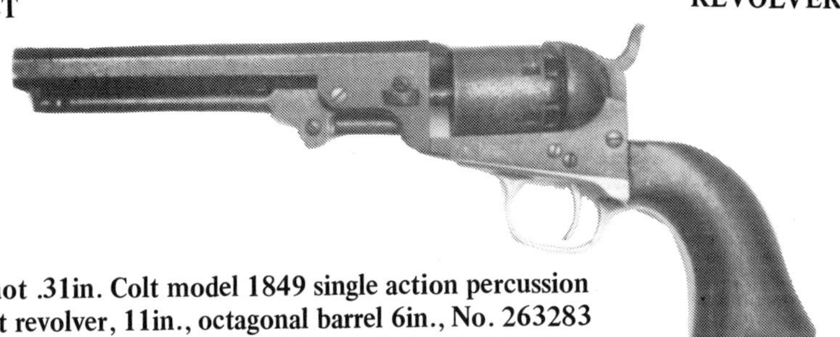

A 6-shot .31in. Colt model 1849 single action percussion pocket revolver, 11in., octagonal barrel 6in., No. 263283 (matching) barrel stamped 'Address Col. Saml. Colt, New York, U.S. America', brass trigger guard and backstrap, polished one-piece walnut grip, underlever rammer, bead foresight, hammer notch rear. $280 £130

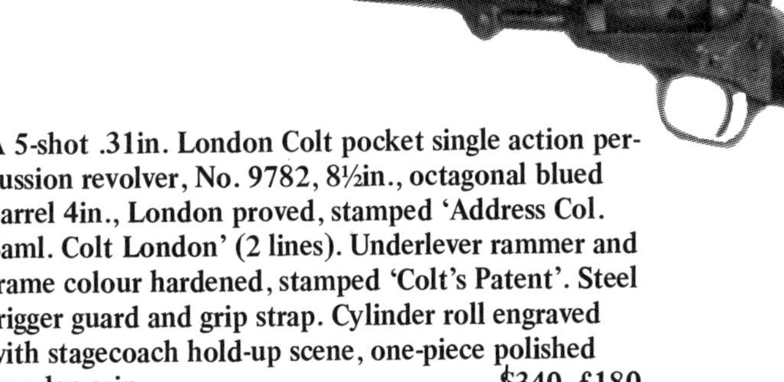

A 5-shot .31in. London Colt pocket single action percussion revolver, No. 9782, 8½in., octagonal blued barrel 4in., London proved, stamped 'Address Col. Saml. Colt London' (2 lines). Underlever rammer and frame colour hardened, stamped 'Colt's Patent'. Steel trigger guard and grip strap. Cylinder roll engraved with stagecoach hold-up scene, one-piece polished wooden grip. $340 £180

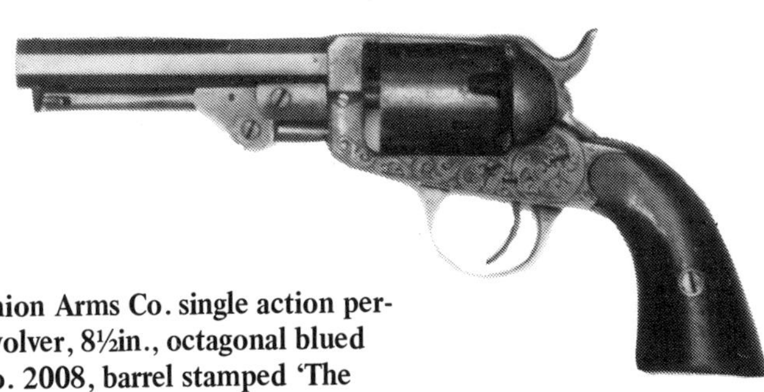

A 5-shot .31in. Union Arms Co. single action percussion pocket revolver, 8½in., octagonal blued barrel 4 3/8in., No. 2008, barrel stamped 'The Union Arms Co.', polished walnut grips, brass trigger guard, underlever rammer, plain cylinder closed frame. $455 £190

A 6-shot .31in. Colt pocket single action percussion revolver, 11in., octagonal barrel 6in., London black powder proof, one-piece walnut grip, steel trigger guard and backstrap, underlever rammer, unfluted cylinder with traces of stagecoach scene, white metal bead foresight, hammer notch rear. $450 £190

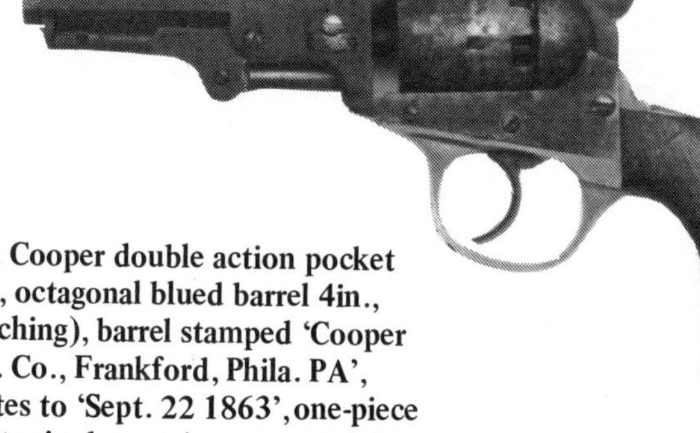

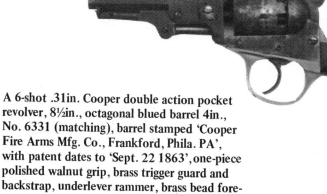

A 6-shot .31in. Cooper double action pocket revolver, 8½in., octagonal blued barrel 4in., No. 6331 (matching), barrel stamped 'Cooper Fire Arms Mfg. Co., Frankford, Phila. PA', with patent dates to 'Sept. 22 1863', one-piece polished walnut grip, brass trigger guard and backstrap, underlever rammer, brass bead foresight, hammer notch rear. $450 £190

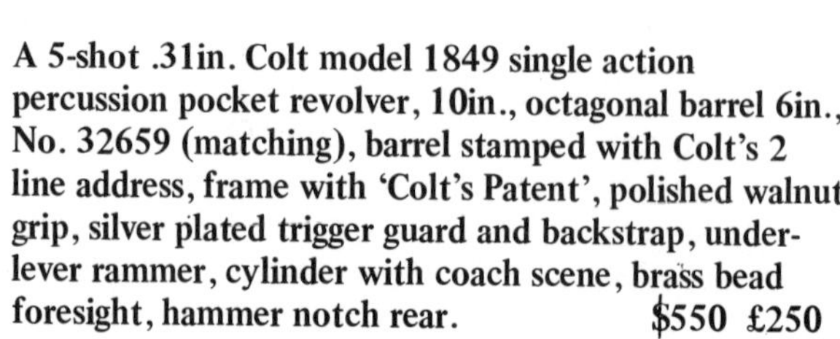

A 5-shot .31in. Colt model 1849 single action percussion pocket revolver, 10in., octagonal barrel 6in., No. 32659 (matching), barrel stamped with Colt's 2 line address, frame with 'Colt's Patent', polished walnut grip, silver plated trigger guard and backstrap, under-lever rammer, cylinder with coach scene, brass bead foresight, hammer notch rear. $550 £250

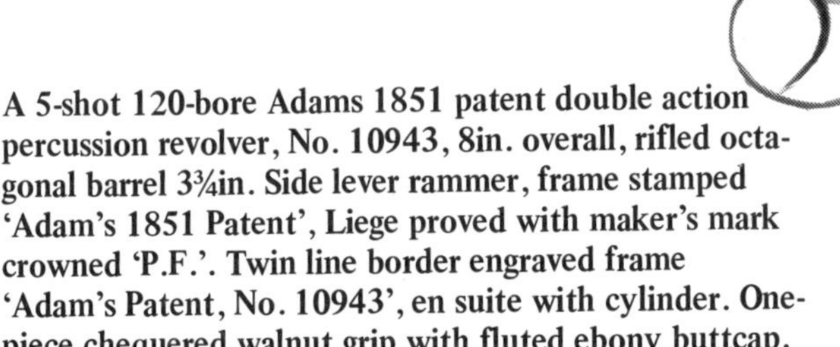

A 5-shot 120-bore Adams 1851 patent double action percussion revolver, No. 10943, 8in. overall, rifled octagonal barrel 3¾in. Side lever rammer, frame stamped 'Adam's 1851 Patent', Liege proved with maker's mark crowned 'P.F.'. Twin line border engraved frame 'Adam's Patent, No. 10943', en suite with cylinder. One-piece chequered walnut grip with fluted ebony buttcap. $635 £260

A 5-shot .28in. Colt model 1855 Root's patent single action percussion pocket revolver, 7¾in., round barrel 3½in., No. 7879, barrel stamped with maker's name and address, cylinder also with patent dates, one-piece polished walnut grips, spur trigger, underlever rammer, closed frame, round side plate to left side of frame, side mounted hammer. $660 £300

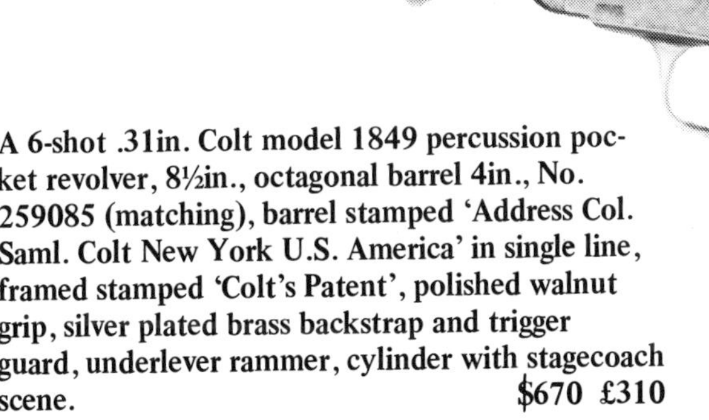

A 6-shot .31in. Colt model 1849 percussion pocket revolver, 8½in., octagonal barrel 4in., No. 259085 (matching), barrel stamped 'Address Col. Saml. Colt New York U.S. America' in single line, framed stamped 'Colt's Patent', polished walnut grip, silver plated brass backstrap and trigger guard, underlever rammer, cylinder with stagecoach scene. $670 £310

A 7-shot .22in. rimfire Smith & Wesson model No. 1 second model single action pocket revolver, 7in., barrel 3 3/16in., No. 14638, octagonal ribbed barrel stamped 'Smith & Wesson, Springfield, Mass', in its mauve velvet lined and fitted box. $1,100 £470

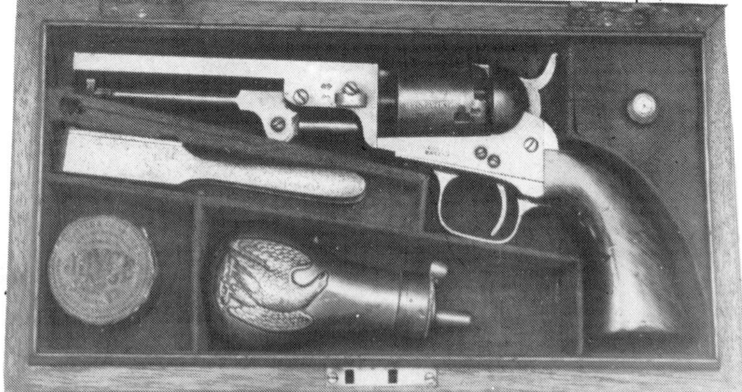

A 5-shot .31in. Colt pocket single action percussion revolver, No. 4074, 10in., octagonal barrel 5in., London proved. In its red velvet lined and fitted mahogany case. $1,100 £500

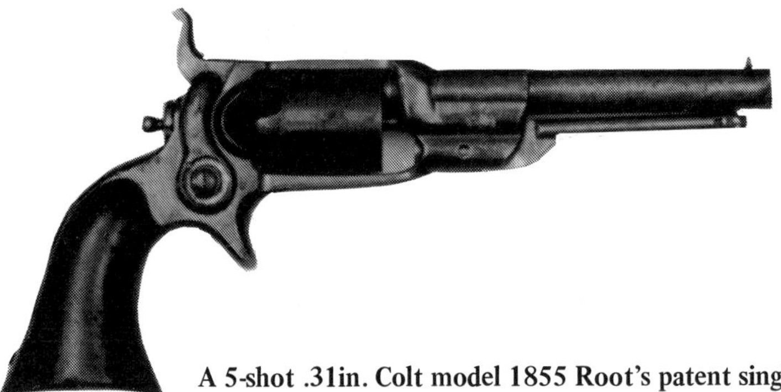

A 5-shot .31in. Colt model 1855 Root's patent single action pocket percussion revolver, 9in., round barrel 4½in., No. L. 9291 (matching), London black powder proof, barrel stamped 'Address Col. Colt New York U.S.A.', frame stamped '31 Cal' behind hammer. Polished one-piece walnut grip, spur trigger, underlever rammer, side mounted hammer, unfluted cylinder stamped 'Colt's Patent', brass bead foresight. $1,200 £500

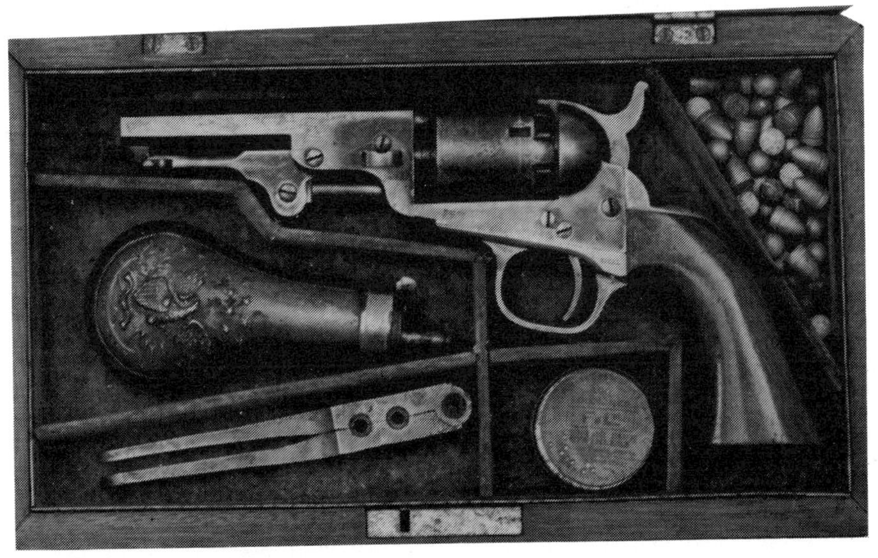

A 6-shot .31in. Colt model 1849 single action percussion pocket revolver, 8½in., octagonal barrel 4in., No. 285316, barrel stamped 'Address Col. Saml. Colt, New York, U.S. America' in single line, frame stamped 'Colt's Patent' and trigger guard '31 Cal'. Polished one-piece walnut grip, brass trigger guard and backstrap, underlever rammer. $1,920 £800

A 5-shot .36in. Colt model 1862 Police single action percussion revolver, 9½in., barrel 4½in., No. 16520 (matching including wedge), polished walnut grip, brass trigger guard and backstrap stamped '.36 Cal', semi-fluted rebated cylinder, round barrel stamped with Colt's name and address and provided with underlever rammer, brass bead foresight, hammer notch rear.
$270 £115

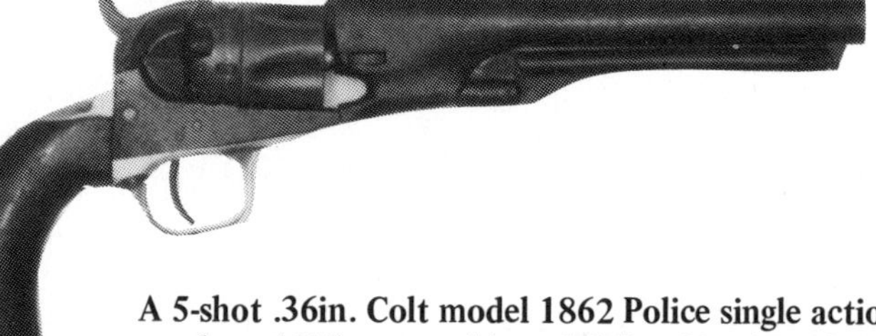

A 5-shot .36in. Colt model 1862 Police single action percussion revolver, 11½in., round barrel 6½in., No. 15243, barrel with 'Address Col. Saml. Colt New York U.S. America' and frame with 'Colt's Patent', walnut grip brass backstrap and trigger guard stamped '.36 Cal', underlever creeping rammer, streamlined barrel, fluted rebated cylinder, brass bead foresight, hammer notch rear. $385 £160

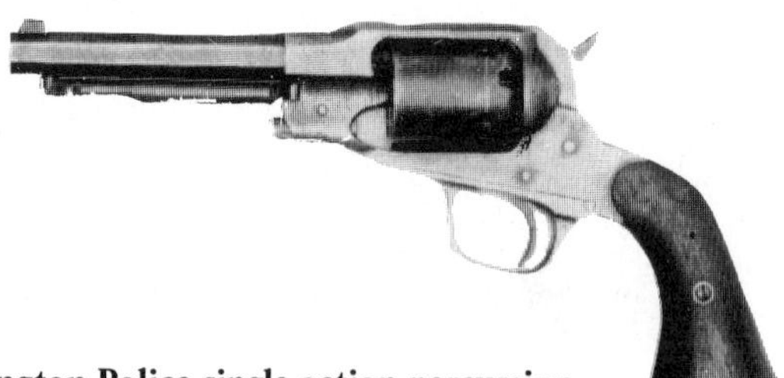

A 5-shot .36in. Remington Police single action percussion revolver, No. 5871, 9¼in., octagonal barrel 4½in., stamped 'Patented Sept. 14 1858, E. Remington & Sons, Ilion, New York, U.S.'. Underlever rammer, plated brass trigger guard. Steel frame and gripstrap. Two-piece polished walnut grips.
$400 £200

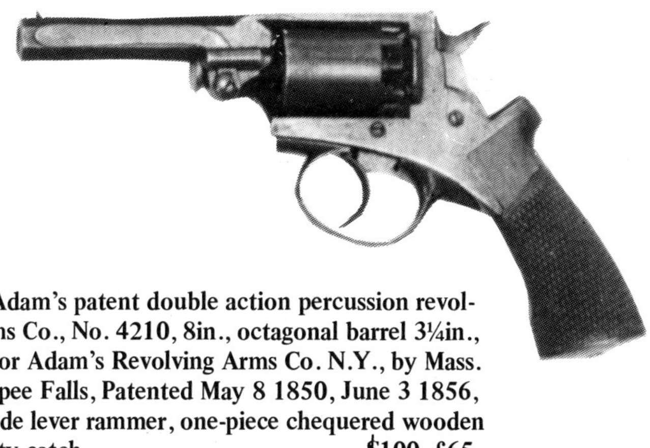

A 5-shot .31in. Adam's patent double action percussion revolver by Mass. Arms Co., No. 4210, 8in., octagonal barrel 3¼in., stamped 'Made for Adam's Revolving Arms Co. N.Y., by Mass. Arms Co., Chicopee Falls, Patented May 8 1850, June 3 1856, April 7 1857'. Side lever rammer, one-piece chequered wooden grip. Sliding safety catch. $100 £65

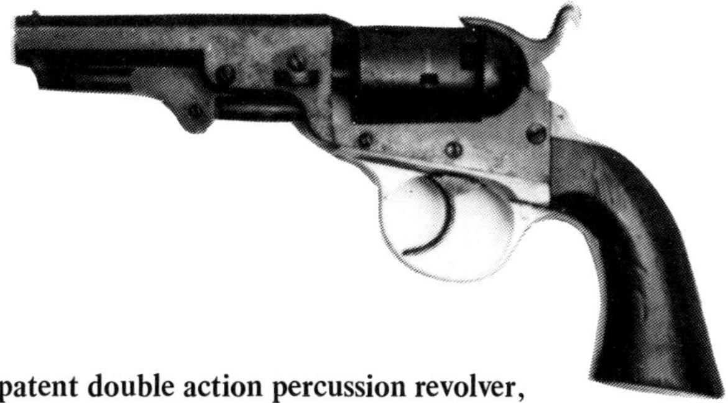

A 5-shot .31in. Cooper's patent double action percussion revolver, No. 6825, 8½in., octagonal barrel 4in., stamped 'Cooper's Firearms Mfg. Co. Frankford, Phila PA' with patent dates to Sept. 22 1863. Underlever rammer, steel frame, brass trigger guard and grip frame. One-piece polished wooden grip. $245 £100

A 6-shot .31in. Moore's patent teat fire single action revolver, 7in., No. 26273, round barrel 3¼in., stamped 'National Arms Co., Brooklyn, N.Y.'. Foliate engraved brass frame, sheathed trigger. Cylinder stamped 'D. Williamson's Patent, May 17 1864', hinged extracting lever. Two-piece wooden grips. $340 £140

A 6-shot .36in. model 1851 Colt Navy single action percussion revolver, No. 110691 (all matching), 13in., octagonal barrel 7½in., stamped 'Address Col. Saml. Colt, New York, U.S. America', underlever rammer. Frame stamped 'Colt's Patent', cylinder stamped 'Colt's Patent No. 110691'. Brass trigger guard and grip strap, one-piece wooden grip. $430 £175

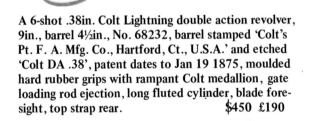

A 6-shot .38in. Colt Lightning double action revolver, 9in., barrel 4½in., No. 68232, barrel stamped 'Colt's Pt. F. A. Mfg. Co., Hartford, Ct., U.S.A.' and etched 'Colt DA .38', patent dates to Jan 19 1875, moulded hard rubber grips with rampant Colt medallion, gate loading rod ejection, long fluted cylinder, blade foresight, top strap rear. $450 £190

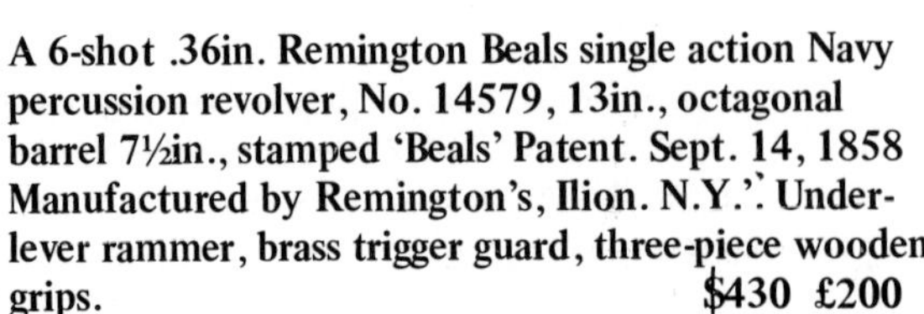

A 6-shot .36in. Remington Beals single action Navy percussion revolver, No. 14579, 13in., octagonal barrel 7½in., stamped 'Beals' Patent. Sept. 14, 1858 Manufactured by Remington's, Ilion. N.Y.'. Under-lever rammer, brass trigger guard, three-piece wooden grips. $430 £200

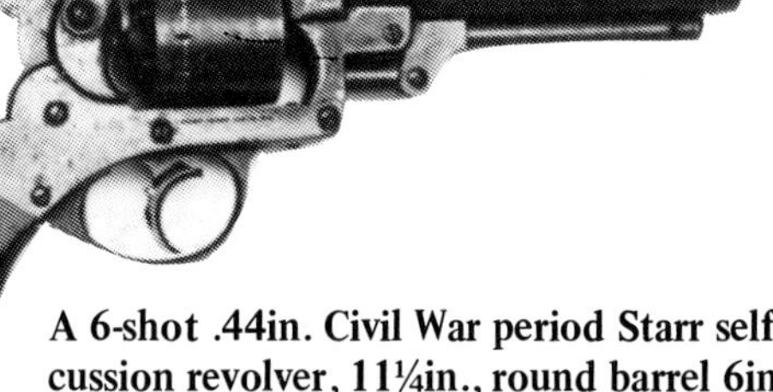

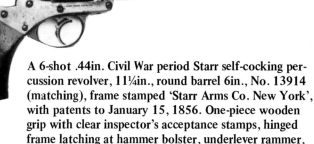

A 6-shot .44in. Civil War period Starr self-cocking percussion revolver, 11¼in., round barrel 6in., No. 13914 (matching), frame stamped 'Starr Arms Co. New York', with patents to January 15, 1856. One-piece wooden grip with clear inspector's acceptance stamps, hinged frame latching at hammer bolster, underlever rammer, plain cylinder with double set of stop notches, blade foresight, hammer notch rear. $440 £200

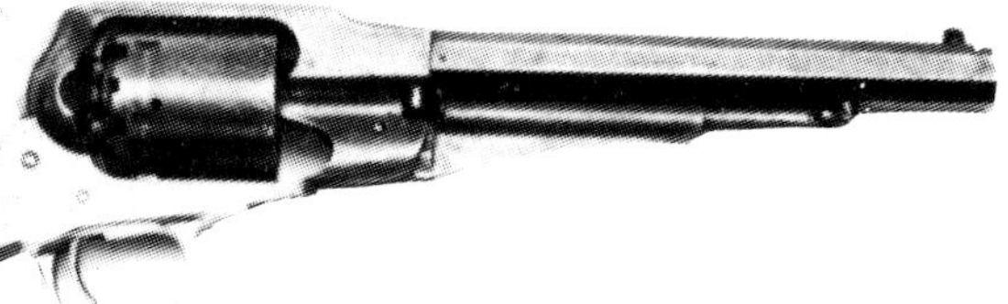

A 6-shot .44in. Remington New model single action percussion Army revolver, 13½in., octagonal barrel 8in., No. 122978, barrel stamped with maker's name and address, polished walnut grips, brass trigger guard, underlever rammer, blade foresight, top strap notch rear, plain cylinder. $505 £230

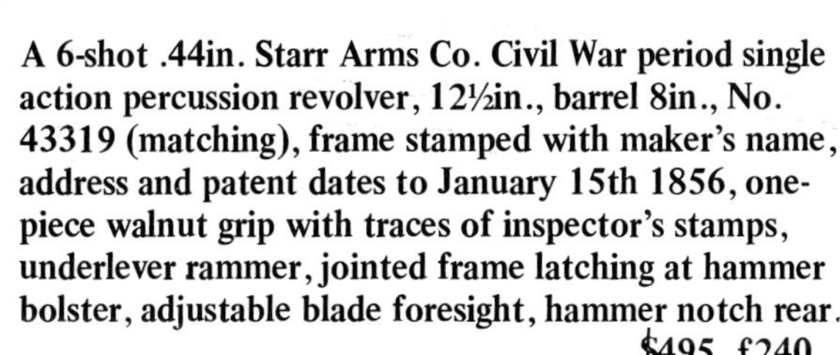

A 6-shot .44in. Starr Arms Co. Civil War period single action percussion revolver, 12½in., barrel 8in., No. 43319 (matching), frame stamped with maker's name, address and patent dates to January 15th 1856, one-piece walnut grip with traces of inspector's stamps, underlever rammer, jointed frame latching at hammer bolster, adjustable blade foresight, hammer notch rear. $495 £240

A 6-shot .44in. Rodgers & Spencer Civil War period single action Army percussion revolver, 13in., octagonal barrel 7½in., No. 1331, flared wooden grips with inspector's cartouche 'RRB', steel backstrap and trigger guard, closed frame with unfluted plain cylinder, underlever loading, white metal foresight, top strap rear. $520 £240

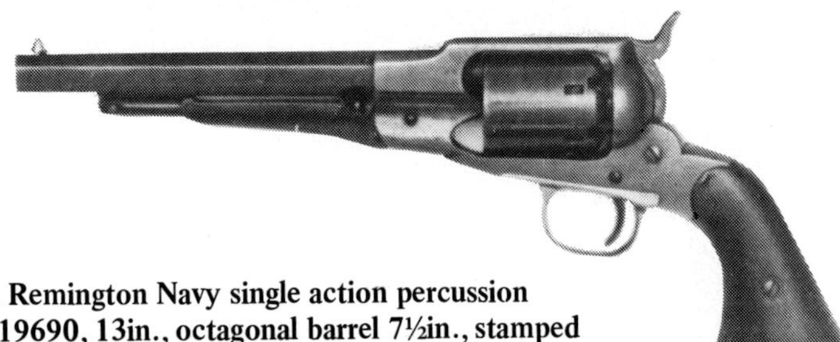

A 6-shot .36in. Remington Navy single action percussion revolver, No. P19690, 13in., octagonal barrel 7½in., stamped 'Patented Dec. 17, 1861. Manufactured by Remington's Ilion, N.Y.', underlever rammer, foliate engraved with cut-out for cylinder axis pin to slide. Foliate engraved hammer, brass trigger guard, two-piece wooden grips. $520 £240

A 6-shot .44in. Remington New model single action percussion revolver, 14in., octagonal barrel 8in., No. 19685, barrel engraved 'Patented Sept. 14 1858, E. Remington & Sons, Ilion. New York U.S.A.', walnut grips, brass trigger guard, underlever rammer, closed frame, blade foresight, top strap rear, grips stamped with inspector's mark. $540 £250

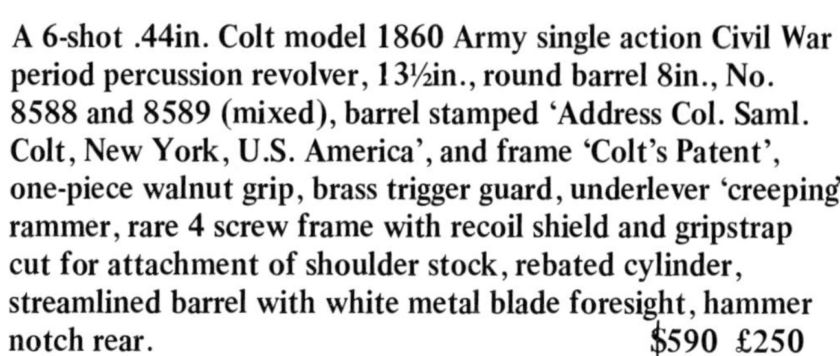

A 6-shot .44in. Colt model 1860 Army single action Civil War period percussion revolver, 13½in., round barrel 8in., No. 8588 and 8589 (mixed), barrel stamped 'Address Col. Saml. Colt, New York, U.S. America', and frame 'Colt's Patent', one-piece walnut grip, brass trigger guard, underlever 'creeping' rammer, rare 4 screw frame with recoil shield and gripstrap cut for attachment of shoulder stock, rebated cylinder, streamlined barrel with white metal blade foresight, hammer notch rear. $590 £250

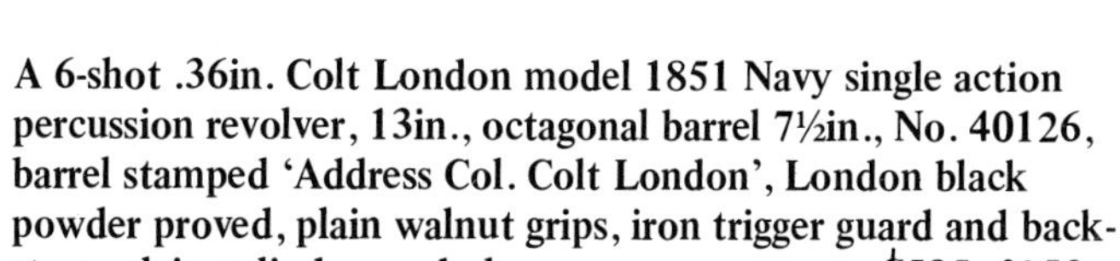

A 6-shot .36in. Colt London model 1851 Navy single action percussion revolver, 13in., octagonal barrel 7½in., No. 40126, barrel stamped 'Address Col. Colt London', London black powder proved, plain walnut grips, iron trigger guard and backstrap, plain cylinder, underlever rammer. $585 £250

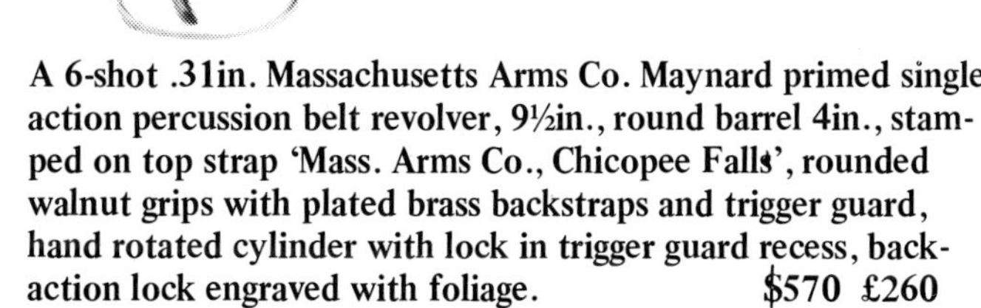

A 6-shot .31in. Massachusetts Arms Co. Maynard primed single action percussion belt revolver, 9½in., round barrel 4in., stamped on top strap 'Mass. Arms Co., Chicopee Falls', rounded walnut grips with plated brass backstraps and trigger guard, hand rotated cylinder with lock in trigger guard recess, back-action lock engraved with foliage. $570 £260

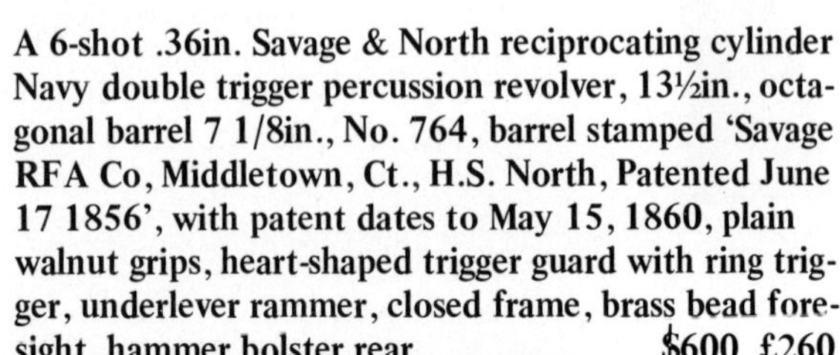

A 6-shot .36in. Savage & North reciprocating cylinder Navy double trigger percussion revolver, 13½in., octagonal barrel 7 1/8in., No. 764, barrel stamped 'Savage RFA Co, Middletown, Ct., H.S. North, Patented June 17 1856', with patent dates to May 15, 1860, plain walnut grips, heart-shaped trigger guard with ring trigger, underlever rammer, closed frame, brass bead foresight, hammer bolster rear. $600 £260

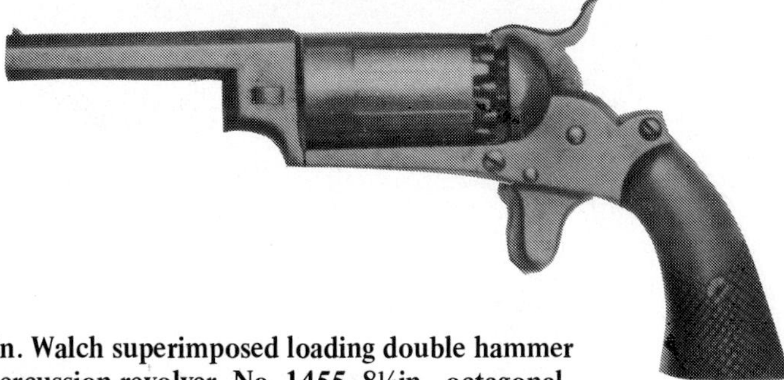

A 10-shot .31in. Walch superimposed loading double hammer single action percussion revolver, No. 1455, 8½in., octagonal barrel 3¼in., stamped 'Walch Fire Arms Co. New York Patd. Feb. 8 1859', brass frame, sheathed trigger fires first right hammer, then left. Two-piece part chequered horn grips. $555 £270

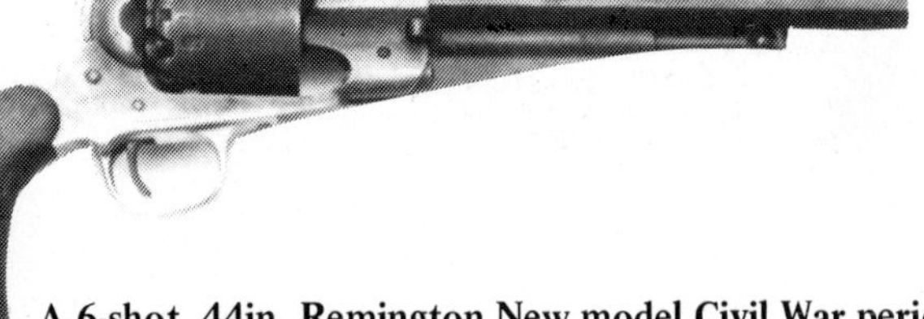

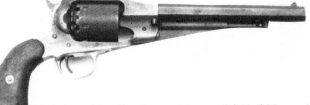

A 6-shot .44in. Remington New model Civil War period single action percussion revolver, 13½in., octagonal barrel 8in., No. 87461, barrel stamped with maker's address, patent date and 'New Model', walnut grips, brass trigger guard, underlever rammer, unfluted cylinder, bead foresight, top strap rear. $625 £270

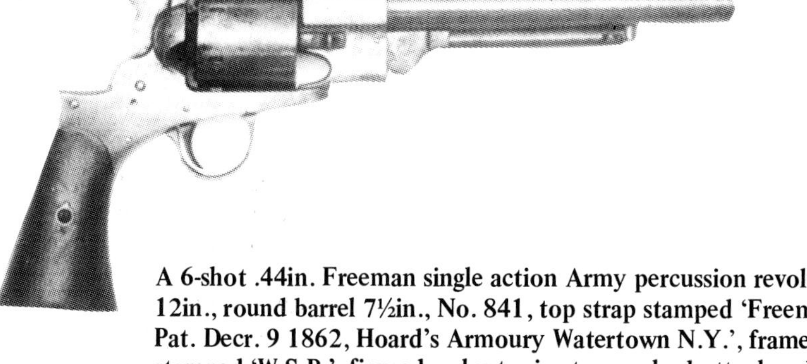

A 6-shot .44in. Freeman single action Army percussion revolver, 12in., round barrel 7½in., No. 841, top strap stamped 'Freeman's Pat. Decr. 9 1862, Hoard's Armoury Watertown N.Y.', framed stamped 'W.S.B.', figured walnut grips to angular butt, closed frame with underlever rammer, patent cylinder pin locking latch, plain cylinder, angular frame. $650 £270

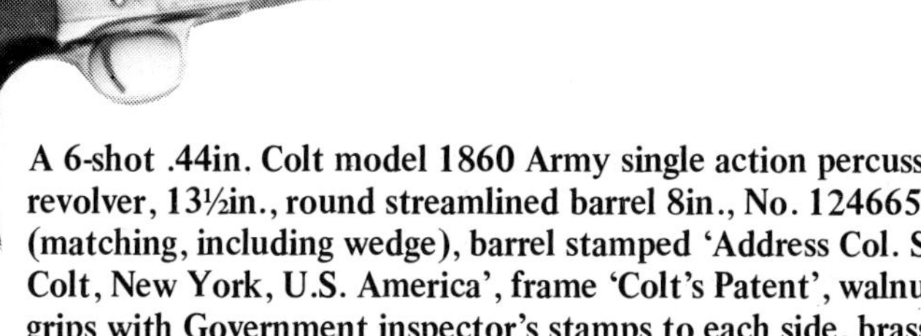

A 6-shot .44in. Colt model 1860 Army single action percussion revolver, 13½in., round streamlined barrel 8in., No. 124665 (matching, including wedge), barrel stamped 'Address Col. Saml. Colt, New York, U.S. America', frame 'Colt's Patent', walnut grips with Government inspector's stamps to each side, brass trigger guard, cut for shoulder stock, underlever 'creeping' rammer, rebated cylinder, white metal blade foresight, hammer notch rear. $660 £270

A 6-shot .44in. Rodgers & Spencer single action percussion revolver, 13in., octagonal barrel 7½in., No. 3701, top strap struck 'Rodgers & Spencer Utica NY', two-piece walnut grips to flared butt, underlever rammer, plain cylinder. $645 £280

A 6-shot .36in. Colt model 1851 Navy single action percussion revolver, 12in., octagonal barrel 7½in., No. 25669, barrel with maker's name and New York address, plain walnut grip, brass trigger guard and backstrap, underlever rammer, cylinder with Naval engagement scene, brass bead foresight, hammer notch rear. $755 £310

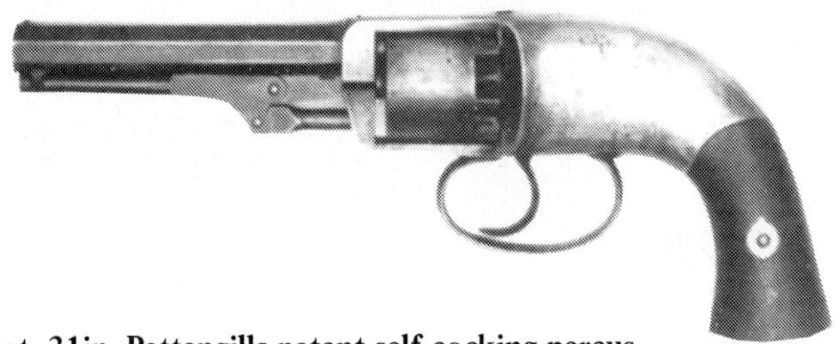

A 6-shot .31in. Pettengills patent self-cocking percussion Navy revolver, 9½in., octagonal barrel 4½in., No. 105, cylinder straps stamped 'Pettengills Patent 1856' and 'Raymond & Robitell Patent 1858', plain wooden grips, rounded action body with enclosed hammer, underlever rammer, sighted barrel. $755 £310

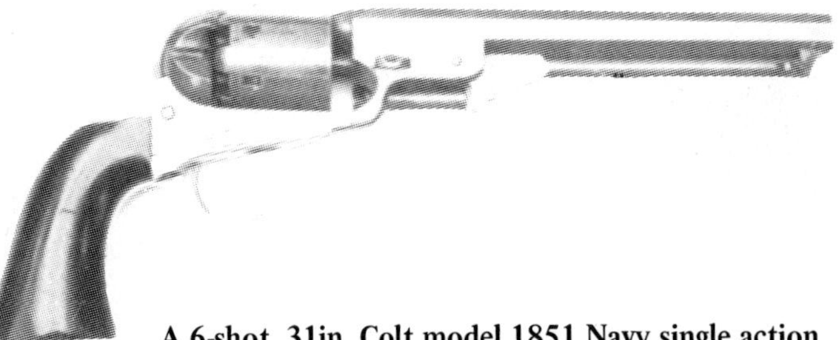

A 6-shot .31in. Colt model 1851 Navy single action percussion revolver, 13in., barrel 7½in., No. 182627 (matching), barrel with maker's name and address, brass trigger guard and backstrap, underlever rammer, cylinder with 60% visible Naval scene. $745 £310

A 6-shot .36in. Colt model 1851 single action Navy percussion revolver 13in., octagonal barrel 7½in., No. 698 (matching), London proved and the barrel stamped 'Address Col. Colt London', brass trigger guard and backstrap, polished one-piece walnut grip, underlever rammer, sighted barrel, with hammer notch foresight, cylinder with 30% Naval scene and London proofs. $725 £330

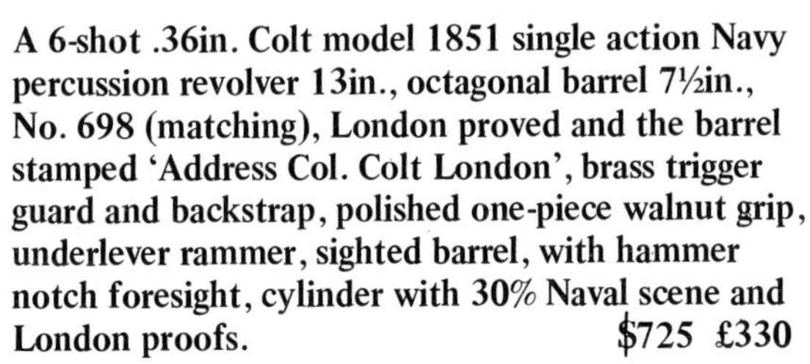

A 6-shot .44in. Remington New Model single action Army percussion revolver, 13in., octagonal barrel 8in., No. 29443, barrel with patent dates and maker's name and address, polished walnut grips, brass trigger guard, closed frame, underlever rammer, white metal blade foresight and top strap rear, plain cylinder with stop notches. $790 £330

A 6-shot .36in. Colt model 1851 Naval single action percussion revolver, 13in., barrel 7½in., No. 127718 (matching), barrel stamped 'Address Col. Saml. Colt, New York, US America', polished rosewood grip, brass trigger guard and backstrap, underlever rammer, frame stamped 'Colt's Patent', the standing breech cut with capping channel on right side, brass bead foresight, hammer notch rear. $780 £340

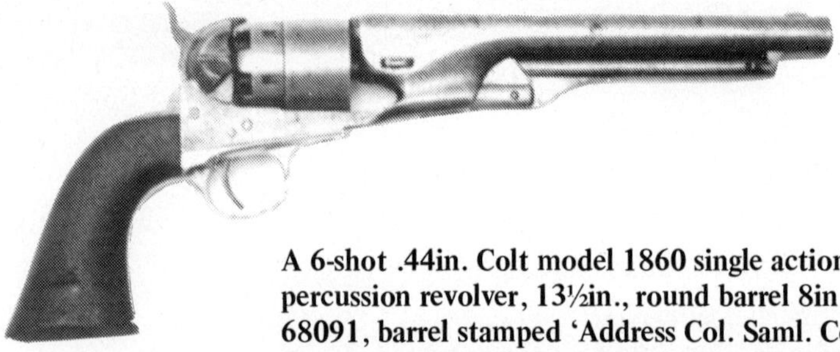

A 6-shot .44in. Colt model 1860 single action Army percussion revolver, 13½in., round barrel 8in., No. 68091, barrel stamped 'Address Col. Saml. Colt, New York, US America' frame with 'Colt's Patent', one-piece wooden grip, brass trigger guard and iron backstrap, frame with recoil shield cut for shoulder stock, creeping underlever rammer. $865 £360

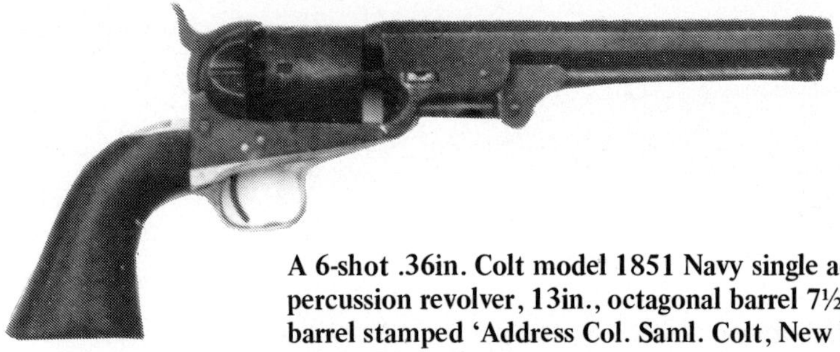

A 6-shot .36in. Colt model 1851 Navy single action percussion revolver, 13in., octagonal barrel 7½in., barrel stamped 'Address Col. Saml. Colt, New York, US America' frame with 'Colt's Patent' and trigger guard '36 Cal', one-piece polished walnut grip, brass backstrap and trigger guard, underlever rammer, unfluted cylinder, silver blade foresight, hammer notch rear. $895 £380

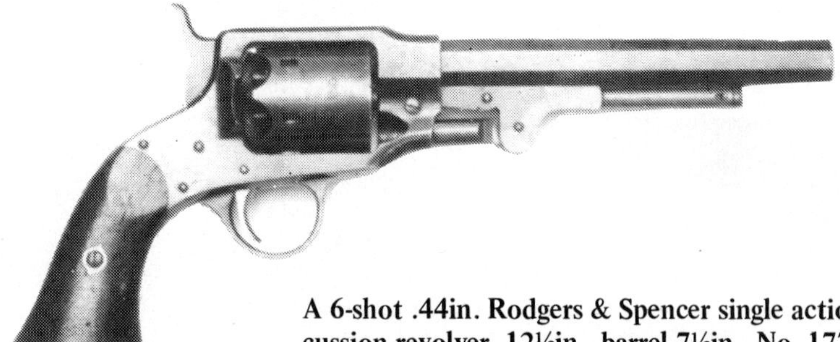

A 6-shot .44in. Rodgers & Spencer single action percussion revolver, 12½in., barrel 7½in., No. 1771, frame stamped with maker's name and address, wooden flared grips with inspector's stamp, underlever rammer, closed frame, plain cylinder, octagonal barrel with bead foresight, top strap rear. $805 £390

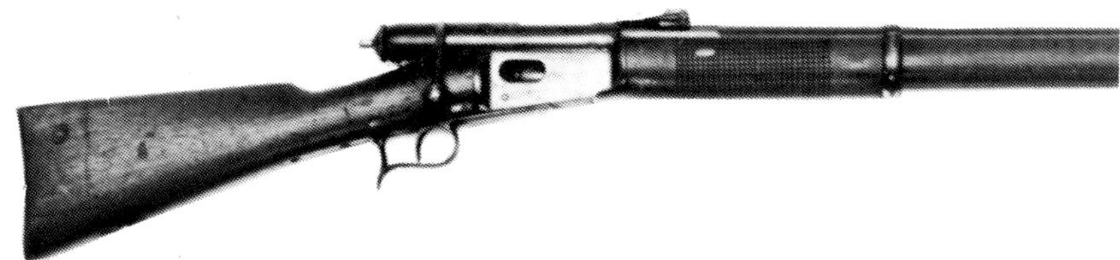

A .577in. Snider patent Enfield breech loading 2 band Military rifle, 48½in., barrel 30½in., regulation walnut stock with iron mounts, barrel with bayonet lug and barley corn foresight, ladder tangent rear to 900 yds., complete with cleaning rod. $90 £40

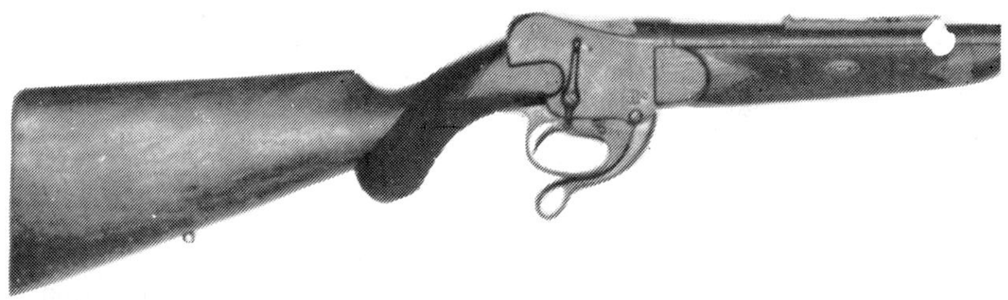

A single shot .450in. Westley Richards falling block underlever opening sporting rifle, smooth bored to 24-bore, 45in., ovoid barrel 28in., with matted top flat stamped 'Westley Richards & Co., London', heavy scroll engraved frame with maker's name and address and 'Patent', chequered walnut pistol grip stock with iron buttplate, chequered crosskeyed fore-end, with horn cap, barrel with bead foresight and 4 folding leaf and tangent rearsight to 1,000 yds. $260 £120

A single shot 15mm. Russian Krnka breech loading Military rifle, 53in., barrel 36in., No. 16949, dated 1865, brass mounted fullstock, the buttplate struck with double headed eagle, three iron barrel bands, barley corn foresight, tangent rear, brass breech with swing-out block, back action side lock with angled hammer nose. $200 £105

A .577in. Volunteer 3 band 1853 pattern Enfield percussion rifle, 55½in., barrel 39in., Birmingham 25-bore proof marks, tangent ladder rearsight to 900 yds. Walnut fullstock, twin line border engraved lock, regulation brass mounts, steel sling swivels, barrel bands and original ramrod. $310 £135

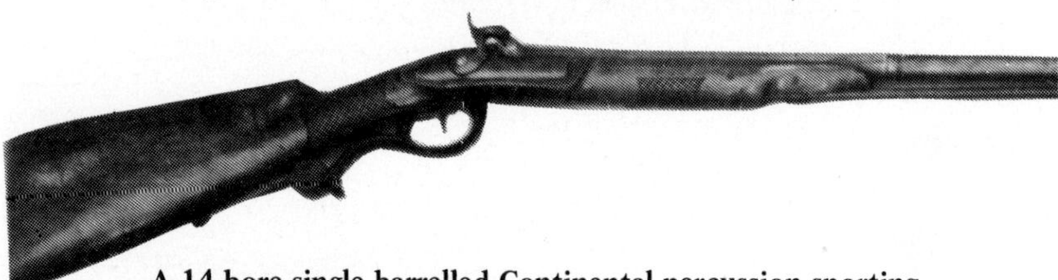

A 14-bore single barrelled Continental percussion sporting rifle, 45in., half octagonal barrel 30½in., ribbed step, deep 8 groove rifling. Halfstocked, slightly rounded hardened lock and hammer. Wooden trigger guard. $345 £150

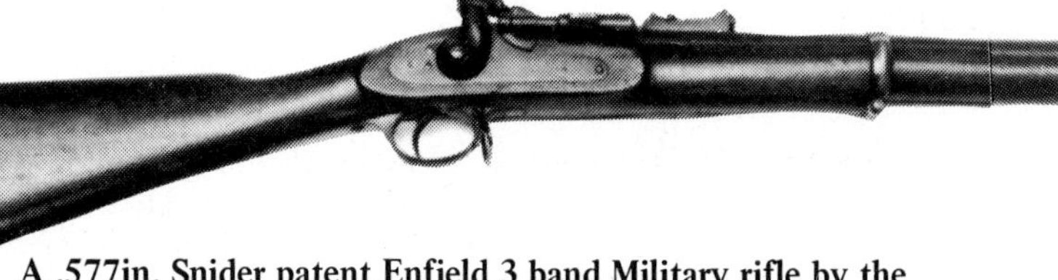

A .577in. Snider patent Enfield 3 band Military rifle by the London Small Arms Co. Ltd., 55½in., barrel 37½in., regulation walnut stock with brass furniture, sling swivels and iron barrel bands, blued barrel with barley corn foresight, tangent ladder rear to 900 yds. $345 £160

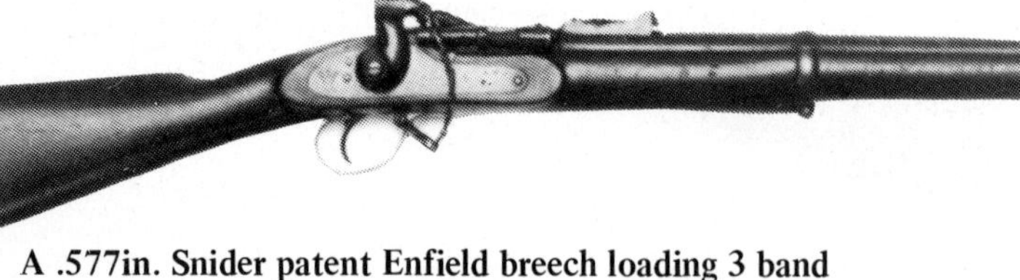

A .577in. Snider patent Enfield breech loading 3 band Military rifle, 54in., barrel 36½in., regulation brass mounted walnut stock with sling swivels and 3 iron barred bands, barley corn foresight, tangent rear to 950 yds., complete with square headed cleaning rod and chained nipple protector. $350 £160

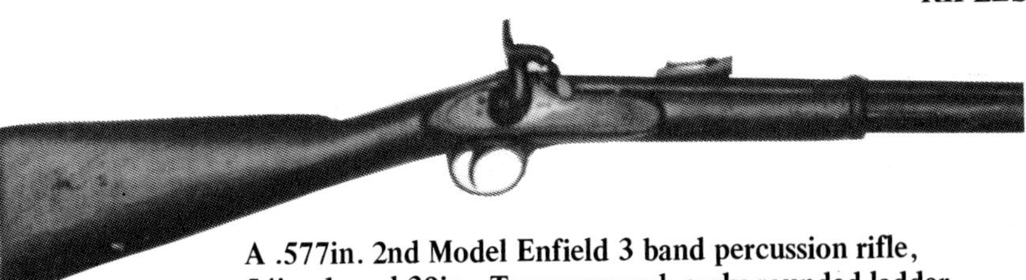

A .577in. 2nd Model Enfield 3 band percussion rifle, 54in., barrel 39in., Tower proved, early rounded ladder rearsight to 1,000 yds. Fullstocked, regulation brass mounts, 3 spring retained solid steel barrel bands. Butt stamped with Pimlico 1860 mark. $385 £175

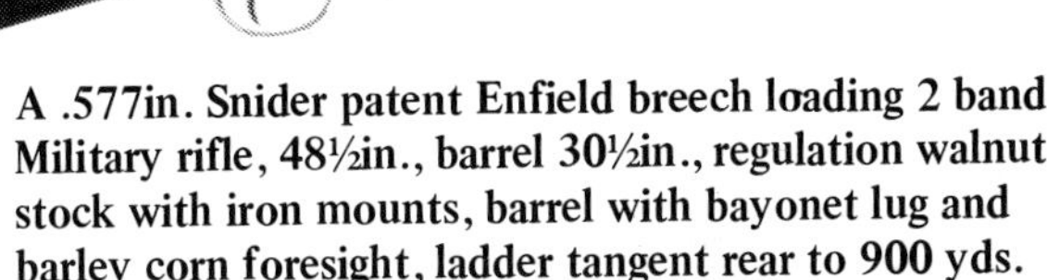

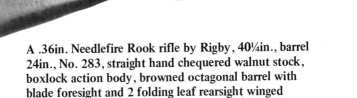

A .577in. Snider patent Enfield breech loading 2 band Military rifle, 48½in., barrel 30½in., regulation walnut stock with iron mounts, barrel with bayonet lug and barley corn foresight, ladder tangent rear to 900 yds. $400 £180

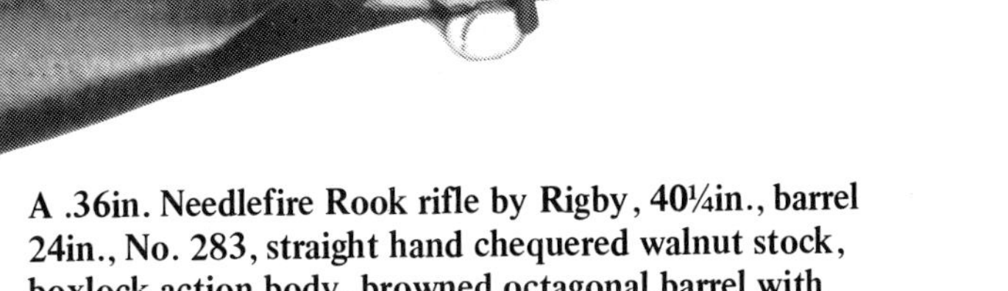

A .36in. Needlefire Rook rifle by Rigby, 40¼in., barrel 24in., No. 283, straight hand chequered walnut stock, boxlock action body, browned octagonal barrel with blade foresight and 2 folding leaf rearsight winged screw at hammer bolster to open breech. $410 £200

A .577in. Volunteer 3 band 1853 pattern Enfield percussion rifle, 55½in., barrel 39in., Birmingham 24-bore proof marks, tangent ladder rearsight to 900 yds. Walnut fullstock, twin line border engraved lock stamped with crown and 'Tower 1861'. $400 £200

A .577in. 3 band Volunteer percussion Enfield Military rifle by Potts & Hunt, London, 55½in., barrel 39in., London proofs, regulation walnut fullstock with brass buttplate, trigger guard, 3 iron barrel bands, sling swivels, barley corn foresight and tangent ladder rear to 900 yds. $475 £250

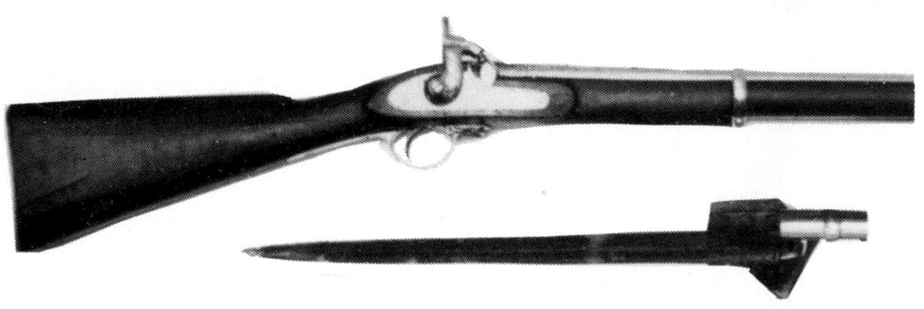

A .577in. Tower Enfield 3 band Volunteer percussion rifle, 55¼in., barrel 39in., Birmingham proofs, regulation brass mounts, walnut stock, the buttplate stamped 'G.F.C. 7', iron barrel bands and sling swivels, steel ramrod, tangent rear sight to 900 yds., with correct socket bayonet with brass mounted leather sheath. $600 £250

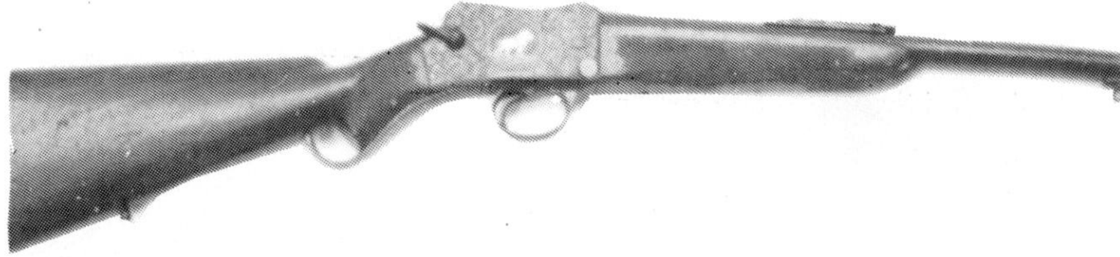

An S.S. .577/450in. Francotte Martini action sporting rifle, 45in., barrel 28½in., No. 15484, chequered walnut pistol grip stock with sling eye, steel buttplate with trap, chequered fore-end, round barrel with matted top flat, barley corn foresight, 3 folding platinum lined leaf rearsights to 400 yds. and ladder to 1100 yds. $615 £260

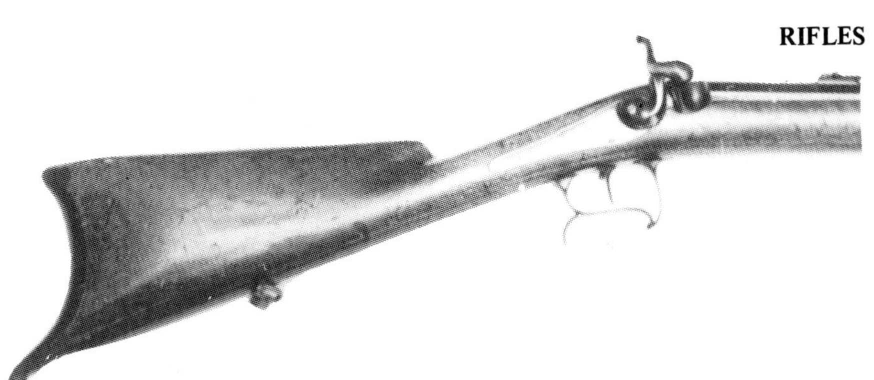

A Continental 30-bore percussion fullstocked rifle, 47in., barrel 30½in., figured walnut stock with cheekpiece, heavy iron butt cap of Schutzen type with elongated toe, single set trigger within scrolling spurred trigger guard barrel held to stock by means of 3 crosskeys, iron ramrod with bulbous terminal blade foresight, ladder rear to 800 metres. $550 £270

A .702in. 3rd Model Brunswick pattern Military percussion rifle, so called 'Sikh Brunswick', 45¾in., barrel 30in., Tower proved, rifled for the belted ball, fixed and single leaf hinge-up rearsight. Fullstocked, lock engraved 'Tower 1860' with crowned 'V.R.' Regulation brass mounts, hinged patchbox in butt, scrolled trigger guard. Steel ramrod, lanyard loops and bayonet bar. $575 £315

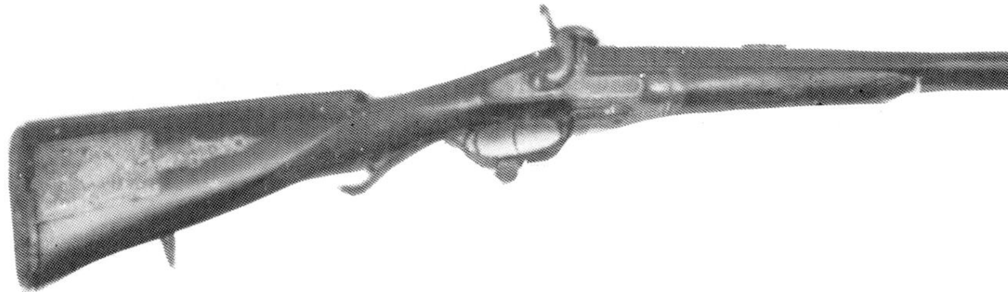

An S.S. 20.9mm. underlever opening pin-fire big game sporting rifle, 48in., barrel 30¾in., the part round part octagonal browned twist barrel engraved 'G. L. Rasch Hve Buchsenmacher in Braunschweig', chequered walnut stock with cheekpiece, rubber buttplate, rope border and foliate scroll engraved trap for 2 cartridges. $755 £320

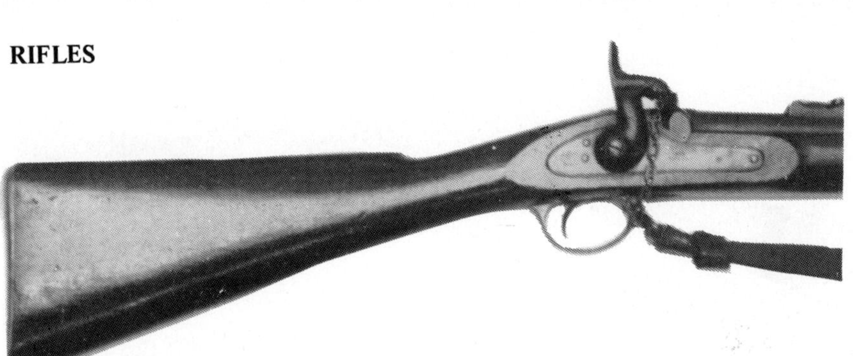

A .577in. Volunteer 3 band pattern 1853 Enfield percussion rifle, 55in., barrel 39in., bearing Birmingham 25-bore proof marks, full length walnut stock with brass buttplate, trigger guard, fore-end cap and side nail cups, iron screw retained bands, barrel with barley corn foresight, tangent ladder rear to 900 yds. $840 £350

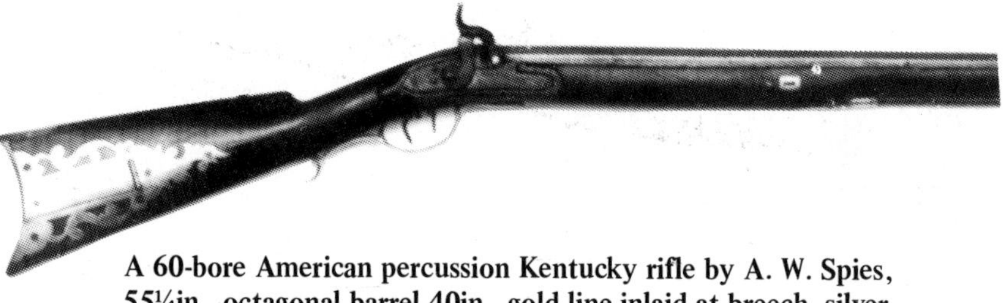

A 60-bore American percussion Kentucky rifle by A. W. Spies, 55¼in., octagonal barrel 40in., gold line inlaid at breech, silver safety plug. Fullstocked, stepped lock foliate engraved with 'A. W. Spies Warranted', detented action. Double set triggers, brass furniture, ornamental patchbox, sprung lid released by button under stock, spurred trigger guard. $990 £450

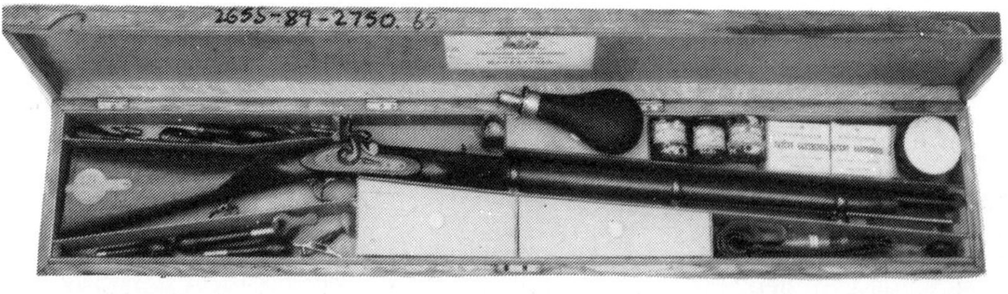

A .451 Whitworth's patent percussion target rifle, 49in., barrel 33in., No. B26, barrel engraved 'Whitworth Patent' with Birmingham proof marks for 52-bore. Crisp figured chequered walnut fullstock with colour hardened iron buttplate, patchbox with sprung border engraved lid fitted with friction roller, sling swivels. In its pigskin lined and fitted oak case. $5,940 £2,750

A .44-40in. Marlin model 1894 'safety' lever action repeating sporting rifle 41½in., barrel 24in., No. 112165, the barrel stamped 'Marlin Firearms Co. New Haven, C.T. U.S.A.' and patent dates to August 1, 1893, take-down octagonal barrel with tube magazine and lever release at frame, walnut stock with heavy crescent buttplate, short metal capped fore-end, white metal blade foresight, spring wedge elevator rear, action with loading port.

$125 £65

An 18-bore Austrian percussion sporting gun by Frantz Stockal of Vienna, converted from flintlock, 39½in., octagonal barrel 24½in., engraved 'Frantz Stockal', with traces of maker's marks. Fullstocked, rounded lockplate engraved 'in Wien'. Plain flat inlaid brass furniture with foliate silhouette finials, brass overlaid wooden trigger guard, carved cheekpiece with incised foliate decoration.

$325 £170

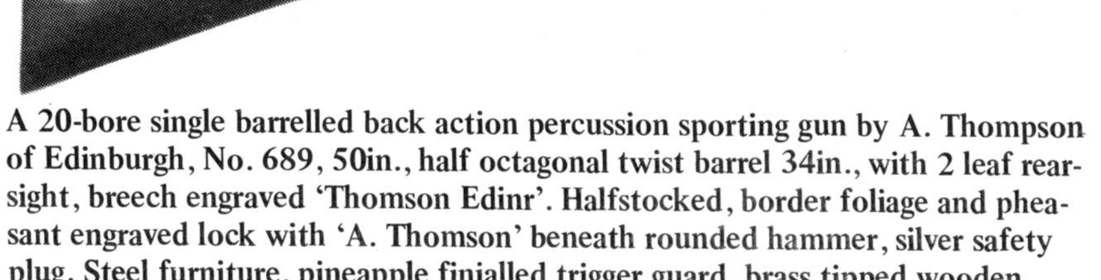

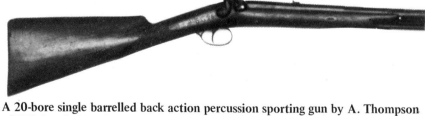

A 20-bore single barrelled back action percussion sporting gun by A. Thompson of Edinburgh, No. 689, 50in., half octagonal twist barrel 34in., with 2 leaf rear-sight, breech engraved 'Thomson Edinr'. Halfstocked, border foliage and pheasant engraved lock with 'A. Thomson' beneath rounded hammer, silver safety plug. Steel furniture, pineapple finialled trigger guard, brass tipped wooden ramrod with brass capped worm, horn fore-cap, white metal barrel wedge plates.

$420 £190

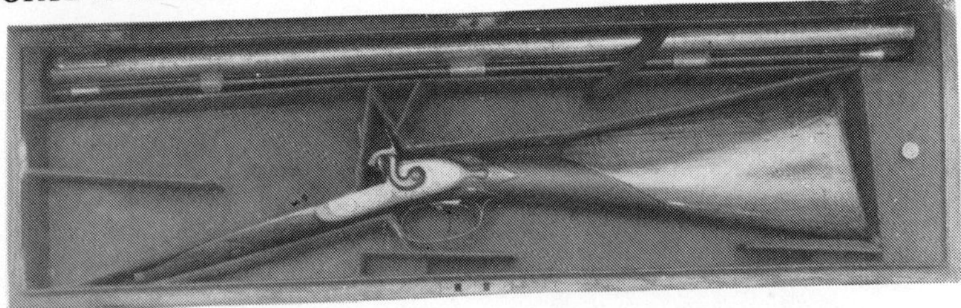

A 12-bore double barrelled percussion sporting gun, 46½in., twist barrels 30in., with platinum safety plugs. Halfstocked, lockplates and trigger guard well engraved with naturalistic rutting stags, does in arborial landscape. Foliate engraved steel furniture and hammers. Chequered small and fore of stock, gold shield-shaped escutcheon, brass tipped wooden ramrod. In its green baize lined fitted oak case. $430 £200

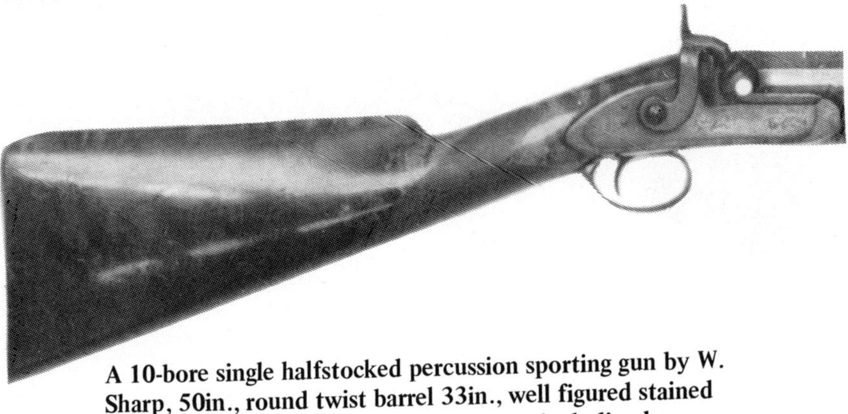

A 10-bore single halfstocked percussion sporting gun by W. Sharp, 50in., round twist barrel 33in., well figured stained birdseye beech stock with iron furniture, including long spurred buttcap, trigger guard, blank white metal wrist escutcheon and crosskey plates, horn capped fore-end, platinum nipple bolster vent. $550 £230

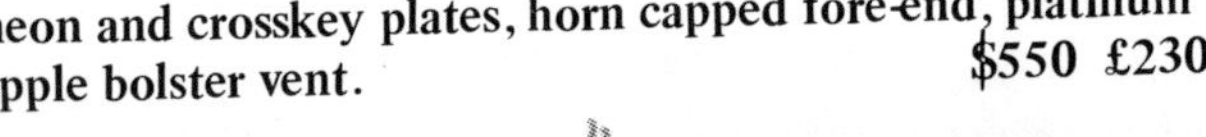

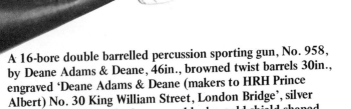

A 16-bore double barrelled percussion sporting gun, No. 958, by Deane Adams & Deane, 46in., browned twist barrels 30in., engraved 'Deane Adams & Deane (makers to HRH Prince Albert) No. 30 King William Street, London Bridge', silver safety plug. Halfstocked, engraved locks, gold shield-shaped escutcheon engraved 'JWB'. $695 £290

A double barrelled 12-bore x 2½in. top lever opening boxlock ejector sporting gun by Hollis, Bentley & Playfair, 44¼in., barrels 27 7/8in., No. 89538, chequered straight hand figured walnut stock with blank silver escutcheon, scalloped action junction and teardrop finial. In its green baize lined and fitted canvas convered case, containing jointed rod and cleaning jags. $720 £300

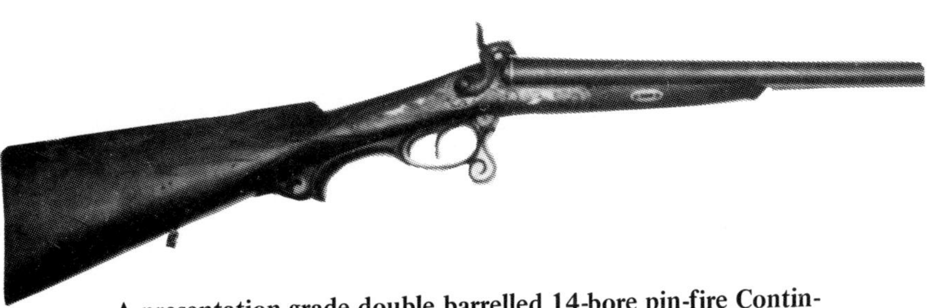

A presentation grade double barrelled 14-bore pin-fire Continental underlever opening sporting gun by Rosch Steyer & Co., 47in., barrel 31 1/8in., chequered walnut stock with cheekpiece, sling swivel, horn trigger guard extension and steel buttplate. $720 £300

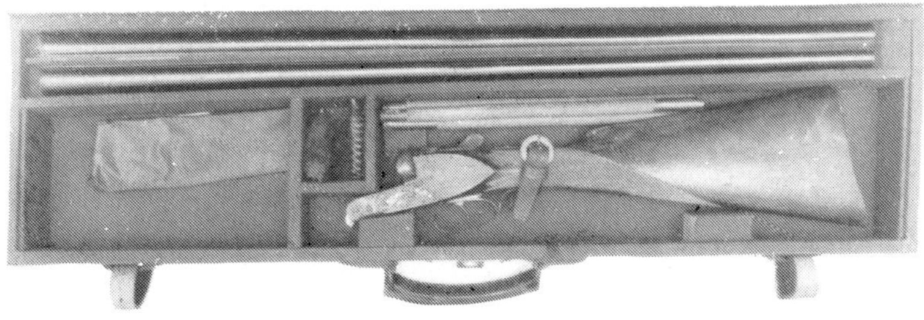

A double barrelled 12-bore x 2¾in., top lever opening hammerless boxlock ejector sporting gun by Anton Sodia, 45½in., barrels 29½in., chequered walnut stock, 2-piece heel and toe plates, blackened barrels with broad matted raised rib, in its green baize lined case. $660 £305

A double barrelled 16-bore pin-fire underlever opening Continental hammer sporting gun by W. O. Werke, 46½in., barrels 30 5/8in., figured walnut stock with chequered wrist, cheekpiece, iron butt-plate, sling swivel and scrolled horn trigger guard extension, browned twist barrels. Back action locks. $650 £330

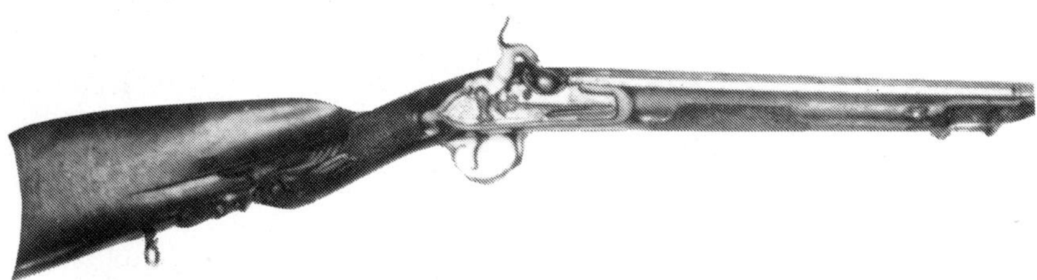

A 16-bore single barrelled Spanish miquelet percussion sporting gun by Bascaran & Asola, dated 1824, 50½in., half octagonal swamped barrel 35in. Halfstocked, steel furniture, silver inlaid star-shaped foresight, steel sling swivels. French walnut stock well carved, chequered small and fore of stock. $880 £400

A .450in. Soper pattern breech loading sporting rifle, 44½in., barrel 28in., No. 519, breech engraved 'W. Soper inventor Patentee and Manufacturer Reading', chequered walnut pistol grip stock with two-piece engraved head and toe plate, bead foresight and folding ladder rear to 500 yds. In its green baize lined and fitted leather case with nipple key, .450 brass mould. $1,815 £825

INDEX